THE CULTURE OF
VERTEBRATE EMBRYOS

THE CULTURE
OF
VERTEBRATE
EMBRYOS

D. A. T. NEW, M.A., Ph.D.

Member of the Scientific Staff of the
Medical Research Council, and Fellow
of Fitzwilliam College, Cambridge

LOGOS PRESS
ACADEMIC PRESS

© D.A.T. New 1966

Published by
LOGOS PRESS LIMITED
in association with
ELEK BOOKS LIMITED
2 All Saints Street, London, N.1

Distributed by
ACADEMIC PRESS INC.
111 Fifth Avenue, New York, N.Y. 10003
and
ACADEMIC PRESS INC. (*London*) LIMITED
Berkeley Square House, Berkeley Square, London, W.1

Library of Congress Catalog Card Number 66–21081

PRINTED IN GREAT BRITAIN BY
UNWIN BROTHERS LIMITED
WOKING AND LONDON

Contents

Text Figures

Plates

Introduction

Which vertebrate embryos can be grown in culture? How can they be obtained? Can one be sure of obtaining them at a particular time? What culture methods are available and how successful are they? What types of experiment can embryos in culture be used for?

These are the main questions that I have had in mind while writing this book. Although I have been primarily concerned to describe methods for growing and observing embryos in the laboratory and classroom, I have added other information where it has seemed particularly relevant. Obviously there are severe limits to the amount that can be included in a work of this size, and I have felt that it would be more useful, both to research embryologists and to biology teachers, to deal fairly fully with a few embryos rather than scrappily with many. The chosen few have been selected partly because of their proven value for research, and known or potential value for teaching, and partly to represent all the five main classes of vertebrates. It must be emphasised, however, that this is *a* choice and not *the* choice. Other embryos may be as good or better for particular purposes or under particular circumstances, and for this reason I have tried where possible to indicate briefly the range of other material available, together with some sources of information on it.

Biology teachers are sometimes discouraged from making much use of live embryos by the supposed difficulty of obtaining the embryos at the right times for particular classes. One method—hallowed by tradition—of avoiding the problem is to abandon living embryos altogether and to give each student a box of sections to draw. This cures the teacher's headache, and in moderation can be a valuable medicine for the student, but the temptation to administer it in lethal doses has in the past lost many good students from embryology. Fortunately there is no longer any excuse for an excessively necrophilic approach. Thanks to the accumulated experience of embryologists during the last few decades, it is now possible, if the right animals are used, to obtain live eggs or embryos of mammals, birds, amphibia and fish at any required hour on any day of the year, and in some cases to obtain, within fairly narrow limits, a particular stage of embryonic development at a specified time. Of course the *occasional* crisis in the classroom may still occur, when for some unaccountable reason the embryos have failed to appear, but this is a

A*

well known hazard with any living material and all biology teachers know how to deal with it.

In planning work with living embryos, and in estimating the degree of success obtained from different culture techniques, it is always useful, and sometimes essential, to have detailed information on the normal development of the embryos concerned. The kind of information required is contained in the tables of development which have been published from time to time for various embryos, but unfortunately these tables are mostly scattered among various biological journals and specialist embryological monographs, and are not always readily available. I have therefore included in this book a detailed table of normal development for one of the recommended embryos in each class, to meet the special needs of those working with these embryos, as well as to provide a general idea of the main types of embryonic development in the different classes of vertebrates.

Culturing vertebrate embryos is more than a convenient way of looking at them. Many embryos, and particularly those of amniotes, are normally so inaccessible that experiments on them are often only possible when the embryos are grown in culture. In the past, each improvement in culture technique has been followed by a rapid advance in embryological knowledge, and there is every reason to suppose that the same sequence will continue to occur. For many embryos the existing techniques still have severe limitations, and I greatly hope that among those who use the methods described in this book, some will be stimulated to try and improve them.

Strangeways Research Laboratory,   DENIS NEW
    Cambridge.
January 1966.

Acknowledgements

The preparation of this book would have been impossible without the generous help that I have received from experts in particular fields of embryology. For advice on fish I am particularly indebted to Professor J. M. Oppenheimer, Dr. Sydney Smith and Professor T. Yamamoto; on amphibia to Dr. E. M. Deuchar and Dr. A. F. W. Hughes; on reptiles to Dr. A. d'A. Bellairs and Professor A. Raynaud; and on mammals to Dr. M. F. Hay. I would also like to thank the many other kind people who have sent valuable information in response to what must often have been rather tiresome requests for details of particular techniques. Especially I am indebted to Professor Dame Honor B. Fell for her encouragement and helpful advice throughout the course of the work. Needless to say the final decision on what to include and what to leave out has been made by me, and therefore the responsibility for any shortcomings in this book is entirely mine.

I am also very grateful to my wife, Dr. J. K. New, and to Mrs. J. R. Wallage for help with indexing and proof reading.

For permission to reproduce illustrations to the following tables of embryonic development, I am indebted to the various authors and publishers of the works in which the tables first appeared: Stages of *Fundulus* development by P. B. Armstrong and J. S. Child in the *Biological Bulletin;* stages of *Xenopus* development by P. D. Nieuwkoop and J. Faber, North Holland Publishing Co.; stages of *Lacerta* development by J-P. Dufaure and J. Hubert in *Archives d'Anatomie Microscopique et de Morphologie Expérimentale;* stages of chick development by V. Hamburger and H. L. Hamilton in the *Journal of Morphology*. Some of the other illustrations in the book have also previously appeared elsewhere, and I am grateful to the publishers of the following journals for permission to reproduce them: *Comptes-Rendus de l'Académie des Sciences, Discovery, Journal of Embryology and Experimental Morphology, Journal of the Fisheries Research Board of Canada, Laboratory Investigation, New Biology (Penguin Books), Proceedings of the Royal Institution, Proceedings of the Royal Society*.

CHAPTER 1

Apparatus and Materials

INSTRUMENTS

A good low-power binocular dissecting microscope is essential for most work with embryos, and for culturing the embryos of birds and mammals a reliable incubator is necessary. Apart from these the apparatus required is simple and inexpensive. Provided standard zoological dissection instruments of good quality are available, the only extra instruments needed are two watchmakers forceps, two cataract knives, and an assortment of pasteur pipettes of various sizes. This will be sufficient for making cultures of all the embryos described in this book, except mammalian eggs for which micro-pipettes are needed. A few other instruments may be necessary for making fine operations on the embryos.

Binocular dissecting microscope

A magnification range of ×5 to ×25 is sufficient for most purposes, though it is useful to have higher magnifications for mammalian eggs. The working distance (objective to specimen) and visual field should be as large as possible. It is often an advantage to examine embryos by transmitted light and the microscope should have provision for substage illumination. A zoom lens is convenient but not important.

Watchmakers forceps

These forceps have very fine tips. When not in use they must be stored carefully with the tips protected. They should frequently be examined under the dissecting microscope and if necessary reground on an oilstone. Unless the tips meet exactly the forceps are useless. (Obtainable from S. Rampling, 1 Rose Crescent, Cambridge, U.K.)

Cataract knives

Knives with narrow blades about 2·5 cm. long are a convenient size. When they first arrive from the manufacturer the blades are too thick and rigid. The end third of the blade should be ground on an oilstone until it is thin and flexible. It should frequently be examined under the dissecting microscope to make sure that the cutting edge is smooth and sharp and the tip ends in a perfect point. (Obtainable from John Weiss & Son Ltd., 287 Oxford Street, London.)

Microburner

This is useful in making micropipettes, glass bridges, and needles. An adequate microburner can be made by connecting a syringe needle to the gas supply with rubber tubing. The tip of the needle should be cut off to give a circular aperture. The gas emerging from the needle will give a tiny flame, which can be controlled by a clamp on the rubber tubing.

Micropipettes

Standard pipettes are not sufficiently controllable for handling objects as minute as mammalian eggs or the smaller embryonic grafts. For these purposes pipettes should be made from 2 mm. bore glass tubing drawn out to 0·5 mm. or less at the tip. An adequate "teat" can be made by attaching a piece of rubber tubing 2 mm. bore and 1–2 cm. long to the pipette and closing the end by inserting a short length of glass rod (Plate 1.A). Pipettes of this type are simpler to make than those with a side hole which are sometimes recommended.

Glass bridges

Glass bridges are particularly useful for holding amphibian grafts in position until they are healed in (Fig. 30, p. 179). They are made from rectangular pieces of glass 3–4 mm. wide and 10–12 mm. long cut from cover slips with a diamond. The edges of each rectangle should first be smoothed by passing them slowly through the flame of a microburner. Then holding one end of the rectangle with forceps the other is placed in the flame until it bends over under its own weight. Several bridges should be made, bent at a variety of angles. Each bridge must be capable of standing firmly on its two ends.

Needles

Mounted metal needles, or Borradaile knives (obtainable from S. Rampling, 1 Rose Crescent, Cambridge, U.K.), ground to a fine tip, are the most easily made cutting instruments for transplantation and extirpation experiments, but glass needles have been widely used in the past and are still often recommended. The end of a piece of glass rod is drawn out in a bunsen flame until it tapers to a fine thread of glass. It is then further drawn out in the microburner, and broken off leaving a needle of required length attached to the glass rod handle. Needles of varying thickness, length and shape should be prepared since requirements vary according to the particular operation and embryo.

Very fine needles can be made from tungsten. A piece of tungsten wire is mounted on a length of glass rod or tube, and the end of the wire dipped in molten sodium nitrite $NaNO_2$. It emerges with an extremely sharp point.

ASEPTIC TECHNIQUE

Culturing vertebrate embryos often involves removing the surrounding membranes and other structures that provide a natural defence against infection, and growing the embryos in media in which bacteria and moulds can flourish. Unless aseptic precautions are taken with such embryos failure is certain. The precautions need not be elaborate, and no special "sterile operating room" is necessary; any room which can be kept reasonably free of dust and draughts is adequate. But instruments and culture vessels must be sterilised, and as far as possible operations should be done under cover. Culture media must either be sterilised or prepared from sterile ingredients.

Most apparatus can be effectively sterilised by heating in a dry oven at 140°C for 1–1½ hours. Silicone rubber tubing, teats, etc., can be treated in the same way, but "natural" rubber is rapidly destroyed at this temperature and is best sterilised in an autoclave at 115°C; rubber teats for pipettes need not be sterilised provided they are kept very clean. Apparatus that has been sterilised in covered containers will remain sterile so long as the container is not opened, and can be stored until required.

Saline solutions without bicarbonate are usually sterilised by heating in an autoclave at about 115°C (700 g./cm.^{2} or 10 lb./in.^{2}) for 30 mins., or at about 121°C (1050 g./cm.^{2} or 15 lb./in.^{2}) for 20 mins. Salines containing bicarbonate or other substances decomposed by heating, are sterilised by vacuum or pressure filtration through a sintered glass or sterimat filter (obtainable from A. Gallenkamp &

Co., 17–19 Sun Street, London, E.C.2). Alternatively the saline can be made in two parts, one part containing the bicarbonate or other heat-labile substances sterilised by filtration, and the remainder sterilised by autoclaving. Some natural media used in embryo culture, such as blood plasma and egg albumen, do not require sterilising provided they have been obtained aseptically from healthy animals.

The operating bench must be arranged so that the embryos, media and instruments have the maximum protection from airborne bacteria and other micro-organisms. There are probably as many ways of doing this as there are embryologists, and personal whim can be left to determine the details. Plate 1.B shows one arrangement that gives good results. The instruments are supported on a rack under a perspex cover to the right of the operator, and all operations to the embryos are performed either under the cover in the centre of the bench, or under the cover over the microscope stage. The instruments are frequently rinsed in the beaker of boiling water, and all except the knives and pipettes are passed through the bunsen flame each time they are brought into contact with the embryos or culture media.

As further protection against infection antibiotics can often be added to the culture media; details of this are given in the accounts of particular embryos.

CULTURE MEDIA AND OTHER MATERIALS

Saline solutions (see p. 3 for sterilising salines).

All quantities are for anhydrous salts unless otherwise stated.

	Grams per litre of solution			
	NaCl	KCl	$CaCl_2$	$NaHCO_3$
Holtfreter Ringer	3·5	0·05	0·10	0·02
(amphibian)	6·5	0·14	0·12	0·10
(chick)	9·0	0·42	0·24	
(for *Oryzias* eggs— Yamamoto)	7·5	0·20	0·20	0·02*

(*Adjust to give pH 7·3)

Tyrode (1910) saline
        8·00 gm. NaCl   0·05 gm. $NaH_2PO_4 \cdot 2H_2O$
        0·20 gm. KCl   1·00 gm. $NaHCO_3$
        0·20 gm. $CaCl_2$ 1·00 gm. glucose
        0·10 gm. $MgCl_2 \cdot 6H_2O$ Water to make 1 litre

(Tyrode, in his original publication, did not state whether the calcium chloride, magnesium chloride and sodium phosphate contained water of crystallisation, but the above is the formula now most commonly used.)

Pannett and Compton (1924) saline
    Solution A   12·11 gm. NaCl
                 1·55 gm. KCl
                 0·77 gm. $CaCl_2$ } in 100 ml. water
                 1·27 gm. $MgCl_2 \cdot 6H_2O$
    Solution B   0·189 gm. Na_2HPO_4 } in 100 ml. water
                 0·019 gm. $NaH_2PO_4 \cdot 2H_2O$

Store solutions A and B separately. Add 4 ml. of A and 6 ml. of B to 90 ml. of distilled water just before use.

Hanks (1949) saline
        8·00 gm. NaCl   0·06 gm. KH_2PO_4
        0·40 gm. KCl   0·06 gm. $Na_2HPO_4 \cdot 2H_2O$
        0·14 gm. $CaCl_2$ 0·35 gm. $NaHCO_3$
        0·10 gm. $MgCl_2 \cdot 6H_2O$ 1·00 gm. glucose
        0·10 gm. $MgSO_4 \cdot 7H_2O$ 0·02 gm. phenol red
                1 litre distilled water

(This is the formula most commonly used, but Hanks and Wallace in their original publication omit the magnesium chloride and add instead 0·20 gm. of the hydrated magnesium sulphate.)

Krebs–Ringer bicarbonate (Cohen, 1957).
    Solutions   Gms. per 100 ml. distilled water
       1   0·90   NaCl
       2   1·15   KCl
       3   1·22 $CaCl_2$
       4   2·11 KH_2PO_4
       5   3·82 $Mg SO_4 \cdot 7H_2O$
       6   1·30 $NaHCO_3$

These solutions are all isotonic (with rat serum) and hence when mixed in any proportions yield mixtures which are isotonic. To prepare Krebs–Ringer bicarbonate they are mixed together in the following proportions:

$$100 \text{ parts of solution } 1$$
$$4 \quad ,, \qquad ,, \quad 2$$
$$3 \quad ,, \qquad ,, \quad 3$$
$$1 \quad ,, \qquad ,, \quad 4$$
$$1 \quad ,, \qquad ,, \quad 5$$
$$21 \quad ,, \qquad ,, \quad 6$$

The mixture is then gassed with 5% CO_2 to give required pH (p. 8). (It may be found convenient to make up solutions 1 to 5 in concentrations five times those listed. The more concentrated solutions are stable for months when stored in the cold. The mixed Krebs–Ringer solution will keep in the cold for about a week.)

Plasma, serum and embryo extract

Methods of obtaining blood plasma and serum are described in full in books on tissue culture techniques such as those of Parker (1961) and White (1954), and will not be described in detail here.

Mammalian plasma clots very easily and is difficult to prepare without the addition of anticoagulants. It is usual therefore to obtain plasma for culturing from adult fowls. Small quantities (up to 50 ml.) of blood can be taken repeatedly from the same bird from a wing vein, or by cardiac puncture; but unless very small amounts are taken, withdrawals of blood should be spaced at intervals of at least several weeks, otherwise the quality of the plasma is liable to decline. Larger amounts can be obtained at one time by inserting a cannula into the carotid artery under anaesthesia and bleeding the bird to death. The blood is collected in centrifuge tubes lined with wax or silicone and surrounded by ice (these precautions are necessary to prevent clotting). The blood cells are thrown to the bottom of the tube by centrifugation and the plasma is then decanted and stored in a refrigerator until required. It will keep without appreciable deterioration for a week, and may still be adequate for some purposes after longer periods.

Serum can be prepared from bird or mammalian blood by allowing the blood to clot, breaking up the clot with a glass rod, and then centrifuging and decanting the supernatant serum.

Embryo extract is prepared from 10- to 13-day chick embryos, or from mammalian embryos. First the embryo is removed from its investing membranes, washed (with saline) free of extraneous blood, and the gall bladder dissected out and discarded. It is then ground down to the consistency of a thick paste, mixed with an equal volume of Tyrode saline containing 1% glucose, and centrifuged at 3000 r.p.m., for five minutes. The supernatant is "embryo extract".

Plasma, serum, embryo extract and synthetic culture media can also be obtained from:

DIFCO Laboratories, Detroit, Michigan 48201, U.S.A. (The United Kingdom agents are Baird and Tatlock, Freshwater Road, Chadwell Heath, Essex.)
Grand Island Biological Company, 3175 Staley Road, P.O. Box 68, Grand Island, New York 14072, U.S.A.
Burroughs Wellcome & Co., The Wellcome Building, Euston Road, London, N.W.1.

Hormones for inducing breeding

Serum gonadotrophin (under the trade name "Gestyl") and chorionic gonadotrophin ("Pregnyl") are obtainable from Organon Laboratories Ltd., Brettenham House, London, W.C.2. The hormones are supplied in solution in small ampoules ready for injection.

Coloured agar for vital staining

A method commonly used for tracing morphogenetic movements in embryos is to mark the tissues with blocks of agar impregnated with nile blue or neutral red. To prepare the stain-agar, 1–2 gm. agar is added to 100 ml. distilled water and the mixture stirred and boiled gently until the agar is completely dissolved. While the solution is still warm 1 gm. of nile blue or neutral red is added and the solution again stirred until the stain is dissolved. The liquid is poured onto microscope slides to give a thin even layer, and allowed to cool and solidify. The slides with their coating of stained agar are protected from dust and left to dry; they can then be wrapped up and stored indefinitely. When required for vital marking, a small area of the agar is soaked for a few minutes in a drop of water, scraped off the slide, and cut into pieces of suitable size under a dissecting microscope.

SIMPLE METHODS FOR CONTROLLING AND MEASURING O_2 AND CO_2

The effects of increased oxygen and carbon dioxide on development have been less studied in cultures of whole embryos than in those of organs and tissues. There is no doubt however, that with some mammalian embryos, and with chick embryos in certain types of culture, better growth and differentiation is obtained in 60–95% O_2 and 3–5% CO_2 than in air. The extra O_2 presumably assists respiration; and the extra CO_2 maintains a pH of around 7·4, corresponding to that of blood, in media containing physiological levels of bicarbonate.

Culturing embryos in a controlled atmosphere is a much simpler and less expensive procedure than is often supposed. The cultures must be housed in some form of gas-tight container, and where money is no object the containers manufactured by laboratory suppliers are satisfactory; but they are expensive and simple home-made equipment can be equally effective. Fig. 1 shows a gas chamber made from an 800 ml. beaker inverted over a large petri dish; liquid paraffin in the dish provides a gas-tight seal and a glass tube passing in under the spout of the beaker serves for the introduction of gases. Such a chamber will house six cultures in petri dishes of 7 cms. diameter, and will retain without leakage O_2 and CO_2 at any desired concentration for several days. Desiccators are sometimes used as gas chambers, but they are liable to leak slowly and should only be used if provision is made for continual replacement of any gas lost.

Cylinders of oxygen, nitrogen and carbon dioxide, as pure gases or mixed in any proportion, can be obtained from commercial suppliers (e.g. British Oxygen Company, East Lane, North Wembley, Middlesex). A mixture that is convenient for many purposes is 95% O_2 and 5% CO_2. The air in the gas chamber containing the cultures can either be completely flushed out with this mixture, or only partially replaced to give O_2 and CO_2 concentrations intermediate between those of the mixture and of air. Measurements should be made of the volume of gas introduced (e.g. with a flow meter) and of the concentration finally attained in the gas chamber. It is advisable also to check the concentration at the end of the culture period in case any leakage has occurred.

A good method for regulating the CO_2 only, which avoids the need for gas cylinders and flow meters, is that of Pardee (1949). A mixture of diethanolamine, thiourea, HCl and $KHCO_3$ is placed in a small open container in the gas chamber where it acts as a "gas buffer", maintaining the CO_2 at a level determined by the concentration of HCl. The following mixture placed in a chamber of air

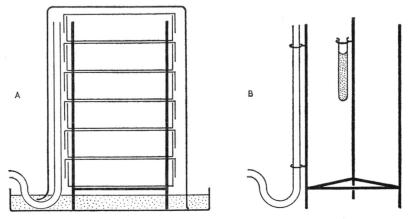

Figure 1.   A simple gas chamber for culturing embryos in controlled concentrations of O_2 and CO_2. A. An 800 ml. beaker (14 × 9·5 cms.) is inverted over a petri dish containing liquid paraffin. This provides capacity for 6 petri dishes (maximum diameter 7·5 cms.) on a stand. Gas is introduced through a tube passing under the spout of the beaker. B. Details of the stand. Made from 3 mm. metal rod, the uprights are 13 cm. long, and each side of the triangle is 7 cm. long. A small glass tube on one upright contains bicarbonate and phenol red for measuring the CO_2 concentration.

(at about 38°C) evolves CO_2 until the concentration in the air is about 5%, and then keeps it at that level:

5 ml. 6N HCl (smaller quantities give lower CO_2 concentrations)
6 ml. 2·2 diethanolamine
15 mg. thiourea
3 gm. $KHCO_3$ (add slowly and stir)
distilled water to make 15 ml.

Measuring CO_2 and O_2 concentrations
For routine determinations of the CO_2 and O_2 levels surrounding embryos growing in gas chambers, simplicity of method is more

important than extreme accuracy. It is rarely necessary to know the concentrations of these gases with an accuracy better than two or three per cent, and elaborate measuring apparatus is all too often used only for gathering dust. On the other hand it is important that measurements be made frequently; estimates of final gas concentrations based on the amount of gas introduced are often erroneous (unless the gas chamber has previously been standardised); so also are assumptions that gas chambers are free of leaks. The following two methods have proved valuable for routine use in embryo culture.

Determination of CO_2 with bicarbonate and phenol red

The pH of a bicarbonate solution in equilibrium with a gas phase containing CO_2 varies according to the equation

$$pH = K + \log\frac{(HCO_3^-)}{(CO_2)}$$

where K is a constant, (HCO_3^-) is the concentration of bicarbonate ions in the solution, and (CO_2) is the concentration of carbon dioxide in the gas phase (see Umbreit 1957 for full discussion). All that is necessary, therefore, for determining CO_2 concentration is a bicarbonate solution of known strength containing a pH indicator.

A 0·01M bicarbonate solution containing phenol red is suitable for determining CO_2 concentrations of 0–10%. Within this range small changes of CO_2 concentration alter the pH sufficiently (see Fig. 2) to give marked changes of colour of the indicator.

A small open tube containing 1–2 ml. of the bicarbonate and phenol red, placed in the gas chamber with the cultures (Fig. 1B), indicates the CO_2 level at any time during the culture period (except during the first hour or two when the bicarbonate and CO_2 are equilibrating). For accuracy in determining the pH of the indicator tube, it should be compared with a set of similar standard tubes containing phenol red at known values of pH.

Determination of O_2 with the Roughton–Scholander analyser

Roughton and Scholander (1943) described a method for measuring the O_2 content of very small samples of blood, by means of an instrument, the "analyser", which consisted essentially of a small syringe joined to a graduated capillary tube (Fig. 3B–E). A measured volume of blood was drawn into the analyser together with solutions containing ferricyanide, bicarbonate and acetic acid. This released a relatively large volume of CO_2 into the barrel of the syringe, together with the gases combined and dissolved in the blood. The CO_2 was absorbed with sodium hydroxide, and the length of the remaining small bubble of gas was measured in the capillary tube before and

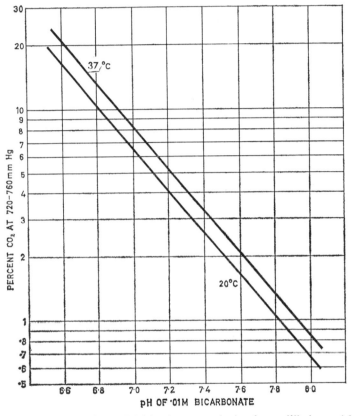

Figure 2. pH of 0·01M bicarbonate solution in equilibrium with gas phase containing CO_2. Upper line: at 37°C. Lower line: at 20°C. (Calculated from data of Umbreit 1957.)

after absorption of the O_2 with pyrogallol. The O_2 concentration of the blood could then be calculated. The same method is applicable to determinations of O_2 in culture media; and a modification of the method can be used for routine determination of O_2 levels in gas chambers, as follows:

Apparatus and materials required:

(i) A Roughton–Scholander (R-S) analyser with a retort stand and clamp to hold it. The analyser is made by fusing a 1 ml. glass syringe to a length of capillary tubing. It is important that the syringe

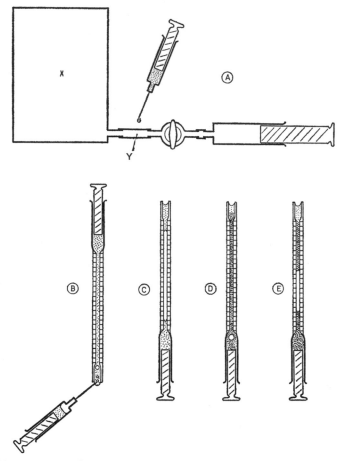

Figure 3. Method of determining the O_2 concentration in a gas chamber by means of the Roughton–Scholander analyser. See text for details.

should have a metal clip to hold the plunger steady. The capillary tubing should be of 0·5–1·0 mm. bore and graduated with 35–55 divisions 2 mm. apart. A short piece of tube ("reservoir") of 3 mm.

bore and 15 mm. length is fused to the capillary tube at its free end.

(ii) A 10 ml. syringe connected to a short length of rubber tubing, with a clip or stopcock at the syringe end of the tubing.

(iii) A 1 ml. hypodermic syringe and needle, kept standing in a beaker of water with the tip of the needle submerged.

(iv) Another small syringe and needle containing pyrogallol solution. The solution is made by dissolving 15 gm. of powdered pyrogallol in 100 ml. 20% sodium hydroxide, and is stored under a 1–2 cm. layer of liquid paraffin in a rubber-stoppered bottle.

Procedure (see Fig. 3):

1. Connect the 10 ml. syringe and rubber tubing to the gas chamber x, open the stopcock, withdraw the plunger of the syringe to the 10 ml. mark, and quickly close the stopcock (A). This draws the air in the rubber tube y into the barrel of the syringe and replaces it with a sample of gas from the gas chamber.

2. Draw a little water into the R-S analyser and eliminate all air bubbles; hold the analyser in a clamp with the plunger uppermost (B).

3. Draw a little water into the 1 ml. hypodermic syringe, insert the needle into the rubber tube y, and draw in about 0·1 ml. of gas. Inject a small bubble of this gas into the reservoir of the analyser (B). (Great care must be taken that no air enters the hypodermic syringe. Except when injecting gas into the analyser the syringe should always be held with the needle downwards and the needle should be kept full of water to act as a seal.)

4. Draw the bubble of gas into the barrel of the analyser, invert the analyser, push the bubble into the capillary tube and measure its length (C). (If the bubble is larger than the capacity of the capillary tube, part of it can be allowed to escape through the water in the reservoir.)

5. Add a little pyrogallol under the water in the reservoir of the analyser. Draw the bubble down into the barrel and slowly draw the pyrogallol over it (D). After about a minute push the bubble back into the capillary tube and again measure its length (E).

6. Calculate the percentage of oxygen in the sample from the measurements of the bubble before and after addition of the pyrogallol. (If the gas sample contains a few per cent of carbon dioxide (p. 10) this largely dissolves in the water in the syringes before the first measurement of the gas bubble is made; allowance must be made for this.)

7. To increase the accuracy of the determination the mean should be taken of measurements on two or three samples of the gas. Further accuracy may sometimes be gained by taking all readings of the gas bubble with the R-S analyser immersed in a constant temperature water bath; but this is usually unnecessary provided wide fluctuations of temperature are avoided.

LIVE FOOD—*Artemia, Daphnia, Drosophila, Enchytraeus, Tubifex*

Cultures of one or more of these five organisms will provide all the food required by many urodele larvae, and by newly metamorphosed urodeles and anurans. They can also be used for feeding many small fish. If other insects or worms are required reference should be made to *The UFAW handbook on the care and management of laboratory animals*, 2nd ed., 1957, edited by A. N. Worden and W. Lane-Petter, where culture methods for a variety of different species are described.

Artemia salina. *The brine shrimp*

Artemia is conveniently bought from dealers in the form of the dried eggs. These eggs, provided they are kept very dry, will remain viable for several years. They provide a very convenient source of nauplii larvae, valuable as food for small fish and amphibian larvae. When the nauplii are required some eggs are sprinkled into a vessel of seawater, or substitute saline made by dissolving sea salt crystals (or even domestic salt) at the rate of about 12 gms. per litre. At a temperature of 20–25°C the nauplii hatch in one to two days. They are attracted to light and if the container is placed near a window or lamp they will concentrate on the illuminated side and can be pipetted out. The simplest way to dispose of the salt water before using the nauplii as food is to filter them through fine muslin or similar material.

Daphnia

Despite the extensive literature on the culturing of Daphnia there appears to be no method that can be relied upon to produce adequate numbers from a given culture at a given time. Much the best policy therefore is to keep several cultures going simultaneously so that at least one will be likely to have a flourishing colony when it is required. Any type of tank or tub can be used and the Daphnia can be adequately fed on any of a variety of foods. Dried skim milk, dried yeast, bone meal, soya bean meal, an emulsion of liver, the outer leaves of lettuce plants and fresh animal manure have all been used successfully. Cultures should be started in only a small quantity of water which is gradually increased as the animals multiply. The amount of food to be added can only be judged by trial and error; strong putrefaction and cloudiness of the water is an indication of excess food; slow growth of the colony may indicate too little.

Fankhauser (1963) recommends Hyman's (1941) lettuce culture procedure. New cultures are started in 8- to 12-litre aquaria with 5–6 cm. of water, to which one boiled lettuce leaf is added. After this medium has been standing for two to three days to develop a sufficient number of bacteria as food, it is inoculated with a liberal number of Daphnia. As the Daphnia multiply the water level is raised at intervals to 20 cm. and new lettuce leaves are added as the old ones sink and disintegrate.

Most species of Daphnia do best at temperatures around 20°C. In very large tanks the water must be aerated with an aquarium pump (Gordon, 1950). The appearance of ephippia or winter eggs in the brood chamber of the females is an indication of adverse conditions.

Drosophila

Drosophila breeds very rapidly and is simple to rear. Milk bottles stoppered with cotton wool are commonly used as culture chambers and are very convenient. The bottles are first heat sterilised and then nutrient medium is poured into them. Sufficient medium for 12 one-pint bottles can be made as follows:

Add 17 gms. agar to 50 ccs. water in a beaker on a water bath. Boil gently until dissolved. Add 5 ccs. of 20% Moldex solution, stirring rapidly (other mould inhibitors may be used, provided they are not harmful to yeast or flies and are used in the quantities recommended by the suppliers). Then pour in 90 ml. molasses, stirring to prevent the molasses being burnt.

Mix 87 gm. cornmeal, 25 gm. dried yeast and 250 ml. water, and pour the mixture into the molasses agar solution. Stir every 3 minutes for 25–30 minutes until thick enough (pasty). This medium sets to a solid jelly when it is cold.

Pour about 2 cms. depth of medium into each bottle. Soak filter papers in 3% Moldex, sterilise at 80°C and place one in each bottle. The filter papers are rolled into a cylindrical shape, and should be large enough to extend from the surface of the medium almost to the top of the bottle. They provide a surface on which the larvae can pupate.

Tubes of *Drosophila melanogaster* can be bought from most biological supply firms. The sexes can be distinguished by the presence of 5 narrow transverse black bands on the abdomen of the female, and 2 or 3 transverse bands and a large black area at the tip of the abdomen of the male. A few flies of each sex should be placed in each bottle. Eggs will soon be found deposited on the surface of the medium, and after a fortnight the bottle will be crowded with flies of the next generation.

Most strains of Drosophila can be cultured adequately at room temperatures around 20°C but they develop more rapidly at 25–30°C.

Drosophila can be conveniently transferred from one bottle to another by making use of the fact that they are strongly attracted by light. If the two bottles are held mouth to mouth with the empty one nearest to a window or lamp the flies will move into it. Tapping the side of the bottle they are leaving speeds them up.

For examination the flies can be anaesthetised with ether. They should be transferred to an empty bottle and a plug of cotton wool soaked in ether applied to its mouth until all the flies are motionless.

The non-flying mutants such as "vestigial-wing" are useful for feeding amphibia, but multiply less rapidly in culture than the "wild" type.

Enchytraeus albidus. "White worms"

These small annelid worms can be obtained from dealers and grown in boxes of soil 10–20 cm. deep. The soil should be light and porous and contain plenty of disintegrating rotten wood or sterilised humus. It must always be kept moist, but not wet and soggy. The best temperature is 15°–20°; the worms do not thrive well above 22°C (Gordon 1950). White bread, cooked cereals, or boiled potatoes, soaked in milk, or boiled oats or oatmeal are all good foods. The food should only be given in small quantities and not left on the surface, otherwise it will merely grow moulds. It is best placed in small depressions about 5 cm. below the surface and covered over with soil. When the worms are required they will be found concentrated round these depressions. Enchytraeus worms are hermaphrodite and lay their eggs in cocoons like earthworms. They breed freely in the boxes, and after a time the colonies consist of worms of all sizes.

Tubificid worms

Worms sold under the name of "Tubifex" often contain tubificid worms of other genera, particularly *Limnodrilus*. They are all useful food for fish and amphibia, but carry with them the risk of infection from their natural habitat which is frequently decaying sewage. In the words of Gordon (1950) "no matter how highly Tubifex and related aquatic worms may be recommended to the aquarist, he will do well to remember that these worms are organisms of aquatic filth". Before they are used as food they should be thoroughly washed in running water for about 48 hours. Besides washing the worms externally this will also allow time for the contents of the alimentary canals to be evacuated.

For a continuous culture (Lehmann 1941, Fankhauser 1963) worms are placed in glass bowls with 1·5–2·5 cm. of washed sand and 3–5 cm. of water. The temperature should be kept around 22°–26°C, and the worms fed on live bakers' yeast pressed into pellets of pea size and buried in the sand. The adult worms are hermaphrodite, and during the greater part of the year will mate and deposit cocoons, from which young worms will emerge, 3–9 per cocoon.

SOURCES OF ANIMALS

Rabbits and the small laboratory rodents are best obtained from one of the breeders approved by the Laboratory Animals Centre of the Medical Research Council, which maintains a Register of Accredited Breeders throughout the United Kingdom. Further information can be obtained from M.R.C. Laboratory Animals Centre, Woodmansterne Road, Carshalton, Surrey.

Fertile hens' eggs for incubation are usually available from any commercial hatchery. Reptiles, and some species of amphibia, may present more of a problem. Several reptiles including adults of *Lacerta vivipara* and *Anguis fragilis*, can be obtained in season from L. Haig & Co. Ltd., Beam Brook, Newdigate, Surrey. The same firm also supplies a variety of amphibia, including the Mexican axolotl, though the supply of this last species is at present unreliable. The common British amphibia are also supplied by the Freshwater Biological Association, The Ferry House, Far Sawrey, Ambleside, Westmorland.

Live *Xenopus laevis* toads can be obtained direct from the Inland

Fisheries Department, South Africa. The cost at present (May 1965) is one shilling (sterling) per adult male and two shillings and six-pence per adult female, plus packaging and transport costs. The toads travel well by ship or plane and can be delivered in good health to most parts of the world. Enquiries should be sent to the Senior Fisheries Officer, Division of Inland Fisheries, Private Bag 14, Stellenbosch, Rep. of South Africa. Importing into the United Kingdom, including special care and delivery of the toads, can be arranged by Thomas Cook and Son, 45 Berkeley Street, London, W.1.

Regrettably most biological suppliers, at least in the United Kingdom, appear not to include Xenopus and the axolotl in their regular catalogues, and it is to be hoped that this situation will im-prove as the demand for these useful animals increases. It is sometimes possible to purchase a breeding pair from a university or research laboratory maintaining a colony. In cases of difficulty in obtaining these or other species of amphibia and reptiles, the Zoological Society, Regent's Park, London, N.W.1, can sometimes help with useful advice.

Trout and trout eggs are available in season from the Freshwater Biological Association and from L. Haig and Co. (addresses as above), and from the Midland Fishery, Nailsworth, Gloucestershire; also from various trout hatcheries whose advertisements appear from time to time in such publications as the *Fishing Gazette* and *The Field*. The medaka and other aquarium fish can be obtained from aquarium suppliers; such firms frequently advertise in *The Aquarist* and *Water Life*. A recommended source of fish in the U.S.A. is Beldt's Aquarium Inc., Hazelwood 21, Missouri.

REFERENCES

COHEN, P. P. (1957). Methods for preparation and study of tissues. In *Manometric techniques and tissue metabolism* (W. W. Umbreit, R. H. Burris, J. F. Stauffer, Eds.). Revised ed. Burgess. Minneapolis.
FANKHAUSER, G. (1963). Amphibia. In *Animals for Research* (W. Lane-Petter, Ed.). Academic Press, London & New York.
GORDON, M. (1950). Fishes as laboratory animals. In *The care and breeding of laboratory animals* (E. J. Farris, Ed.). John Wiley and Sons, New York.
HANKS, J. H. & WALLACE, R. E. (1949). Relation of oxygen and temperature in the preservation of tissues by refrigeration. *Proc. Soc. exp. Biol. Med.*, **71**, 196–200.

HYMAN, L. H. (1941). Lettuce as a medium for the continuous culture of a variety of small laboratory animals. *Trans. Amer. Micr. Soc.*, **60**, 365–70.

LEHMANN, F. E. (1941). Die Zucht von *Tubifex* fuer Laboratoriumszwecke. *Rev. Suisse Zool.*, **48**, 559–61.

PANNETT, C. A. & COMPTON, A. (1924). The cultivation of tissues in saline embryonic juice. *Lancet* **205**, 381–4.

PARDEE, A. B. (1949). Measurement of oxygen uptake under controlled pressures of carbon dioxide. *J. biol. Chem.* **179**, 1085–91.

PARKER, R. C. (1961). *Methods of tissue culture.* 3rd ed. Paul B. Hoeber, New York.

ROUGHTON, F. J. W. & SCHOLANDER, P. F. (1943). Micro-gasometric estimation of the blood gases. 1. Oxygen. *J. biol. Chem.*, **148**, 541–50.

TYRODE, M. V. (1910). The mode of action of some purgative salts. *Arch. int. Pharmacodyn.*, **20**, 205–23.

UMBREIT, W. W. (1957). Carbon dioxide and bicarbonate. In *Manometric techniques and tissue metabolism* (W. W. Umbreit, R. H. Burris, J. F. Stauffer, Eds.). Revised ed. Burgess, Minneapolis.

WHITE, P. R. (1954). *The cultivation of animal and plant cells.* Ronald Press, New York.

CHAPTER 2

Mammals

In all but the most primitive mammals the environment provided for the developing embryo by the maternal organism is of such complexity, and is regulated with such precision, that it is hardly surprising that most attempts to reproduce it in culture have met with little success. However, in recent years techniques have been devised which have made it possible to grow in culture the embryos of some species during two periods of development: from the cleavage to the blastocyst stage (rabbits and mice), and from the early somite to the early limb bud stage (rats and mice). Embryos at these stages develop almost as well in vitro as in vivo; they appear to be unaffected by being cooled during explantation, and the techniques involved are fairly simple.

Methods of housing and maintaining rabbits, rats and mice for laboratory use are fully described in the books edited by Worden and Lane-Petter (1957), and Lane-Petter (1963). As a source of embryos for culturing, mice have the advantage that their embryos develop well when explanted either at cleavage stages, or at early somite stages; they are also somewhat cheaper than rats, and much cheaper than rabbits, to breed and maintain. Unfortunately, mice are more susceptible than rats to virus infections, and the number of embryos (usually 5–10) obtainable from each pregnant mouse is less than that (frequently 12–14 or more) obtainable from each pregnant rat. The blastocysts of mice remain very small (about 0·1 mm. diam.) until they implant on the uterus, whereas those of rabbits enlarge very considerably (to 4–5 mm. diam.) during the three days preceding implantation—though this enlargement does not always occur normally in culture.

References to studies on other mammalian eggs in culture, and to many successful experiments on transferring eggs between the uteri of different individuals, can be found in the valuable book by Austin (1961). Eggs and blastocysts, particularly of mice, have also been studied after transfer to the anterior chamber of the eye (Runner

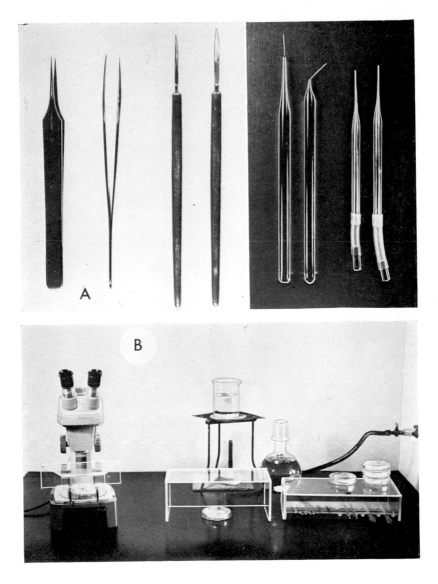

PLATE I

Instruments.

A. Embryological instruments. Watchmakers forceps, cataract knives, glass needles, micropipettes. $\times \frac{1}{2}$.

B. Operating bench. Aseptic precautions include perspex covers over the instruments, microscope stage, etc., and frequent rinsing of the instruments in the beaker of boiling water.

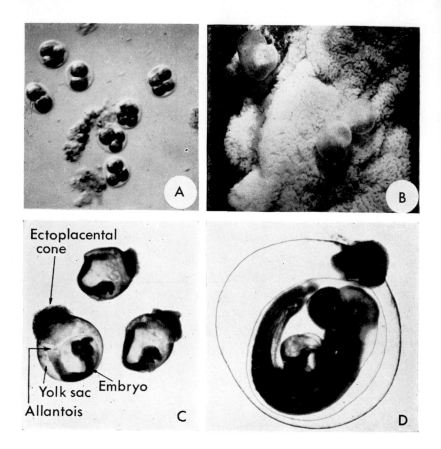

Ectoplacental cone

Yolk sac Embryo

Allantois

PLATE 2

  A. Mouse eggs at the 2- to 4-cell stage together with cellular debris, as obtained from the oviducts (see p. 23). Such eggs develop in culture to blastocysts. × 80.

  B. Rabbit blastocysts implanting on uterine endometrium in culture (Glenister 1961). × 9.

  C. Post-implantation rat embryos of early somites stages, with embryonic membranes, as explanted. × 10.

  D. Rat embryo explanted as in (C) after about 40 hours growth in culture. 25–30 somites, eyes, ears and anterior limb buds have formed, and both embryo and embryonic membranes have greatly enlarged. × 10

1947; Fawcett, Wislocki and Waldo 1947) and other extra-uterine sites (Fawcett 1950; Kirby 1962, 1963a, b; McLaren and Tarkowski 1963). Some recent experiments with advanced embryos, maintained for short periods in vitro by means of blood perfused through the umbilical vessels, are described by Westin, Nyberg and Enhorning (1958—human embryos), Lawn and McCance (1962—pig embryos) and Nixon, Britton and Alexander (1963—sheep embryos).

As far as possible aseptic precautions (p. 3) should be taken when explanting and culturing mammalian eggs and embryos. The use of antibiotics reduces the risk of bacterial growth still further.

Normal tables

The most detailed and fully illustrated table of the normal stages of rat development throughout gestation is that by Henneberg (1937— in German). The development of the external form of the embryo is described, with many illustrations, by Long and Burlingame (1938). Recently Witschi (1962) has published another table for the rat, part of which is reproduced in modified form here on pp. 39–43.

Snell (1941) describes the early development of the mouse, which is very similar to that of the rat but more rapid; equivalent times for the two embryos are shown in the table on pp.39–43. Gruneberg (1943) gives an illustrated table of the normal development of the external form of the mouse from the 9th day of gestation onwards, together with measurements of length. Otis and Brent (1954) provide a table of mouse development, together with much information on the equivalent ages of mouse and human embryos.

Keibel's Normentafeln contains an illustrated table by Minot and Taylor (1905—in English) of the development of the rabbit from the 6th day of gestation onwards, and also tables (in German) for the pig, the deer, the tarsier, the loris and man.

EGGS AND BLASTOCYSTS

The mouse (Mus musculus)

Obtaining eggs and blastocysts

The following information on reproduction in the mouse is largely based on the account by Snell (1941).

Fertilisation occurs in the upper end of each oviduct where the eggs are found usually gathered into clumps, after their discharge from the ovaries. Each egg is surrounded by a transparent, non-

B

cellular membrane, the zona pellucida. Eggs and zona together have a diameter of about o·1 mm. and little enlargement occurs until implantation. The zona pellucida is initially surrounded by follicular cells, but these disperse soon after fertilisation.

The first cleavage occurs about 24 hours after copulation, and subsequent cleavages at intervals of about 12 hours. By the end of the 3rd day (72 hours) the eggs have become morulae of 16–32 cells and at about this time they pass from the oviducts into the uterus. A fluid-filled cavity which rapidly enlarges soon appears among the cells of the morula, and the embryo is then termed a blastula or blastocyst. During the 4th–5th days, the blastocyst emerges from the zona pellucida and implants on the uterine wall.

In mice the onset of heat or oestrus (i.e. the period when the female will accept the male), is usually in the night, most commonly between 10 p.m. and 1 a.m. (The time of oestrus is light regulated and can be made to occur in the daytime if the mice are kept in a room that is light by night, dark in the day.) Ovulation takes place an hour or two after the onset of oestrus and the eggs retain their capacity for fertilisation for about 8 hours. Sperm reach the ovarian end of the oviduct, where fertilisation occurs, within 15 minutes of mating, and retain their fertilising ability for about 6 hours.

The duration of the oestrous cycle varies considerably between different strains and different individuals. It is most commonly 4–6 days, so the chance of a particular female mating on a particular night is about one in five. Copulation is accompanied by the formation of a vaginal plug formed by a mixture of the secretions of the vesicular and coagulating glands of the male. This solid plug usually fills the vagina and persists for 18–24 hours or occasionally longer. It can easily be seen by examination of the vulva, and provides a valuable indication that mating has occurred.

Good results can be obtained by allowing the mice to mate overnight in small cages of one male and two or three females per cage. The following morning the females with vaginal plugs are removed, and later they are killed when the eggs have reached the required age. The presence of the vaginal plug is not a certain indication of fertilisation and some of the females may prove to be without fertile eggs, but most of them should yield 5–10 eggs each.

The proportion of female mice that will mate at a particular time can be increased by inducing oestrus artificially with hormone injections; this also increases the yield of eggs from each mouse ("superovulation"). The injections are effective when administered either to immature animals, as little as four weeks old (Runner and Palm 1953), or to older mature animals. 3–10 i.u. of pregnant mare's serum is injected subcutaneously to stimulate follicle development, and about 40 hours later 3–10 i.u. of human chorionic gonadotrophin (see p. 7 for sources of hormones) is injected intraperitoneally to induce ovulation, which occurs after about a further 12 hours. The males are placed with females at the time of, or soon after, the second injection. Fowler and Edwards (1957) found that 75% of mature female mice could be induced to mate by this procedure, of which about three-quarters became pregnant; the average number of eggs ovulated per female was increased by the injections to about 20 (the average varied from 12–24 according to the strain of mouse). Eggs obtained from a mouse by superovulation are apparently normal and give the same results in culture, or when transferred to other females, as those ovulated in natural oestrus; if they are all left to implant in one female, however, many of the embryos are resorbed, presumably as a result of overcrowding, so that the litter size at birth is no larger than normal.

When the eggs have developed to the required age for culturing the mice are killed by breaking the neck, and the oviducts are dissected out and placed in a small watch glass or cavity slide containing saline. Aseptic precautions must be taken and sterile instruments used in this and all subsequent stages of culturing the eggs. If the eggs are more than three days old they may have entered the uterus, which must then be dissected out together with the oviducts. The eggs can be flushed out of the uterus by means of a stream of saline injected at one end from a syringe or finely drawn pipette. Some workers use the same method to get eggs out of the oviducts, but it is perhaps technically easier to cut the oviduct into short sections and then stroke each section with a needle, squeezing out the contents. Epithelial fragments as well as eggs emerge from the oviduct, but the eggs with their sharply outlined spherical zona pellucida (Plate 2.A) stand out clearly under a dissecting microscope, and can be transferred with a micropipette (p. 2) to the culture vessel.

Several salines such as Tyrode, Hanks or Krebs–Ringer (p. 5) are suitable for collecting the eggs. It is sometimes stated (Austin 1961, p. 103) that the eggs deteriorate less rapidly if substances of high molecular weight are present in the medium, but Whitten (1957a) reported normal development of eight-cell ova in a medium containing only Krebs–Ringer bicarbonate, glucose and simple amino acids. A safe and convenient policy is to collect the eggs in some of the same medium in which they are to be cultured.

Culturing 4-cell and older stages

Hammond (1949) appears to have been the first to obtain marked success with the cultivation of mouse ova. The culture medium consisted of an extract of yolk and albumen from hens' eggs in glucose saline. Groups of one to six ova were placed in sealed vessels containing 2–3 ml. of the medium and 1–2 ml. air, incubated at 37°C and examined after 42–52 hours. No two-cell ova developed beyond the four-cell stage, but some four-cell and all of the eight-cell ova developed to blastulae. A few of the blastulae emerged from the zona pellucida.

Whitten (1956, 1957a,b) found that the pH of Hammond's medium although initially low, rapidly rose to $7 \cdot 8$ if the medium was exposed to the air. He attributed this rise to loss of CO_2 from the egg albumen. Since even eight-cell ova fail to develop at a pH above $7 \cdot 7$ Whitten devised a medium containing Krebs–Ringer bicarbonate saline (p. 5) which, in equilibrium with 5 % CO_2, maintained a pH of $7 \cdot 4$. To the saline was added glucose (1 mg./ml.), streptomycin and penicillin (10 μg./ml.) and thin egg white (1 %) or crystalline bovine albumin (1 mg./ml.). Groups of 10–14 ova in 1 ml. of medium were cultured in agglutination tubes. The gas phase of the tubes was flushed through with 5% CO_2, and the tubes were then tightly stoppered and incubated at 37°C. (If nitrogen was used instead of air, the eggs continued to develop, but in oxygen they died.)

Whitten's method gives good development of eight-cell stages to blastulae and it has been used in several important studies. McLaren and Biggers (1958) employed the technique to culture embryos which were then transferred to the uterus of a foster mother. The embryos were obtained at the 8–16 cell stage and cultured for two days, during which time 87% developed to blastocysts. When transferred to the uterus of a recipient female (technique of McLaren and Michie, 1956) the same proportion (21%) of the blastocysts implanted and continued normal development as in control experiments with uncultured blastocysts transferred directly from one female to another.

Tarkowski (1961, 1964a, b) and Mintz (1964) have demonstrated the remarkable regulative powers of young mouse embryos by successfully rearing composite embryos made by fusing together eggs at mid-cleavage stages. In Tarkowski's experiments the zona pellucida was first removed from 8-cell eggs (p. 26) and drops of medium each containing two naked eggs were pipetted onto the floor of a small dish, under a layer of liquid paraffin. Medium was then withdrawn from each drop so that the two eggs of each pair were squeezed together. After 5–30 minutes 2–4 mm.[3] of a medium similar to that of Whitten was added to each drop, and the cultures were incubated. In 12–16 hours each pair of eggs had completely rounded up into a single morula, leaving no trace of dual origin. After 24–40 hours the composite embryos had reached the blastula stage and when transferred to the oviduct or uterus of a foster mother, 33% implanted and 21% developed further; several survived to term as morphologically normal single embryos, but few developed for long after birth.

The method of culturing embryos in drops of medium under paraffin oil has proved more satisfactory for general use than culturing in stoppered tubes, because it permits easier examination of the embryos under the microscope. Brinster (1963) recommends that the oil be equilibrated with the medium by bubbling 5% CO_2 in air through a mixture of 400 ml. of oil and 20 ml. of medium. Plastic petri dishes 15 × 60 mm. form convenient culture chambers, and 10 ml. of the equilibrated oil is placed in each dish. Small drops (approx. 0·1 ml.) of medium are then placed under the oil (Fig. 4B)

A   B

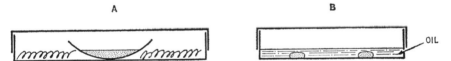

OIL

Figure 4. Two types of culture chamber. A. A watch glass of nutrient medium housed in a petri dish and surrounded by wet cotton wool to maintain humidity. B. Drops of nutrient medium placed under a layer of liquid paraffin in a petri dish.

by means of a micropipette, and several eggs can be cultured in each drop. The petri dishes are incubated in chambers gassed with 5% CO_2 in air bubbled through water.

Culturing 1- and 2-cell stages

Whitten (1957a) found that some 2-cell embryos would develop in vitro if the calcium chloride in the Krebs–Ringer saline were replaced by calcium lactate (L), or if isotonic sodium lactate were added to the medium. In a typical experiment 21 out of 52 2-cell embryos developed to blastulae and it appeared that it was only those ova about to undergo the second cleavage division that were capable of further development. Brinster (1963) cultured several thousand 2-cell ova obtained from superovulated mice, and reported that if the 2-cell ova were taken from the mice 45 hours after the injection of chorionic gonadotrophin (see technique for superovulation described on p. 22) 60–100% developed to blastocysts. Brinster's culture medium was almost identical with that of Whitten. He used Krebs'–Ringer bicarbonate saline as described on p. 5 except that the proportion of NaCl was reduced to 91·5 parts and that of $CaCl_2$ to 2 parts; to this was added 8·5 parts of isotonic sodium lactate, 1 mg./ml. crystalline bovine albumin, 100 U./ml. penicillin and 50 μg./ml. streptomycin. In a careful study of the requirements of 2-cell mouse ova Brinster (1965) concluded that energy for development can be supplied by lactate, pyruvate, oxaloacetate or phosphoenolpyruvate, but not by glucose, fructose, ribose, glucose-6-phosphate, fructose-1, 6-diphosphate, acetate, citrate, α-ketoglutarate, succinate, fumarate or malate; a supply of fixed nitrogen is needed, but this can be provided either by bovine serum albumin or by mixtures of its constituent amino acids; the ova can develop in the pH range 5·87–7·78 (optimum about 6·82) and in the osmolarity range 0·2002–0·3542 osmols (optimum 0·2760).

No satisfactory method has yet been devised for culturing 1-cell ova explanted from the oviducts. However, Biggers, Gwatkin and Brinster (1962) cultured whole Fallopian tubes on a complex chemically defined medium and obtained development of fertilised ova inside the tubes from 1-cell to blastocyst.

Removal of the zona pellucida

Methods for removing the zona pellucida from mouse eggs are described by Austin (1961), Tarkowski (1961), Mintz (1962) and Gwatkin (1964). A variety of chemical treatments will dissolve the membrane, but most of these impair the viability of the egg. It is possible to remove the membrane with fine glass needles, but this is very tedious and often results in injury to one or more of the blastomeres. The best results have been obtained with the following two methods:

Tarkowski (1961) removed the zona pellucida from 8-cell stages by rapidly sucking each egg into a micropipette. The pipette, of internal diameter 65 u. was attached by rubber tubing to a compressible rubber bulb. When the egg was sucked into the pipette the zona pellucida ruptured and the naked egg escaped undamaged. The size of the pipette and the suction pressure applied proved critical for the success of the operation, but many undamaged eggs were obtained capable of further normal development.

Mintz (1962, 1964) has developed a technique for removing the zona pellucida by means of pronase, an enzyme first isolated in Japan from a strain of the mould *Streptomyces griseus*. She recommends the following procedure. A $0 \cdot 5 \%$ solution of the enzyme is made up in bicarbonate-free Hanks balanced salt solution (p. 5) or in any other saline commonly employed in mammalian cell cultivation, and sterilised by filtration. In the refrigerator this solution remains stable for at least a week. Shortly before use, it is warmed to 37°C under 5% CO_2 until the pH, initially high, is approximately neutral. The solution may be allowed to cool when the eggs are transferred to it. The zona pellucida is digested in about 3 minutes, and the eggs are then washed four times in culture medium. 2-cell eggs usually show abnormal cleavage patterns after the zona is removed, but 8-cell eggs continue to develop normally to blastocysts.

The rabbit (*Oryctolagus cuniculus*)

Obtaining eggs and blastocysts

In the rabbit there is no definite oestrous cycle. Waves of follicles are constantly maturing, and most of the time the animals are in oestrus. Ovulation is not spontaneous, as in rats and mice, but follows the stimulus of mating with the buck; this causes the release of gonadotrophic hormone from the anterior pituitary, and leads to ovulation about 10 hours later. Sperm in the female reproductive tract retain their capacity for fertilisation for about 30 hours, and the ova remain fertilisable for 6–8 hours (see reviews by Bishop 1961 and Blandau 1961).

The technique of superovulation described by Pincus (1940) has frequently been used to increase the number of ova yielded by each doe. Does 4–6 months old are given six subcutaneous injections at 12 hour intervals of anterior pituitary (gonadotrophic) hormone, and 8–12 hours after the last of these injections a further injection of the same hormone is made intravenously to induce ovulation. Just before the intravenous injection the animals are mated. This method often gives a yield of 30–50 or more fertile eggs per rabbit, as compared with the usual 6–12. Hafez (1964) induced superovulation in does by means of 150–200 i.u. of pregnant mare's serum injected subcutaneously in three equal doses on three successive days, followed by 50 i.u. of human chorionic gonadotrophin injected intravenously in one dose (see p. 7 for obtaining gonadotrophic hormones). Kennelly and Foote (1965) give data on the effect of various treatments with commercially prepared hormones on rabbits of different ages.

Lewis and Gregory (1929) found that rabbit eggs attain the 2-cell stage 22–25 hours after mating, 4-cell after 25–32 hours, 8-cell after 32–41 hours and 16-cell after 41–47 hours; the blastocoel and inner cell mass appear at about 70 hours. During this period the diameter of egg and zona pellucida remains fairly constant at about 0·1–0·2 mm. As the egg passes along the oviduct it receives a covering of mucin (formerly termed the "albumen coat") which may be of a thickness equal to, or greater than, the diameter of the egg itself. The egg (=blastocyst) enters the uterus on the 4th day. After this, secretion of fluid into the blastocoel causes rapid enlargement of the blastocyst, and it reaches the relatively enormous size of about half a centimetre in diameter by the time of implantation on the 7th day. This expansion stretches the mucin and zona pellucida layers until their combined thickness is no more than a few microns.

When the eggs are required, the does can be killed by a sharp blow on the back of the head. However, if the eggs have reached the blastocyst stage and are in the uterus, some workers prefer instead to kill the animals with an overdose of nembutal, and then to bleed them out by cutting the throat; this leaves less blood in the uterine vessels and makes the subsequent operation easier. When the oviduct or uterus has been dissected out, the eggs can be obtained by flushing; a pipette or syringe of suitable size is inserted into one end of the tube and fluid injected to wash the eggs out at the other end. Exposure to protein-free solutions is generally considered harmful to the eggs, and if salines such as Tyrode or Hanks (p. 5) are used it is probably advisable to add a little serum or thin egg white; alternatively the eggs can be collected in some of the same medium as that used for culturing. To obtain large blastocysts (i.e. after the 5th day) it is better to open the entire length of the uterus on the anti-mesometrial side by carefully tearing with two pairs of forceps, and then to remove the blastocysts individually in a wide pipette, spoon-ended spatula or bone scoop.

It is possible to recover eggs from living animals under anaesthesia (Austin 1961, p. 105, Chang 1952) but in some countries, including the United Kingdom, this operation is illegal except under a vivisection licence.

Culturing eggs and blastocysts

Many studies have been made on rabbit eggs in vitro, since the initial experiments of Brachet (1912, 1913). The culture medium most commonly used has been rabbit plasma (liquid) or serum, with or without the addition of embryo extract (p. 6); it is doubtful whether the embryo extract improves the medium. Chang (1949) cultured 2-cell ova in a variety of sera for 24 hours, examined them for cleavage divisions, and then transferred some of them to the uterus of foster mothers to test the capacity of the cultured eggs for further development. He found that rabbit serum gave the best results (84% normal cleavage), but good results were also obtained with serum from the horse (80%), rat (75%), and guinea-pig (71%). In dog serum only 55% of the eggs continued normal cleavage, and in pig serum only 45%. Serum from man, sheep, cattle, goat or fowl contained an ovicidal factor which killed most or all of the eggs within 10 minutes; this ovicidal factor was, however, thermolabile and could be destroyed by heating the sera to 55°C for 30 minutes. Lutwak-Mann, Hay and Adams (1962) found fowl (cock) serum satisfactory for culturing 6-day blastocysts. Cole, Edwards and Paul (1966) find Waymouth's MB752/1 solution supplemented with 5% calf serum and 2% human serum a reliable medium for culturing cells taken from embryos, as well as for intact eggs and blastocysts. Smith (1949) states that 0·02% streptomycin in the medium allows eggs to develop while preventing bacterial growth, and reduces the need for aseptic precautions. The usual incubation temperature is 37°C.

The eggs and blastocysts can be cultured on microscope slides, a method very convenient for microscopy and photography (e.g. Lewis and Gregory 1929, Smith 1949); a drop of medium containing the embryo is held between the slide and a raised coverslip sealed on with wax. Alternatively the embryos can be cultured in small stoppered tubes, in watch glasses in petri dishes (Fig. 4A, p. 25), or in drops of medium under a layer of paraffin oil (as described for the mouse—p. 25, Fig. 4B). Fertilised uncleaved eggs readily develop to 8-cell stages and in the more successful cultures a proportion may

B*

develop to young morulae. Lutwak-Mann *et al.* (1962) cultured 6-day blastocysts for 24 hours and obtained development of the primitive streak and extra-embryonic mesoderm; this appears to be the limit of embryonic development that can be obtained at present from explanted blastocysts. A good method for close examination of the cells of the blastocysts after they have been fixed is that of Moog and Lutwak-Mann (1958) in which the blastocysts are torn open and prepared as flat mounts.

Rabbit eggs transferred to the uterus of a foster mother after a period in culture can continue normal development, and this has been utilised by Chang (1959) in one of the few convincing demonstrations of fertilisation of mammalian eggs in vitro. 266 eggs recovered 2 to 3 hours after ovulation were added to a suspension of sperm in saline and then incubated for 18 hours in serum. At the end of this time 55 of the eggs appeared to have undergone normal cleavage into four cells, and 36 of these were transferred to six unmated does. Two of the recipients did not become pregnant, but the other four yielded 15 young.

Rabbit eggs are remarkably resistant to cold and can develop normally after storage at temperatures of 0°C or lower (see Austin 1961 for references).

Blastocyst expansion

Lewis and Gregory (1929) studied blastocysts developing under cover slips on microscope slides and found that in these conditions the blastocysts failed to expand normally. Any enlargement quickly caused a break in the trophoblast and zona pellucida resulting in loss of blastocoel fluid and collapse of the blastocyst; the trophoblast then healed and the cycle of enlargement and collapse was repeated.

Several later workers have observed similar behaviour of blastocysts in culture. However, Pincus and Werthessen (1938) cultured blastocysts in chambers through which 30 ml. of serum aerated with 77% N_2, 19% O_2, 3% CO_2 was constantly circulated, and found that many of the blastocysts explanted at 68–77 hours after mating expanded to over 4·0 mm. diameter, though more slowly than in vivo. Glenister (p. 44) and Cole *et al.* (1966) obtained good expansion of blastocysts grown in small quantities (2 ml.) of static medium after removal of the zona pellucida. Glenister (1963) found that the proportion expanding was greatly increased when the cultures were incubated in 95% O_2 and 5% CO_2; in such cultures 66% of the blastocysts expanded as compared with 9% in air. It is not at present certain which are the essential requirements for blastocyst expansion, but it may be significant that in all these successful cultures the medium was equilibrated with 3–5% CO_2.

Removal of the zona pellucida

Rabbit blastocysts, unlike those of the mouse, do not emerge spontaneously from the zona pellucida in culture.

The mucin layer and zona pellucida can be removed by tearing the zona open with watchmakers forceps. Alternatively both layers can be digested away by treatment with a 0·1–1·0% (w/v) solution of the enzyme pronase (Cole *et al.* 1966) in Hanks saline (p. 5). A few minutes in the enzyme is sufficient to remove the mucin and zona layers from blastocysts, but younger stages may require up to 45 minutes. It is advisable therefore to add 2–3% of serum to the Hanks saline to avoid a long exposure of the embryos to protein-free solution. With embryos younger than the 32-cell stage the action of the enzyme can be assisted by drawing the embryos in and out of a fine pasteur pipette to split the zona pellucida. Immediately the zona is removed the embryos must be washed thoroughly in enzyme-free solution.

Edwards (1964) found that if the zona pellucida were removed from 1- or 2-cell eggs, cleavage of the blastomeres continued but they failed to cohere, each egg giving rise to colonies of up to 32–64 separated cells all of the same type. Cole *et al.* (1966) have found that some 4- or 8-cell embryos behave similarly after removal of the zona pellucida; but other 4- or 8-cell embryos, and those at later cleavage stages, after a few days in culture give rise to small blastocysts and layers of trophoblast-like epithelial cells, which migrate over the floor of the (plastic) container. When embryos are explanted at the blastocyst stage (5–6 days after mating), and the zona is removed, the rapid outward migration of the trophoblast cells pulls many of the blastocysts into a flat layer of cells; to obtain normal development of a naked blastocyst in culture it is essential therefore to prevent contact between the blastocyst and the culture dish.

Daniel (1961) showed that fragmented blastocysts have considerable powers of reorganisation in culture. When 5-day old blastocysts were divided into several parts, each part formed within 24 hours a small hollow sphere with a trophoblast wall and an "inner cell mass". As many as eight new "blastocysts" of this kind could be obtained from one original blastocyst, and more spheres could be obtained by subdividing the new "blastocysts".

Implantation in culture

Glenister (1961a, b, 1962, 1963) has devised a method for studying implantation of the rabbit blastocyst in vitro (Plate 2.B). Thin strips of endometrium 0·5 to 1 cm.² are dissected off an opened uterus and stretched on pieces of rayon (cellulose acetate) fabric, which are placed on a solid medium in a watch glass as in the method of Shaffer (1956). The watch glass is housed in a petri dish culture chamber (Fig. 4A, p. 25). Blastocysts are obtained from does 6½ to 7 days after mating and the zona pellucida is removed with watch-makers forceps. Before the blastocysts are transferred to the explanted endometrium, a layer of fluid to support them in the culture is provided by 9–12 drops of liquid medium placed over the endometrium. After 2–3 days in culture, the explants on their pieces of rayon are transplanted to another watch glass containing fresh medium.

In the first cultures of this type made by Glenister, the solid medium consisted of an agar clot containing chick embryo extract, egg albumen and Tyrode solution; it was made up in bulk by adding 10 ml. of egg albumen in 20 ml. of Tyrode saline to 100 ml. of 0·6% agar in warm Tyrode saline, and then adding 10 ml. of chick embryo extract (p. 7) to the mixture; 15 drops of this medium were placed in each watch glass and allowed to cool and solidify. Serum, obtained from the doe providing the blastocysts, was used for the liquid medium over the endometrium. In later experiments (1963) the medium was varied, e.g. (1) a solid base of agar containing albumen only, with a liquid layer of a complex chemically defined medium (Tissue culture medium "199", from Glaxo Laboratories Ltd., Greenford, England), or (2) an entirely liquid medium ("199") in which the explants were supported on a wire-mesh platform. In some experiments oestrogen and progesterone hormones were added.

In such cultures tissues of the embryo proper develop only irregularly, but the blastocysts implant and the trophoblast invades the endometrium in a manner similar to that in vivo. It appears to make no difference whether the endometrium is obtained from the same doe as the blastocysts, from another pregnant doe, or from an adult virgin doe. The proportion (about three-quarters) of blasto-cysts which implants successfully also varies little with the type of nutrient medium used, except that in media containing added hormones the proportion is reduced. When the cultures are incubated in 95% O_2 and 5% CO_2 instead of air, a much higher proportion of the blastocysts expand normally, and remain expanded, and the trophoblast undergoes more advanced differentiation into syncytial and cellular layers.

POST-IMPLANTATION EMBRYOS

Most early attempts at culturing post-implantation embryos met with very little success. However, Jolly and Lieure (1938) obtained limited development of rat and guinea-pig embryos explanted into homologous serum at stages between primitive streak and a few somites. They report that of their explanted rat embryos 37% developed an embryonic axis with a rhythmically beating heart, but only 9% a functioning blood circulation; none formed limb buds or a circulation in the allantois. Nicholas and Rudnick (1934, 1938) appear to have had a similar degree of success with rat embryos cultured in heparinised rat plasma and embryo extract. Waddington and Waterman (1933) explanted rabbit blastodiscs of primitive streak to 3-somite stages onto plasma clots; in the most successful cultures a 6–9 somite embryo was obtained with neural tube and beating heart, but without any blood circulation. Smith (1964) cultured mouse embryos of 4–8 somites on nutrient agar clots, after tearing the yolk sac and amnion so that the embryos flattened out; the cultures were incubated for 18–20 hours in 5% CO_2 in air, and the embryos developed up to the 16-somite stage, but without a blood circulation.

Rat and mouse embryos on plasma clots

Better development of post-implantation embryos has been obtained by New and Stein (1963, 1964) by culturing early somite stages of mouse and rat embryos, with the yolk sac intact, on the surface of plasma clots. Descriptions of the development of these embryos (which are very similar) during normal gestation are given by Snell (1941—mouse) and Witschi (1956—rat). The clots are made in watch glasses enclosed in petri dishes, as in the classic organ culture technique of Fell and Robison (1929), and the cultures are incubated in 60% O_2 and 3–5% CO_2.

The details of the culture method are as follows. Adult female rats or mice are housed with males for 12 hours, and those then found to have copulation plugs are removed and later examined for embryos. (See p. 22 for mating behaviour in mice. Oestrus in rats also normally occurs at night, but can be varied by altering the timing of the light and dark periods; the commonest duration for the oestrous cycle is 4 days.) Development of the embryos to a stage suitable for explanting (Witschi stages 14–16; see p. 40) takes 10–11 days in rats and 8–9 days in mice. The culture chambers consist of petri dishes 7–8 cm. in diameter containing watch glasses of about 4 cm. diameter (Fig. 4A, p. 25). The embryos and nutrient medium are placed in the watch glass, which is surrounded by cotton wool soaked in water or saline to maintain a humid atmosphere.

The clots are made of 3 parts chick plasma and 1 part of an extract from ground-up chick, rat or mouse embryos (p. 7). It is not necessary to measure the quantities of plasma and embryo extract exactly, and a convenient way of making a series of clots is to pipette into each watch glass a certain number of drops of each ingredient. Pasteur pipettes of 1 mm. bore at the tip are suitable for this, one pipette being used for the plasma and another for the embryo extract. Fifteen drops of plasma and five drops of embryo extract make a clot suitable for four or five embryos. The mixture in each watch glass is stirred and spread into an even pool of liquid immediately both ingredients have been added. Coagulation begins in a minute or two, and after about ten minutes the clot is firm enough to be used for culturing.

In rats and mice, somite stage embryos are completely surrounded by uterine decidual tissue, which has proliferated to such an extent that it blocks the uterine lumen and produces a series of easily visible swellings in the uterus. The method of explanting the embryo is shown in Fig. 5. The pregnant females are killed by breaking the neck, and each uterine horn is transferred to a watch glass containing Tyrode saline (p. 5); the uterine wall is then torn open with forceps, care being taken not to squeeze the embryos or damage them with the points of the forceps, and the pear-shaped decidual swellings are dissected out. The most difficult part of the operation is the removal of the embryo and its membranes from the decidua, and from this stage onwards it is essential to work under a dissecting microscope. The best method is to make a meridional incision in the broad end of the decidual "pear" (arrow in Fig. 5B), preferably cutting along the groove representing the remains of the uterine lumen, and then to tear the decidua into two equal halves. The embryo and its membranes are usually left intact and adhering to one of the halves (Fig. 5C) from which they can easily be dissected.

Surrounding the embryo is Reichert's membrane with its adherent endoderm and trophoblast cells, and the next stage is to

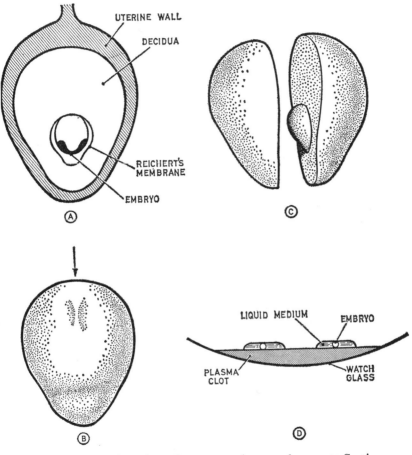

Figure 5. Explantation of mouse and rat embryos. A. Section through uterus of 8-day pregnant mouse or 10-day pregnant rat. Decidua surrounds embryo and blocks uterine lumen. B. Decidua after removal of uterine muscle layers. Decidua is next separated into two halves (from point indicated by arrow) and c. Embryo and membranes can then be easily dissected out. D. After removal of Reichert's membrane, embryo with yolk sac and ectoplacental cone is placed on plasma clot in a drop of nutrient medium.

remove it. Dissecting away the membrane is not difficult if it is first torn open with very fine watchmakers forceps. A good place to grasp it in the forceps is just above the middle of the embryo, where it usually stands further away from underlying tissues than elsewhere.

The explant now consists of a sphere of yolk sac with the embryo at one pole and the ectoplacental cone at the other (Plate 2.c). It is transferred to the clot in a drop of embryo extract (normal strength or diluted with saline) which is spread until its surface is just level with the top of the explant (Fig. 5D). The explant is arranged with the ectoplacental cone to one side.

The cultures are housed in gas chambers (p. 8) in an atmosphere of 3–5% CO_2 and 60–90% O_2, and incubated at 37°C.

With practice the explantation of each embryo need take no more than 5–10 minutes. Delays of up to 3 hours between killing the mouse or rat and transferring the embryos to the incubator seem to have no effect on embryonic development, and it is unnecessary to operate so hurriedly as to risk wounding the embryos. With reasonable care all the embryos in a uterus can be transferred undamaged to the culture vessels. Small injuries to the yolk sac usually heal and do not hinder embryonic development.

Explanted mouse embryos grow in culture for up to 40 hours and develop a functioning blood circulation in the embryo and yolk sac, and often in the allantoic "placenta". The yolk sac enlarges up to 4 mm. diameter and gradually sinks into a cavity which it digests in the clot, thus bringing the circulating blood into close contact with the clot over a wide area. Despite this close contact the yolk sac does not form any cellular adhesion with the clot; cells from the ectoplacental cone, however, become firmly attached to the clot and migrate for a short distance into and over it. Embryonic development may continue up to the 30–35 somite stage with the formation of prominent anterior and posterior limb buds.

Development of rat embryos in culture is very similar to that of mouse embryos, except that the explants grow somewhat larger (yolk sac diameter up to 5 mm.), the allantoic circulation rarely develops, and the most advanced stage of embryonic development that can be attained is about 28–30 somites with only the anterior limb buds prominent (Plate 2.D).

As long as a good blood circulation is present, both rat and mouse embryos develop at about the same rate in vitro as in vivo, forming about 8 extra somites every 12 hours.

Some factors affecting development in culture
Only a few of the many factors that might affect development of post-implantation rat and mouse embryos in culture have been examined (New and Stein 1964). Experiments to compare mouse embryo extract with chick embryo extract as a constituent of the clot and of the liquid medium, showed that both give the same results. However, differences in age of the embryos at explantation, or of O_2 or CO_2 concentration during incubation, have marked effects on the amount of development and duration of survival.

(i) Development of embryos explanted at different stages.
Fig. 6 shows the survival rates of mouse embryos explanted at different stages between primitive streak and 12 somites. In general

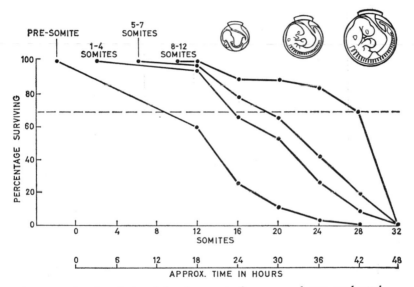

Figure 6. Survival and development of mouse embryos explanted at pre-somite, 1–4 somite, 5–7 somite, and 8–12 somite stages. Broken line indicates two-thirds surviving.

the older embryos grow better, but few develop beyond the 32-somite stage. Development of the pre-somite embryos is usually poor; mortality is high and those that develop are often abnormal and stunted.

Embryos can be explanted at stages more advanced than 12

somites, and a higher proportion then develop to 30–35 somites, but not further.

Similar results are obtained with rat embryos.

(ii) O_2 and CO_2.

Fig. 7 shows the survival rates of mouse embryos cultured in air containing 4–5% CO_2 compared with those in air containing 4–5% CO_2+60% O_2. The histogram indicates the combined results of

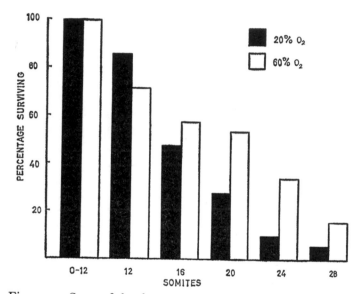

Figure 7. Stage of development reached in culture, as indicated by number of somites, of mouse embryos explanted at 0–12 somites and grown in 20% O_2 (solid rectangles) or 60% O_2 (open rectangles).

experiments with embryos explanted at all stages between head fold and 12 somites, and shows that in general the addition of O_2 to the air in the culture chambers much improves embryonic development. (The extra O_2 is apparently not beneficial, and may even be harmful, to pre-somite stages, however.)

In an experiment designed to test the effect of the CO_2 on the development of embryos explanted at stages between head fold and 12 somites, embryos cultured in air with 4–5% CO_2 were compared with controls cultured in air. The extra CO_2 appeared to benefit embryos of all ages, and the proportion (55%) of embryos in the

CO_2 cultures that developed to the 20-somite stage was more than twice that (24%) of the controls.

Rat embryos in serum

New (1966) has found that rat embryos will grow as well in rat serum as on plasma clots. Blood is obtained by inserting a 10 ml. hypodermic syringe into the dorsal aorta, at the junction of the iliac arteries, of rats anaesthetised with ether. A No. 2 hypodermic needle is suitable, and both syringe and needle must be siliconed to prevent premature clotting. 5–10 ml. of blood can be drawn from each rat, which is then killed. The blood is transferred to centrifuge tubes where it is allowed to clot, and the clot is then freed from the tube wall with a knife and left overnight to contract and release the serum. The following day the tubes are centrifuged (3000 r.p.m. for 15 minutes) and the serum decanted off.

Each embryo is placed in a watch glass containing 0·5–1·0 ml. of the serum, and incubated in petri dish culture chambers in 60% O_2 and 3% CO_2, as for plasma clot cultures.

Good results are obtained with serum from male or female (pregnant or non-pregnant) rats. In serum from other mammals or from the chick, however, development of the rat embryos is often poor.

NORMAL STAGES IN THE EARLY DEVELOPMENT OF THE RAT (AND MOUSE)

The following table of early stages of rat development is based on the complete table of development by Witschi (1962). Age (2nd column) = days after mating, i.e. approximately time from fertilisation plus 8 hours. Size (3rd column) = largest dimension of embryo in natural position (largest and smallest dimensions of blastocysts and chorionic vesicles are given in parentheses).

The early development of the mouse is very similar to that of the rat. The times of development of mouse stages corresponding to those of the rat are given in parentheses in the 2nd column. After the first few cleavage divisions, development in the mouse remains about 2 days ahead of the rat.

STAGE	AGE days	SIZE mm.	

FERTILISATION TO BLASTULA

STAGE	AGE days	SIZE mm.	
1	$1\frac{1}{2}$	·07	1 Cell (in oviduct)
2	$2\frac{1}{2}$ (Mouse 1)		2 Cells ,,
3	$3\frac{1}{2}$		4 Cells ,,
4	$3\frac{1}{2}$–4 (M.2)		8–12 Cells ,,
5	4		Morula (in uterus)
6	$4\frac{1}{2}$	(·08 × ·03)	Early blastocyst ,,
7	$5\frac{1}{2}$	(·12 × ·05)	Free blastocyst ,,

GASTRULA (*Implantation*)

8	$6\frac{1}{2}$ (M.$4\frac{1}{2}$)	(·28 × ·07)	Implanting blastocyst, with trophoblastic cone and inner cell mass. Outgrowth of endoderm (hypoblast).
9	7–$7\frac{1}{2}$		Diplotrophoblast. Inner cell mass (pendant) covered with endoderm.
10	$7\frac{1}{2}$–8	(·3 × ·1)	Near complete implantation. Pendant begins differentiation into embryonic and extra-embryonic parts.
11	8–$8\frac{1}{2}$	(·5 × ·1)	Completion of implantation. Primary amniotic cyst. Ectoplacental cone.

PRIMITIVE STREAK

12	9 (M.7)	(1·04 × ·26)	Connecting ectochorionic and amniotic cavities. Rudiments of amniotic folds. Start of third layer formation, and of primitive streak. Blastemas of heart and of pericardium.

NEURULA STAGES

13	$9\frac{1}{2}$	1·0 (1·4 × ·45)	Presomite neurula. Fusion of chorio-amniotic folds; chorio-amniotic stalk. Neural plate. Embryo curved dorsally.
14	1c (M.8)	1·5 (1·8 × 1·1)	Pendant with three cavities: ectochorionic cyst, exocoelom, and amniotic cavity. Ectochorionic cyst collapsing. Allantoic stalk projects into exocoelom. Somites 1–4 (occipital). Neural plate. Paired tubular hearts; initiation of myocardial contractions. Start of fore-gut formation. Embryo bent dorsally.
15	$10\frac{1}{2}$	2·0 (1·1 × 2·2)	Ectochorionic cyst fused with ectoplacenta and with allantoic stalk. Regression of peripheral (distal) yolk sac and trophectoderm (diplotrophoblast). Somites 5–12

STAGE	AGE days	SIZE mm.	

(cervical). Partly closed neural tube. Optic sulcus. Otic placode. Single tubular heart, beating. 1st aortic arch. Oral membrane ruptures. Primitive thyroid pit. Nephric blastema cord. Gonia in endoderm. Embryo bent dorsally.

16 | 11 (M.9) | 2·4 (2·2 × 3·4) | Disc and yolk-sac placentas. Somites 13–20 (upper thoracic). Three primordial brain vesicles. Six rhombomeres. Upper neuropore closes, at 17 somites. Hypophyseal placode. Nasal placodes. Optic bulbs. Otic cups. Aortic arches I and II. Circulation established. Appendicular folds. Liver primordium. Embryo reverses, curves ventrally.

17 | 11½ | 3·3 | Somites 21–25 (lower thoracic). Lower neuropore closes, at 24 somites. Hypophyseal cup. Olfactory placodes. Optic bulbs and stalks. Closing otic cups. Aortic arches I, II and III. Liver. Dorsal pancreas. Yolk stalk closes at level of 15th somite, and resorbs. Rudiments of nephric ducts and tubules. Gonia in mesentery. Primitive streak disappears. Tailbud becomes organised. Arm- and leg-buds recognisable.

TAILBUD STAGES

18 | 12 (M.10) | 3·8 | Somites 26–28 (upper lumbar). Tel-, di-, mes-, met- and myelencephalon. Wide hypophyseal cup. Olfactory placodes. Lens placodes. Otic vesicles closed. Three aortic arches, I regressing; IV in preparation. First indication of separation of left and right heart chambers. Thyroid vesicle constricting. Laryngotracheal groove, paired lung buds. Stomach. Liver trabeculae. Nephric duct approaches cloacal region. Arm-buds recognisable.

19 | 12–12½ | 4·2 | Somites 29–31 (lower lumbar). Hypophysis a wide cup. Beginning invagination of optic bulbs and lens placodes. Otic vesicles with short endolymphatic ducts. Four aortic arches, I regressing, IV still small. Cervical folds. Trachea begins separation from oesophagus. Growing tips of nephric

STAGE	AGE days	SIZE mm.	
			ducts meet with the nephric papillae of cloaca. Small solid ureterbuds. Gonadal folds begin to form. Appendicular folds and buds.
20	12–12½	5·0 (4·7×5·2)	Somites 32–33 (upper sacral). Aortic arch II regressing; III and IV well developed; V very slender, irregular.
21	12½		Somites 34–35 (lower sacral). Aortic arches III and IV large, sometimes one or both of the V arches well developed.
22	12½–13	5·2	Somite 36 (first caudal). Hypophyseal cup closely applied to frontal wall of infundibulum. Deep, simple olfactory pits. Lens cup begins to close. Nervous layer of retina thicker than pigment layer. Otic vesicles with endolymphatic duct. Four aortic arches: III, IV are large, V, VI are very slender. Cervical fold. Thyroid separating from epithelium of tongue. First pharyngeal pouch touches ectoderm; second ruptured; third touches ectoderm. Larynx; trachea mostly free. Vesicular lungs. Stomach. Duodenum; hepatopancreatic duct; ventral pancreas. Start of umbilical herniation. Indifferent gonadal folds. Primitive mesonephric tubules, mostly solid. Nephric duct, without continuous lumen, fused with the cloacal nephric papillae. Mammary welts.
23	12½–13 (M.11)	5·6 (4·5×5·8)	Somites 37–38 (caudal). Lens sacs with fairly large pore. The first cervical ganglion has completely regressed. The ganglion of the second cervical nerve (sixth somite) now a convenient landmark in counting somites. In addition to four arches as in preceding stage, also a VII (pulmonary) arch or plexus. Thyroid connected with surface epithelium by slender cord of cells. Larynx differentiation. Mesonephric tubules and ducts without continuous lumen; no renal corpuscles.
24	12½–13	6·0	Somites 39–40 (caudal). Lens sacs with closing pore. Thyroid a solid body. Thymus primordia. In heart, atrioventricular cushions and septa in evidence (primordia). Cloaca begins dividing.

STAGE	AGE days	SIZE mm.	

FULL EMBRYO

25   13   6·2   Somites 41–42 (caudal). Occipital somites dispersing. Hypophyseal pouch wide open to oral cavity, flattened against frontal surface of infundibulum. Deep olfactory pits with median pockets (vomero-nasal organs). Lens sacs detach from epidermis, differentiate into epithelium and fibre parts. Nervous layer of retina four times as high as pigment layer. Otic vesicle laterally compressed, saccular and utricular parts. Aortic arches III, IV, and VI well developed; V very irregular, vanishing; VII (pulmonary) consolidating. Deep cervical sinus. Adrenal cortical blastema. Ureter buds imbedded in metanephric blastema. Indifferent sex glands. Armbuds at somite levels 8–14, about as high as long. Legbuds at somite levels 28–31, smaller.

REFERENCES

AUSTIN, C. R. (1961). *The mammalian egg.* Blackwell. Oxford.

BIGGERS, J. D., GWATKIN, R. B. L. & BRINSTER, R. L. (1962). Development of mouse embryos in organ cultures of fallopian tubes on a chemically defined medium. *Nature,* **194,** 747–9.

BISHOP, D. W. (1961). Biology of spermatozoa. In *Sex and internal secretions.* (Young, Ed.) Ballière, Tindall, & Cox, London.

BLANDAU, R. J. (1961). Biology of eggs and implantation. In *Sex and internal secretions.* (Young, Ed.) Ballière, Tindall & Cox, London.

BRACHET, A. (1912). Développement *in vitro* de blastodermes et de jeunes embryons de mammifères. *C.R. Acad. Sci.,* Paris, **155,** 1191–3.

BRACHET, A. (1913). Recherches sur le determinisme héréditaire de l'oeuf des mammifères. Développement *in vitro* de jeunes vésicules blastodermiques du lapin. *Arch. Biol.,* Paris **28,** 447–503.

BRINSTER, R. L. (1963). A method for *in vitro* cultivation of mouse ova from two-cell to blastocyst. *Exp. Cell Res.,* **32,** 205–8.

BRINSTER, R. L. (1965). Studies on the development of mouse embryos *in vitro.* I. The effect of osmolarity and hydrogen ion concentration. II. The effect of energy source. III. The effect of fixed-nitrogen source. *J. exp. Zool.,* **158,** 49–58, 59–68, 69–78.

CHANG, M. C. (1949). Effects of heterologous sera on fertilised rabbit ova. *J. gen. Physiol.,* **32,** 291–300.

CHANG, M. C. (1952). Fertilisability of rabbit ova and the effects of temperature *in vitro* on their subsequent fertilisation and activation *in vivo.* *J. exp. Zool.,* **121,** 351–81.

CHANG, M. C. (1959). Fertilisation of rabbit ova *in vitro*. *Nature*, **184,** 466.

COLE, R. J., EDWARDS, R. G. & PAUL, J. (1966). Cytodifferentiation and embryogenesis in cell colonies and tissue cultures derived from ova and blastocysts of the rabbit. *Devl. Biol.* In press.

DANIEL, J. C. Jr. (1961). Reconstruction of rabbit blastocysts *in vitro*. *Amer. Zool.*, **1,** 444. (Abstract.)

EDWARDS, R. G. (1964). Cleavage of one- and two-celled rabbit eggs *in vitro* after removal of the zona pellucida. *J. Reprod. Fertil.*, **7,** 413–5.

FAWCETT, D. W. (1950). The development of mouse ova under the capsule of the kidney. *Anat. Rec.*, **108,** 71–91.

FAWCETT, D. W., WISLOCKI, G. B. & WALDO, C. M. (1947). The development of mouse ova in the anterior chamber of the eye and in the abdominal cavity. *Amer. J. Anat.*, **81,** 413–43.

FELL, H. B. & ROBISON, R. (1929). The growth, development and phosphatase activity of embryonic avian femora and limb buds cultivated *in vitro*. *Biochem. J.*, **23,** 767–84.

FOWLER, R. E. & EDWARDS, R. G. (1957). Induction of superovulation and pregnancy in mature mice by gonadotrophins. *J. Endocrin.*, **15,** 374–84.

GLENISTER, T. W. (1961a). Organ culture as a new method for studying the implantation of mammalian blastocysts. *Proc. Roy. Soc. B.*, **154,** 428–31.

GLENISTER, T. W. (1961b). Observations on the behaviour in organ culture of rabbit trophoblast from implanting blastocysts and early placentae. *J. Anat.*, **95,** 474–84.

GLENISTER, T. W. (1962). Embryo-endometrial relationships during nidation in organ culture. *J. Obstet. Gynaec. Brit. Comm.*, **69,** 809–14.

GLENISTER, T. W. (1963). Observations on mammalian blastocysts implanting in organ culture. In *Delayed implantation*. (Enders, Ed.) Rice University. Semicentennial Publications.

GRUNEBERG, H. (1943). The development of some external features in mouse embryos. *J. Heredity*, **34,** 88–92.

GWATKIN, R. B. L. (1964). Effect of enzymes and acidity on the zona pellucida of the mouse egg before and after fertilisation. *J. Reprod. Fertil.*, **7,** 99–105.

HAFEZ, E. S. E. (1964). Effects of over-crowding *in utero* on implantation and foetal development in the rabbit. *J. exp. Zool.*, **156,** 269–88.

HAMMOND, J. Jr. (1949). Recovery and culture of tubal mouse ova. *Nature*, **163,** 28–9.

HENNEBERG, B. (1937). Normentafel zur Entwicklungsgeschichte der Wanderratte (*Rattus norvegicus* Erxleben). In Keibel's *Normentafeln zur Entwicklungsgeschichte der Wirbeltiere*. Gustav Fischer, Jena.

JOLLY, J. & LIEURE, C. (1938). Recherches sur la culture des oeufs des mammifères. *Arch. Anat. micr.*, **34,** 307–74.

KEIBEL, F. (Ed.) (1897 etc.) *Normentafeln zur Entwicklungsgeschichte der Wirbeltiere*. Gustav Fischer. Jena.

KENNELLY, J. J. & FOOTE, R. H. (1965). Superovulatory response of pre- and post-pubertal rabbits to commercially available gonadotrophins. *J. Reprod. Fertil.*, **9,** 177–88.

KIRBY, D. R. S. (1962). The influence of the uterine environment on the development of mouse eggs. *J. Embryol. exp. Morph.*, **10**, 496–506.

KIRBY, D. R. S. (1963a). Development of the mouse blastocyst transplanted to the spleen. *J. Reprod. Fertil.*, **5**, 1–12.

KIRBY, D. R. S. (1963b). The development of mouse blastocysts transplanted to the scrotal and cryptorchid testis. *J. Anat. Lond.*, **97**, 119–30.

LANE-PETTER, W. (Ed.) (1963). *Animals for research.* Academic Press. London and New York.

LAWN, L. & McCANCE, R. A. (1962). Ventures with an artificial placenta. 1. Principles and preliminary results. *Proc. Roy. Soc. B.*, **155**, 500–9.

LEWIS, W. H. & GREGORY, P. M. (1929). Cinematographs of living developing rabbit eggs. *Science*, **69**, 226–9.

LONG, J. A. & BURLINGAME, P. L. (1938). The development of the external form of the rat with observations of the origin of the extraembryonic coelom and foetal membranes. *Univ. of Calif. Publ. in Zool.*, **43**, 143–84.

LUTWAK-MANN, C., HAY, M. F. & ADAMS, C. E. (1962). The effect of ovariectomy on rabbit blastocysts. *J. Endocrin*, **24**, 185–97.

McLAREN, A. & BIGGERS, J. D. (1958). Successful development and birth of mice cultivated *in vitro* as early embryos. *Nature*, **182**, 877–8.

McLAREN, A. & MICHIE, D. (1956). Studies on the transfer of fertilised mouse eggs to uterine foster-mothers. 1. Factors affecting the implantation of native and transferred eggs. *J. exp. Biol.*, **33**, 394–416.

McLAREN, A. & TARKOWSKI, A. K. (1963) Implantation of mouse eggs in the peritoneal cavity. *J. Reprod. Fertil.*, **6**, 385–92.

MINOT, C. S. & TAYLOR, E. (1905). Normal plates of the development of the rabbit (*Lepus cuniculus L*). In Keibel's *Normentafeln zur Entwicklungsgeschichte der Wirbeltiere.* Gustav Fischer. Jena.

MINTZ, B. (1962). Experimental study of the developing mammalian egg. Removal of the zona pellucida. *Science*, **138**, 594–5.

MINTZ, B. (1964). Formation of genetically mosaic mouse embryos, and early development of "lethal (t¹²/t¹²)-normal" mosaics. *J. exp. Zool.*, **157**, 273–92.

MOOG, F. & LUTWAK-MANN, G. (1958). Observations on rabbit blastocysts prepared as flat mounts. *J. Embryol. exp. Morph.*, **6**, 57–67.

NEW, D. A. T. (1964). Growing embryos in the laboratory. *Discovery.* **25**, 16–21.

NEW, D. A. T. (1966). Development of rat embryos cultured in blood sera. *J. Reprod. Fertil.* In the press.

NEW, D. A. T. & STEIN, K. F. (1963). Cultivation of mouse embryos *in vitro. Nature*, **199**, 297–9.

NEW, D. A. T. & STEIN, K. F. (1964). Cultivation of post-implantation mouse and rat embryos on plasma clots. *J. Embryol. exp. Morph.*, **12**, 101–11.

NICHOLAS, J. S. & RUDNICK, D. (1934). The development of rat embryos in tissue culture. *Proc. Nat. Acad. Sci.*, **20**, 656–8.

NICHOLAS, J. S. & RUDNICK, D. (1938). Development of rat embryos of egg cylinder to head-fold stages in plasma cultures. *J. exp. Zool.*, **78**, 205–32.

NIXON, D. A., BRITTON, H. G. & ALEXANDER, D. P. (1963). Perfusion of the viable sheep foetus. *Nature*, **199**, 183–5.

OTIS, E. M. & BRENT, R. (1954). Equivalent ages in mouse and human embryos. *Anat. Rec.*, **120**, 33–64.

PINCUS, G. (1940). Superovulation in rabbits. *Anat. Rec.*, **77**, 1–8.

PINCUS, G. & WERTHESSEN, N. T. (1938). The comparative behaviour of mammalian eggs *in vivo* and *in vitro*. III. Factors controlling the growth of the rabbit blastocyst. *J. exp. Zool.*, **78**, 1–18.

RUNNER, M. N. (1947). Development of mouse eggs in the anterior chamber of the eye. *Anat. Rec.*, **98**, 1–17.

RUNNER, M. N. & PALM, J. (1953). Transplantation and survival of un-fertilised ova of the mouse in relation to post-ovulatory age. *J. exp. Zool.*, **124**, 303–16.

SHAFFER, B. M. (1956). The culture of organs from the embryonic chick on cellulose-acetate fabric. *Exp. Cell Res.*, **11**, 244–8.

SMITH, A. U. (1949). Cultivation of rabbit eggs and cumuli for phase-contrast microscopy. *Nature*, **164**, 1136–7.

SMITH, L. J. (1964). The effects of transection and extirpation on axis formation and elongation in the young mouse embryo. *J. Embryol. exp. Morph.*, **12**, 787–803.

SNELL, G. D. (1941). Chapters 1 and 2 in *Biology of the laboratory mouse*. (G. D. Snell, Ed.) Dover Publications. New York.

TARKOWSKI, A. K. (1961). Mouse chimaeras developed from fused eggs. *Nature*, **190**, 857–60.

TARKOWSKI, A. K. (1964a). Patterns of pigmentation in experimentally produced mouse chimaerae. *J. Embryol. exp. Morph.*, **12**, 575–85.

TARKOWSKI, A. K. (1964b). True hermaphroditism in chimaeric mice. *J. Embryol. exp. Morph.*, **12**, 735–57.

WADDINGTON, C. H. & WATERMAN, A. J. (1933). The development *in vitro* of young rabbit embryos. *J. Anat.*, **67**, 355–70.

WESTIN, B., NYBERG, R. & ENHORNING, G. (1958). A technique for the perfusion of the previable human foetus. *Acta paediatr.*, Stockh., **47**, 339–49.

WHITTEN, W. K. (1956). Culture of tubal mouse ova. *Nature*, **177**, 96.

WHITTEN, W. K. (1957a). Culture of tubal ova. *Nature*, **179**, 1081–2.

WHITTEN, W. K. (1957b). The effect of progesterone on the development of mouse eggs *in vitro*. *J. Endocrinol*, **16**, 80–5.

WITSCHI, E. (1956). *Development of vertebrates*. Saunders. Philadelphia and London.

WITSCHI, E. (1962). Development: Rat. In *Growth. VII. Pre-natal Vertebrate Development*. (Altman and Dittmer, Eds.) Biological Handbooks of the Federation of American Societies for Experimental Biology. Washington.

WORDEN, A. N. & LANE-PETTER, W. (Eds.) (1957). *The UFAW handbook on the care and management of laboratory animals*. The Universities Federation for Animal Welfare. London.

CHAPTER 3

The Chick

(*Gallus domesticus*)

The chick embryo has been an object of study at least since the time of the Hippocratic writers, and it played a prominent part in the formulation of most of the theories and speculations of the early embryologists (see Oppenheimer 1955, Needham 1959). The reasons for this long and venerable history are undoubtedly concerned far more with the size of the egg than with any peculiarities of the embryo itself. Development, particularly of the embryonic membranes, proceeds at a rate and on a scale which was spectacular long before microscopes were available to magnify it, and the food value of the egg has always stimulated sufficient agricultural production to provide, as a by-product, a steady supply of material for embryologists.

The same advantages still apply today. In particular, the chick provides a solution to that perennial problem of the embryology teacher—how to obtain embryos of a required stage, at a particular hour, at any time of year, with the minimum of trouble. The feeding and breeding of the adult animals, the source of so many anxieties in obtaining other embryos, can here be safely left to the farmer. If the eggs arrive earlier than required, development can be delayed by keeping them cool—for a few days if necessary; and when they are incubated, growth is so rapid that experiments can often be completed in a fraction of the time required with other material.

Techniques are available for growing the isolated chick blastoderm in culture up to the 4th day of incubation, which makes possible very close observation and fine operations on the earliest stages of development. Later stages are usually studied in ovo through windows cut in the shell. There is rarely any advantage in explanting and culturing the embryo with the yolk intact.

Some valuable books on the chick embryo are: Romanoff and Romanoff (1949)—on the unincubated egg; Needham (1931, 1950) —on embryos in general, but with a considerable amount on the biochemistry and physiology of the chick; Hamilton (1952) and

Romanoff (1960)—the most comprehensive descriptions available of the development and physiology of the embryo and its membranes; Waddington (1952)—on the experimental embryology; *Annals of the New York Academy of Sciences,* Vol. 55 (1952)—contains a symposium on the chick embryo in biological research; Landauer (1961) —on factors affecting hatchability.

A normal table of chick development (Keibel and Abraham 1900), with detailed illustrations, is included in Keibel's Normentafeln. But the table most generally used now is that of Hamburger and Hamilton (p. 84-92). Vakaet (1962) divides the pre-streak and primitive streak periods of development into more stages than Hamburger and Hamilton, an arrangement that will probably prove useful to embryologists studying development of the early blastoderm. Künzel (1962) has published a series of photographs of eggs opened at intervals of one day, which show the changing spatial relationships of embryo and embryonic membranes during development.

STORAGE AND INCUBATION OF EGGS

The agricultural importance of the chick has inspired a large literature on factors affecting hatchability (i.e. percentage of eggs hatching). This has been summarised in the valuable monograph by Landauer (1961) from which several of the following recommendations are taken. For embryological studies requiring embryos of only a few days of incubation, it may not be necessary to treat the eggs quite as carefully, particularly as the main peak of mortality is normally around the 19th day. On the other hand explanted embryos, or embryos in opened eggs, may have special requirements, which will be mentioned in connection with particular techniques.

Storage

Hatchability is affected by both the temperature and duration of storage (i.e. the time between laying and incubating) and also by excessive shaking.

The optimum temperature for storage is 7-15°C. Outside this range the incidence of subsequent embryonic abnormalities is increased and hatchability is reduced. Eggs should therefore neither be stored in a warm room, nor in a refrigerator.

Storing the eggs under optimum conditions for 1-2 weeks does little harm, but if they are kept for longer, hatchability falls off rapidly and reaches almost zero at 6 weeks (Fig. 8). Kaufman (1938) found that embryos developing in eggs that had been stored for 3–5 weeks before incubation had a higher water content and were smaller than controls; hatching was delayed and mortality was particularly high during the early stages of development.

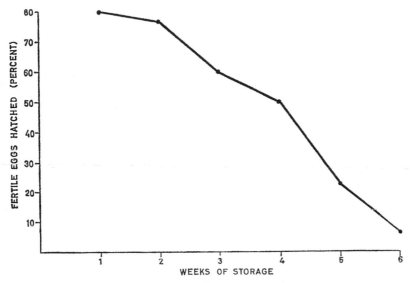

Figure 8. Effect of storage of eggs at optimum temperature (10°C) on percentage hatched. (From data of Olsen & Haynes 1948.)

Violent and prolonged shaking reduces hatchability and increases the incidence of all types of commonly occurring malformations. In some cases it has been confirmed that transport, by rail or by sea, can be harmful, apparently as a result of repeated jarring of the eggs. But mild agitation, such as that incurred in normal careful handling and transport, has little or no effect.

Incubation

Temperature

It is extremely important to maintain the correct temperature during incubation.

Barott (1937) made a particularly careful study of the effects of different temperatures and humidities on hatchability, and his results indicate that the optimum temperature at 60% relative humidity is

38·0°C; hatchability falls off very rapidly with even small deviations from this (Fig. 9). Embryos may begin to develop at temperatures widely different from the optimum, but few survive for long.

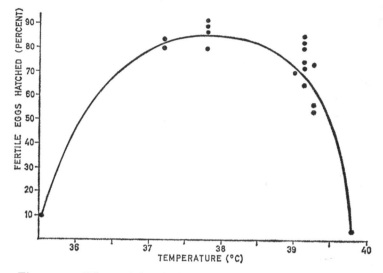

Figure 9. Effect of incubation temperature (at 60% relative humidity) on percentage of fertile eggs hatched. (Barott 1937.)

In the past it was often assumed, by analogy with the conditions of natural incubation, that there should be a temperature gradient declining from upper to lower surface of the eggs. Burke's measurements (1925) suggested that under a sitting hen the bottom of the egg may be as much as 8 degrees C colder than the top. But experiment has failed to show any advantage in reproducing this gradient artificially. Eggs heated uniformly develop just as well as those heated from above.

During early development the embryos are remarkably tolerant of large temporary falls in temperature, as opposed to small prolonged ones. Provided they are cooled sufficiently for development to cease altogether (i.e. to below about 25°C) incubation can be interrupted during the first week for as long as 24 hours with little, if any, harmful effect. The embryos are less resistant to cooling at later stages of incubation, and Ancel (1958, 1959) has shown that even during the first week, if the eggs are kept cold (17°–22°C) for 2–3 days, a proportion of the embryos subsequently develop abnormalities.

Humidity

The development of the chick embryo poses a problem of water conservation in a particularly acute form. The only water available to the embryo during the entire period of incubation is that stored initially in the egg, and this is continually being reduced by evaporation through the shell, which must be porous to permit respiration. If the rate of evaporation is too great the embryo runs out of water before incubation is completed. Excessively dry air in the incubator, therefore, reduces hatchability.

More surprising, and as yet still unexplained, is the fact that high humidity also has harmful effects. According to Barott (1937) the optimum relative humidity at 38°C is 60%, and hatchability falls off fairly rapidly at humidities above or below this. The optimum varies slightly with temperature (Fig. 10).

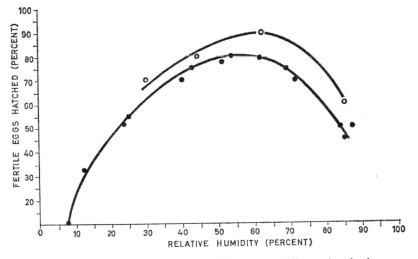

Figure 10.   Effect of relative humidity at two different incubation temperatures on percentage of fertile eggs hatched.
Upper curve: 38°C. *Lower curve:* 39°C (Barott 1937).

O_2 and CO_2

Carbon dioxide concentrations between zero and 1% have little effect on hatchability, but concentrations above 1% lead to slow growth, abnormalities and early death of the embryo. The optimum oxygen concentration is just over 20%, but mortality is only slightly increased by concentrations up to 30%; below 20% or over 30%, however, hatchability falls off rapidly.

During early development the oxygen requirements of the embryo are small, and a few eggs can be successfully incubated, for a few days, in practically any incubator that will maintain the correct temperature. To incubate large numbers of eggs right through to hatching, however, a properly ventilated incubator is necessary.

Turning

The most curious of the requirements for good hatchability is the periodic turning of the eggs during incubation. Eycleshymer (1906) appears to have been one of the first to find that many more chicks hatch successfully from turned than from unturned eggs, and this observation has been confirmed by many later workers. The hatchability of unturned eggs may be as low as 30% or less.

In the nest the eggs are turned frequently by the hen, who shuffles them with her feet and beak. Under the conditions of artificial incubation turning twice a day, alternately clockwise and anticlockwise, until the 18th day, gives good results. Turning four or five times daily gives a slight (6–10%) further increase in hatchability, but it is doubtful if any additional improvement can be gained by turning more than this.

Eggs should not be incubated with the small end upwards because this markedly increases the proportion that develop abnormally, but eggs incubated either horizontally or with the large end upwards develop well. Horizontally incubated eggs are turned by rotating them individually 45°–180° round the long axis; eggs with the large end upwards are tilted 45° to either side of the vertical, usually by tilting the tray on which they stand. Funk and Forward (1960) found that turning either horizontal or vertical eggs through 45° (i.e. total angle 90°) gives 2–3% better hatchability than turning through 30°, but that no advantage is gained by increasing the angle further. 72·5% of their horizontal eggs turned 45° hatched, as compared with 76·7% of the vertical eggs turned 45°.

After the 18th day of incubation it is advisable to place all eggs horizontally and to leave them unturned, otherwise hatching may be hindered.

New (1957) showed that the most important time for turning the eggs is between the 4th and 7th days of incubation (Table 1). Eggs turned during this period hatch nearly as many live chicks as those turned throughout incubation, whereas the hatchability of eggs turned only between the 8th and 11th days of incubation is as low as that of eggs left unturned. Examination by candling suggests that turning the eggs between the 4th and 7th day maintains a layer of lubricating albumen between the shell membranes and chorion, and prevents the formation of adhesions which might lead to the many abnormalities of development frequently found in unturned eggs (see Kaltofen 1961 for further discussion of this problem).

	Infertile	Died 1st week	Died 2nd week	Died 3rd week	Hatched
Turned 4th–7th day	4	1	2	7	21
Turned 8th–11th day	7	7	7	8	6
Turned throughout	4	5	0	2	24
Unturned	6	3	2	15	9

TABLE 1. Effect of turning eggs during incubation. Four batches, each of 35 eggs, were subjected to different turning schedules. Hatchability of eggs turned only between the 4th and 7th days of incubation was nearly as high as that of eggs turned throughout incubation. Hatchability of eggs turned only between the 8th and 11th days was as low as that of eggs left unturned.

When, as in many embryological experiments, a "window" has been cut in the egg, and the smooth surface of the shell membranes has been broken, it is doubtful whether turning is advantageous. It can often be a nuisance in interfering with observation of the embryo, dislodging grafts, etc., and New's results indicate that it is certainly not worth doing after any operation performed later than the 7th day. After earlier operations turning may sometimes be justified, but rarely in experiments completed during the first two weeks of incubation, because most of the embryos that die in unturned eggs do so towards the end of the third week. When development is allowed to continue beyond hatching, the number of live chicks obtained may be reduced by omitting turning, but those that hatch successfully are normal and healthy.

EMBRYOS IN THE SHELL

Development in the opened egg

Aseptic precautions (p. 3) should be taken when eggs are opened. Under appropriate conditions growth of the embryo will continue

C

for several days, or longer, after part of the shell has been removed. Romanoff (1931) devised a simple method for observing embryonic development in opened eggs and studied the duration of survival after the eggs had been opened at different stages of incubation. A circle about 25 mm. in diameter was cut at the blunt end of each egg and the cap of shell and shell membrane removed. A little albumen was poured out to increase the field of observation, and the egg was then placed upright on a wire mesh tray in a glass-topped incubator and covered with a 150 ml. beaker (Fig. 11A); the humidity was maintained at 65%. The duration of survival varied greatly with

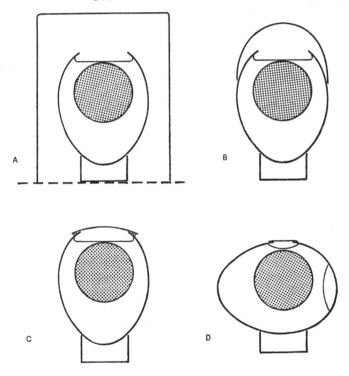

Figure 11. Methods of incubating opened eggs. A. Eggs placed on perforated tray and covered with beaker; humidity maintained at 65% (Romanoff 1931). B. Opening in egg covered with cap of eggshell (Price and Fowler 1940). C. Opening covered with watch glass sealed on with wax (Weiss and Andres 1952). D. Small opening sealed with tape or glass coverslip (or removed piece of shell resealed in position); cavity below the opening can be enlarged by letting air out of the air sac.

the stage at which the egg was opened. In eggs opened before incubation, half the embryos died before the 3rd day and none survived more than 9 days; of those opened on the 3rd or 4th day half
survived to the 16th day, and a few to the 19th day, but the latter
were only two-thirds (20 gms.) of the normal weight; in eggs opened
after 6 days some of the embryos reached hatching.

Instead of covering the opened egg with a beaker, a cap can be
made from the broad-end half of the shell of another egg (Price and
Fowler 1940). The shell membranes are removed from the cap,
which is then sterilised in alcohol. It is not sealed to the opened egg,
and forms a convenient cover if frequent reopening is required
(Fig. 11 B). Weiss and Andres (p. 60) used instead a watchglass
sealed to the shell with wax (Fig. 11 C); some of their embryos, in
eggs opened at 3–4 days of incubation, developed to the end of the
incubation period, and a few hatched.

Moscona (1959) has shown that in opened eggs, the reduction in
CO_2 concentration near the opening causes abnormal development
of the chorion, which becomes squamous and keratinised. This does
not occur if the opening is covered with sellotape or parafilm well
sealed on with wax, or if the eggs are incubated in 5–8% CO_2
(Moscona & Carneckas 1959).

Candling and making windows

Operations on the embryo are usually made through a small
opening or "window", 1 cm. square or less, cut in the side of the
egg (Fig. 11D). This provides a smaller field of observation than in
eggs opened by Romanoff's method, but usually gives considerably
longer survival of the embryo.

Care must be taken in deciding where to cut the window. It is
worth taking trouble to ensure that the window is made over the
embryo, because it is usually difficult to move the egg contents after
the opening has been made.

Candling, i.e. examining the egg by transmitted light, is the best
guide to the position of the embryo. A simple apparatus for candling
eggs can be made by housing a 100-watt electric light bulb in a
light-proof box. An egg-shaped hole, a little smaller than the size
of the eggs, is cut in the top of the box, and the eggs are examined
by placing them over the hole. Success depends on the eye receiving
the maximum of light through the egg and as little as possible from
anywhere else; a cloth or rubber border to the hole gives a better

fit and reduces extraneous light. If possible the apparatus should be used in a dark room.

The blastoderm is usually difficult to locate by candling during the first two days of incubation, though Olsen and Knox (1938) had 90% success with 20-hour blastoderms by examining the eggs through dark blue spectacles, or by using blue or blue-green filters in the candling apparatus. By three days the blood circulation is formed and the network of vessels indicates clearly the position of the embryo and extent of the area vasculosa. Dead embryos can usually be detected by an unusually prominent blood-filled sinus terminalis and the absence of a visible network of vessels. From the seventh to the thirteenth days the chorio-allantoic vascular system can be seen, but after this growth of the embryo makes the egg increasingly opaque except for the air sac.

If the shell contains pigment, examination of the egg contents by candling is difficult, and if much pigment is present it may become impossible. For such eggs, and for those with very young blastoderms, the position of the embryo can only be guessed. Fortunately the guess can often be correct if it is based on the tendency for the yolk to rotate until the blastoderm is at the top of the egg. If the eggs are left undisturbed for at least 30 minutes, and the window is then cut at the highest point on the shell, in a large proportion of the eggs the embryo will be found under the window.

Windows can be cut with a hacksaw blade, ampoule file, or any other instrument with a finely serrated edge. A small-toothed wheel driven by an electric motor does the job rapidly, and is particularly convenient if connected to the motor by a flexible shaft. Square windows of side 5–10 mm. are satisfactory and easy to make. Before opening the egg, aseptic precautions (p. 3) should be taken. The egg and the saw should first be wiped with 70% alcohol, and then the four sides of the square cut in the shell without puncturing the shell membrane. The area of the window is again wiped with alcohol, removing all "sawdust", and the square of shell lifted off the shell membrane with sterile forceps. A drop of saline is placed on the exposed membrane to reduce its tendency to adhere to underlying structures, and the square of membrane is then cut out with a finely pointed scalpel or scissors. It may be helpful to start the cut with a mounted needle. The blastoderm, or at a later stage the chorio-allantois, lies very close to the shell membrane and great care is necessary to avoid damaging it.

The window can be covered with sellotape, parafilm, or a coverslip sealed on to the shell with high melting point wax. Alternatively, the square of shell and shell membrane can be replaced, in which case it is better when making the window to remove them together; they can then be restored in one piece and held in position by wax or sellotape.

Injecting

If the site for an injection needs to be precisely located (e.g. a blood vessel) a window must first be cut in the shell; but for many purposes it is sufficient to make a small hole in the shell and then to inject "blind"; the hole can be made with a mounted needle, or better, with a dentists' drill attached to an electric motor. It should be remembered, however, that the rate of diffusion of injected substances, and hence the rate at which they are taken up by the embryo, can vary greatly according to where they are deposited in the egg, and careless injection can easily lead to disappointingly inconsistent results. The yolk is particularly resistant to diffusion. Measurements of electrical conductivity in the unincubated egg indicate that diffusion through the albumen or vitelline membrane is about 150 times faster than through the yolk (Maurice 1952); Maurice & Fidanza (1952) found that radioactive bromide injected into the albumen was uniformly distributed through the albumen after 1 hour, but the concentration in the yolk was only $2\cdot5\%$ of that in the albumen after 200 hours.

Many text book diagrams designed to show the development of the embryo and its membranes, are very misleading as to the distribution of the various egg contents during the first half of incubation. This is mainly because they take no account of the formation of the sub-blastodermic fluid, which accumulates between the blastoderm and yolk during the first week, and at its maximum reaches about 16–17 ml., i.e. about one-third of the total egg volume (Romanoff 1943a). This fluid is 95% water, and is formed by the blastoderm, which actively absorbs water from the albumen and secretes it from its endoderm surface (New 1956); this mechanism inflates the yolk sac and presses the vascular area close to the shell, where it can form an effective respiratory surface at a time when the chorio-allantois is still very small. During the second week the sub-blastodermic fluid diminishes, most of it being transferred to the amniotic and allantoic fluids.

Fig. 12 shows the location of the yolk, albumen, sub-blastodermic fluid and embryonic membranes during the first half of incubation. By the 4th day the yolk sac almost completely surrounds the yolk. By the 5th day the allantois has extended over more than half of the embryo, and on the 6th day completely covers it. After the 6th day the allantois extends rapidly between the chorion (with which it fuses, forming the chorio-allantois), and yolk sac. By the 8th day it reaches the equator of the yolk sac, and on the 9th day the chorio-allantois starts to extend round the albumen. By the 12th day the entire egg contents are surrounded by the chorio-allantois (Fig. 12D) and the volume of the chorio-allantoic fluid has increased to about 5–6 ml. At about the 13th day the albumen passes through a newly formed opening in the sero-amniotic connection into the amniotic cavity, and the embryo begins to swallow it; during the next three or four days it is all consumed.

To inject without cutting a window in the shell, the eggs should first be examined by candling (p. 55) and compared with diagrams of the contents at the particular stage of incubation. The injection can then be made with reasonable precision if the position of the injection hole and the length of needle inserted are gauged carefully. It must be remembered that during the first half of incubation the egg contents can rotate slowly within the shell, and are only stable when the embryo is at the top (as in Fig. 12). After the injection is made the hole in the shell can be sealed with sterile wax, and the egg returned to the incubator and turned as usual.

Several workers have successfully injected up to 0·1 ml. of solution, or cell suspension, into the allantoic vein of embryos incubated 6 days or more (e.g. Polk, Buddingh & Goodpasture 1938, Beveridge & Burnet 1946, Kent 1961, Solomon 1962). For this it is essential to cut a window in the shell (p. 55), but the shell membrane is left intact. The position of the main allantoic vein is first determined by candling and the shell window is then made above it. The shell membrane is made transparent with a drop of medicinal paraffin and the injection needle passed through it into the vein. A 1 ml. hypodermic syringe with a 30-gauge needle is suitable, and it is usual to inject in the direction of blood flow. Solomon finds that the operation is much easier if the needle is connected to the syringe by 15–20 cm. of thin polythene tubing. Bleeding after removal of the needle from the vein does not seem to be excessive, and development of the embryo continues—in the more successful cases up to

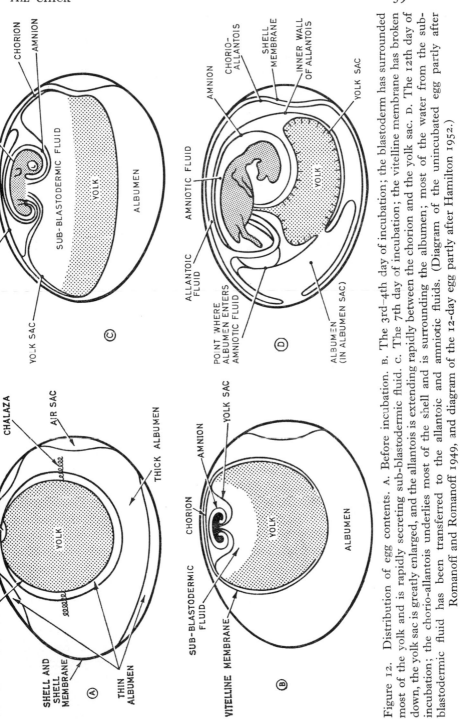

Figure 12.   Distribution of egg contents. A. Before incubation. B. The 3rd–4th day of incubation; the blastoderm has surrounded most of the yolk and is rapidly secreting sub-blastodermic fluid. c. The 7th day of incubation; the vitelline membrane has broken down, the yolk sac is greatly enlarged, and the allantois is extending rapidly between the chorion and the yolk sac. D. The 12th day of incubation; the chorio-allantois underlies most of the shell and is surrounding the albumen; most of the water from the sub-blastodermic fluid has been transferred to the allantoic and amniotic fluids. (Diagram of the unincubated egg partly after Romanoff and Romanoff 1949, and diagram of the 12-day egg partly after Hamilton 1952.)

hatching. The same method can be used for removing samples of blood from the chorio-allantoic vessels.

Drachman and Coulombre (1962) describe an apparatus for continuous infusion of fluids into the chorio-allantoic circulation. A fine cannula made from polythene tubing is inserted into a chorio-allantoic blood vessel and connected to the needle of a 1 ml. syringe. The plunger of the syringe is controlled by a mechanism powered by a synchronous motor, so that it delivers approximately 0·01 ml./hr. of fluid. These workers infused embryos between 6 and 17 days of incubation for periods up to 4 days, and state that many subsequently hatched.

Weiss and Andres (1952), in studying the distribution of pigment cells, obtained prolonged development of embryos following the delicate operation of injecting cell suspensions into yolk sac blood vessels. Injection was made with glass micropipettes with tips 40 to 50μ in diameter, operated by ordinary rubber teats. These were inserted into small branches, about 50μ in diameter, of the vitelline vein of 3- to 4-day embryos. (It was necessary to select small branches in order to avoid excessive haemorrhage.) The eggs were prepared for the operation on the preceding day. "They were fastened in an upright position blunt end upward, and by means of an electric dental saw, the shell segment overlying the air chamber was cut off along a circle of approximately 25 mm. diameter. The severed shell cap was discarded and the edge of the opening was painted with liquid paraffin (i.e. melted wax). The shell membrane was then removed with forceps exposing the underlying embryo which had risen to the top. A warmed watch glass of appropriate size was then placed on top as a transparent cover replacing the shell cap, with the melting paraffin along the edge effecting a tight seal. In this position the eggs were returned to the incubator and left overnight for injection the following day. At that time the glass cap was again removed, a suitable extraembryonic vessel was chosen and the tip of the injection pipette thrust through its wall into the lumen, care being taken to introduce no air. The injection was done under steady, gentle pressure against considerable resistance. Once an injection is under way, it can be continued until nearly the whole blood of the embryo has been replaced. However, it was empirically found best to stop after approximately 0·05 mm.[3] of material had been injected, for larger doses usually proved fatal. According to rough calculations, this standard dose was estimated to contain from 3000 to 5000 cells.

"The injection completed, the pipette was withdrawn, and the heated watch glass replaced on the self-sealing paraffin border, leaving the embryo visible. The eggs were then kept in the incubator standing on end for the rest of the incubation period." In most cases loss of blood at the point of puncture was negligible, and controls injected with Indian ink showed that the injected material was promptly carried through the venous system into the heart, and from there propelled through the arterial system of the embryo and of the yolk sac. The embryos developed for varying lengths of time; most of those that developed up to hatching died during that critical phase, but a few hatched and could be reared further.

More recently Kent (1961) succeeded in injecting small un-measured quantities of Thorotrast suspension into a tributary of the vitelline vein of embryos of 3–6 days' incubation, using a glass micropipette held in a "Singer" micromanipulator under a binocular microscope. After the injection the blood vessel was sealed by cautery with a hot needle. The embryos were all fixed within a few hours of injection and Thorotrast was found in the kidney, liver and other organs.

For some purposes it may be useful to know how much the injection is diluted by the embryonic blood. Rychter, Kopecky and Lemez (1955) give values for the volume of the blood plasma, and of the blood corpuscles, for each day of incubation from the 2nd day onwards, based on measurements of the dilution of known amounts of injected dye. According to them the total blood volume in the 3-day incubated egg is about 0·05 ml., increasing to 0·5 ml. by the 8th day, and 2 ml. by the 14th day.

Replacement of albumen, sub-blastodermic fluid, or yolk

Ryle (1957) studied the effects of exchanging small amounts of albumen and sub-blastodermic fluid between the eggs of large and small breeds of fowl, on the subsequent growth rates of the hatched chicks. She found, as had earlier workers, that any exchange of albumen before incubation caused death of the embryo within a few days. With eggs incubated 3 days, however, the results were much better, and when 5 ml. of albumen (i.e. 10% of the total egg weight) was replaced at this time, up to 40% of the embryos continued development and subsequently hatched. Before exchanging the al-bumen a window (p. 55) was cut in the shell and shell membranes at a position about one-third of the length of the egg from the pointed

c*

end. Then "the egg was laid in the stand with the axis horizontal and the window directed towards the operator. The syringe, fitted with a very wide bore stainless steel needle or cannula, about 3 cm. long, was lowered so that the latter passed down between the shell and the yolk. The egg was alternately moved slightly towards the operator and rotated slightly on its axis, as the syringe was lowered further, until the window was at the highest point and the tip of the needle near the lower face of the shell. With this procedure there is little risk of damaging the yolk. It is essential to get the window at the highest point before withdrawing albumen because the air replacing it will otherwise move into the egg away from the opening and form bubbles. These are extremely difficult to get rid of and prevent the replacement of the full quantity of albumen." The piece of shell removed to form the window was replaced and sealed in position with sellotape, and the eggs were then returned to the incubator and turned as usual.

Exchanges of sub-blastodermic fluid were made between eggs incubated five days. The eggs were candled and a window cut through the shell, but not through the shell membrane, in the region of the area vasculosa. The shell membrane was made transparent with a drop of medicinal paraffin, and a hypodermic syringe inserted through it into the sub-blastodermic fluid (i.e. until the needle tip was just above the axis of the egg—see Fig. 12), care being taken to avoid damage to the major blood vessels of the yolk sac. The egg was held with the window uppermost during this operation, to avoid bubble formation. 2·5 ml. of fluid (i.e. 5% of the total egg weight) was removed and replaced with fluid from another egg. The shell window was replaced and sealed on with sellotape, and the eggs were then returned to the incubator and turned as usual. Fifty per cent hatched.

Removal and replacement of yolk is more difficult because of its high viscosity, but a technique has been devised by Grau, Klein and Lau (1957) in which the yolk is flushed out, and other fluids introduced, through a tube of heat-coagulated albumen formed between the shell and the vitelline membrane. The technique is applicable only to eggs incubated for 2 to $3\frac{1}{2}$ days. Before 2 days the embryo is not sufficiently firmly attached to the vitelline membrane to remain in place during the flushing procedure, and after $3\frac{1}{2}$ days the coagulum cannot be made strong enough.

Fig. 13 shows the stages in the operation. A hole 3 mm. in

diameter is drilled through the shell, but not through the shell membrane, slightly above the equator of the egg. The egg is then returned
to the incubator, where it is kept with the hole downward for a few
minutes, to orient the embryo away from the hole. Next the egg is
supported with the large end upward in a metal cup containing a
few drops of an electrolyte, to assure a good electrical contact, and

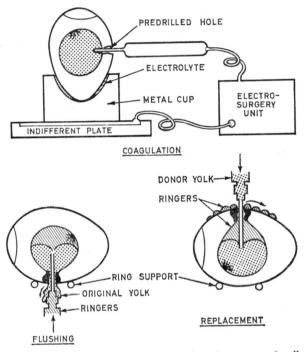

Figure 13.   Three steps in the total replacement of yolk
(Grau, Klein & Lau, 1957.)

the cup is placed on the indifferent plate of an electrosurgical unit.
A straight, sharp, 20 mm. electrode is inserted quickly through the
hole and into the yolk, and the current is turned on for 5–6 seconds.
Then, while the current is maintained, the needle is drawn outward
in a spiral motion, over a period of about 4 more seconds, until the
point is about 5 mm. inside the egg. The current is then turned off
and the needle is withdrawn slowly, carrying with it small amounts
of coagulated yolk. A direct connection should now have been formed

between the inside of the yolk and the outside of the shell through a tunnel surrounded by coagulated albumen.

The egg is supported in a horizontal position with the hole downward and a large bore hypodermic needle is used to clear the tunnel of coagulated yolk and albumen fragments. Next a hypodermic needle, attached by tubing to a reservoir of Ringer saline containing erythromycin (0·1 mg./ml.) and streptomycin (1·0 mg./ml.), is inserted about 15 mm. into the hole, and a pressure of 25–35 cm. of water is used to flush out the yolk. The egg, which is moved occasionally to keep the yolk flowing, is kept warm by a heat lamp. Flushing is completed in 5–15 minutes if the preparation is satisfactory.

The tube of coagulated albumen is quite strong, and may be used repeatedly for injections into the yolk sac, or for studying the effects on embryonic development of materials perfused through the yolk sac. If desired, the yolk can be cut free from the shell, after sealing with paraffin wax, by running an L-shaped knife blade around the inside of the hole.

Several studies have now been made by means of this method of yolk replacement (Klein, Grau and Green 1958, Grau et al. 1962, 1963). Perfusion of the yolk sac with standard tissue culture salines, containing glucose and antibiotics but no other organic substances, gave a median survival time for the embryos of 30 hours. The addition of yolk, amino acids or vitamins to the perfusion fluid did not prolong survival, but addition of dilute albumen, non-fat milk or casein lengthened it to 80 hours. The embryos appeared to benefit from a high potassium to sodium ratio (1 : 5) and a very low level of calcium. In an experiment (Grau et al. 1957) where the yolk was entirely replaced on the third day of incubation by yolk from other eggs (unincubated or 5-day incubated) 38 out of 74 embryos survived the operation, 13 were alive two days later, 3 survived to the twentieth day, and 1 hatched. Walker and Grau (1963) found that when only small amounts (up to 2 ml.) of yolk were supplied to embryos deprived of their own yolk, survival, developmental stage, and body weight, measured 4 or 5 days after the operation, were related directly to the amount of yolk provided.

Vital staining and carbon marking

Morphogenetic movements can be traced in young blastoderms of primitive streak and head process stages by vital staining, though the method is not as effective as with amphibian embryos because the stains diffuse and fade much more rapidly. Pieces of agar impregnated with stain are prepared as described on p. 7.

Eggs incubated for about 18–20 hours usually have primitive streak blastoderms suitable for study, though the exact stage of development reached varies considerably from one egg to another. A window is cut in the shell and shell membrane (p. 55) and any albumen over the blastoderm is removed. The primitive streak is often difficult to see, but can be made more visible by illuminating the blastoderm obliquely with a blue or green light, or briefly placing a piece of nile blue agar or neutral red agar over the centre of the blastoderm until the streak is *lightly* stained. Marks can then be made on the blastoderm at any desired place, by means of small pieces of strongly coloured blue or red agar applied for a few minutes. The agar should be left in position until a clearly defined mark is formed, but not longer.

Nile blue and neutral red readily pass through the vitelline membrane into the blastoderm. Bismarck brown stains the vitelline membrane, and Pasteels (1935, 1936, 1937), in studying gastrulation movements of stained blastoderms in ovo, used this dye for making marks on the membrane to act as reference points.

After staining, the window in the shell is closed, and incubation continued. The blastoderm should be re-examined within 24 hours, preferably by transmitted light in a watch glass of saline (see p. 83 for dissecting blastoderms free of the yolk and vitelline membrane).

Marking with carbon particles, a technique commonly employed with explanted blastoderms, has rarely been used in ovo because of difficulties created by the presence of the vitelline membrane. However, Deuchar (1958) successfully used this method to trace the origin of the tongue muscles of the embryo. Each egg was incubated for 45 hours (to Hamburger and Hamilton stage 10–12). A window was cut in the shell and shell membrane, and carbon particles, moistened with saline, were pushed through the vitelline membrane into one of the first three post-otic somites with a fine tungsten needle. The shell window was replaced, the egg incubated for a further 3–4 days, and the embryo then fixed, sectioned, and the tongue muscle examined for particles. Mortality was high; out of 98 embryos operated only 6 were alive at the end of the experiment (H-H stage 25–28). The main causes of death seemed to be adherence of the vitelline membrane to the shell window, or splitting of the membrane when the original hole made with the needle was rather large; both could probably now be avoided by the use of Silver's technique (p. 67).

Excision, grafting and other operations
(a) During the 3rd and 4th days of incubation.

Prolonged survival of operated embryos can most easily be obtained after operations performed when the embryo is partly or entirely covered by the amnion, but before it is covered by the allantois; i.e. from the later somite to the early limb bud stages during the 3rd and 4th days of incubation. A shell window is cut by the usual methods (p. 55) and the exposed shell membrane moistened and cut away. The vitelline membrane over the embryo is carefully torn open with watchmakers forceps, and if necessary the embryo made more visible by lightly staining it, either before or after removal of the membrane, with a piece of agar impregnated with neutral red or nile blue (p. 7). If the amnion and chorion cover the site of the operation they can be slit open by an upward movement of a fine glass or metal needle inserted into the amniotic cavity along the midline; they will heal back over the embryo after the operation. The window in the shell is closed and incubation of the eggs continued without turning.

If the injury to the embryo is not too severe development may continue for several days, and even lead to the hatching of healthy chicks, as in the classic experiments by Willier and Rawles on the development of feather pigmentation (reviewed by Rawles, 1948), and the more recent study of Székely and Szentágothai (1962) on the reflex movements of supernumerary limbs. The latter authors grafted extra limb buds to embryos on the 3rd day of incubation (Hamburger and Hamilton Stages 19–21), and from about 120 operated embryos obtained 11 hatched chicks.

An important application of the method is the grafting of organ rudiments to the embryonic coelom. First introduced by Hamburger (1938), this technique can give excellent morphological development of grafts, particularly of isolated organs such as limbs, eyes, etc., which can develop from material taken from very young embryos even before the rudiments of the organs are recognisable. Detailed descriptions of the procedure for making coelomic grafts, as well as flank grafts, and grafts of neural crest to the base of the wing buds, are given by Hamburger (1960).

(b) During the 1st and 2nd days of incubation.

For operations in ovo on embryos of less than 48 hours incubation, simple methods may be effective provided the duration of survival required after the operation is short, and the hole made in the vitelline membrane is very small. De Haan (1959) operated on the anterior intestinal portal of young embryos, causing the formation of double hearts, and was able to study their development for periods of up to 4 days, which is longer than is possible by in vitro methods. "Eggs incubated 24–26 hours were cracked in two, and the excess albumen allowed to spill out in such a manner that the yolk remained, supported in the blunt half of the shell. The blastoderm was vitally stained through the vitelline membrane with nile blue sulphate or with neutral red solution containing an antibiotic. With the aid of a hooked tungsten microneedle inserted through the vitelline membrane at the side of the blastoderm, the anterior intestinal portal could be divided in the mid line. . . . Each egg was then placed, open end up, in a polythene cup, and a few ml. of Howard's solution (Howard 1953) was added to maintain humidity. The press fit cover was sealed on and the cup was stored at 37·5°C for further incubation. No 'window' or closure of any kind was made on the egg itself."

Until recently, any hopes of prolonged development after operating on such young blastoderms usually met wth disappointment; but thanks to the careful analysis by Silver (1959, 1960) of the problems involved, the chances of success are now much greater, provided adequate precautions are taken. The cause of many failures is the formation of adhesions between the embryo and vitelline membrane, which result from partial desiccation of the membrane after the thin covering layer of albumen has been disturbed. This can happen not only from evaporation during the operation, but also during subsequent incubation, and is accentuated by the secretory activity of the blastoderm which is continually transferring water from the albumen to the sub-blastodermic fluid (New 1956). Only when the amnion has formed is the danger from drying past. The earlier the stage of the embryo at operation, the longer is the time that must elapse before the amnion is completed, and the greater the probability of harmful adhesions forming.

If a very small hole (e.g. <0·2 mm. diam.) in the vitelline membrane is sufficient for the operation, the egg can be topped up with chick saline or saline albumen after the operation (Grabowski 1956), and this reduces the danger of desiccation. It is advisable also to roll the egg through 180° so that the embryo comes opposite fresh shell membrane.

Where a larger hole in the vitelline membrane is needed, however, this method cannot be used. The effect of adding the "topping up" fluid is then to force the embryo and surrounding blastoderm out through the hole in the membrane. Silver has overcome the problem of obtaining normal development without adding extra fluid by mounting the eggs on horizontal turntables in a saturated atmosphere. The turntables rotate the eggs alternately clockwise and anticlockwise through 90°, and because of the inertia of the yolk, the vitelline membrane and shell membrane are in constant relative movement, so that the vitelline membrane is wetted "in a manner analogous to the wetting of the cornea by the eyelid".

In preliminary tests with this apparatus, using 30-hour incubated eggs in which openings of not less than 0·75 mm. had been made in the vitelline membrane over the embryos, Silver found that out of 18 eggs incubated on the turntables 14 developed to hatching; whereas out of 36 eggs placed in the same incubator but not on the turntables, only 2 reached Stage 19 (Hamburger and Hamilton) and neither of these survived beyond the 7th day. He has subsequently (1962) used the method for studies on extirpation and transplantation of the optic vesicles. The details of the technique as given by Silver (1960) are:

1. Candle the egg and cut window in shell over the blastoderm about 0·5–0·75 cm. square.

2. Place the egg in the operating incubator at 37·5°C and nearly 100% humidity.

3. Candle the egg again and cut window in shell membrane exactly over the embryo.

4. Make opening in vitelline membrane as small as reasonable for experiment required. The position of the opening—over the embryo or to the side—is not important; sticking to the edge of the opening (Silver 1959) will not occur as long as the vitelline membrane remains wet.

5. Twist the egg on the turntable under the microscope at frequent intervals during the experiment and, finally, as an extra precaution, re-wet the whole of the exposed surface, not merely the embryo, with a glass rod or forceps by drawing the peripheral albumen towards the centre, so that it forms an unbroken film. It is

now safe to replace and seal the shell window with wax (adhesive tape is not satisfactory because, whenever the incubator door is opened, dew immediately appears on the undersurface and this moisture must come from fluid over the blastoderm).

6. Replace the egg in the incubator on its own mechanical turntable (90° turn alternately clockwise and anticlockwise, 8 cycles per minute) with the window uppermost and immediately over the central vertical spindle of the table. In theory the centrifugal forces acting on the yolk should then balance each other. Each egg should be left on its turntable until a total incubation time of at least 72 hours has elapsed. By this time the amnion is complete and the circulation well established and anti-drying measures are no longer required.

7. It is thought to be inadvisable to roll the eggs (i.e. the usual procedure of "turning" them at intervals round the long axis) during the subsequent weeks of incubation. It is easy to roll 180° immediately after removing the egg from the turntable, but later the albumen, as it becomes viscid, will stick to the window. Once this has happened further attempts to roll the egg will only produce distortion of its contents.

(c) After the 4th day of incubation.

Operations on the embryo in ovo after the 4th day of incubation are made more difficult by the presence of the allantois, which now partially or completely covers the embryo. However, some operations of this kind have been made successfully. Zwilling (1965) describes operations on the foot plates of 6- and 7-day embryos: "The work was accomplished through a window (about 1 cm.²) which had been made in the shell on day 3. The allantoic membrane was carefully deflected in such a way that the blood vessels were not damaged (a blunt glass probe was used for this) and the amnionic membrane over the limb was exposed. A small hole was torn in the latter over the limb site (watchmakers forceps were used for this) and then I pulled the foot plate through the hole. The greatest difficulty was encountered because of the amnionic contractions and the rocking of the embryo. I minimised this by placing a hair loop around the shank portion of the limb. This had to be held with one hand while all of the operative work was done with a fine steel needle held in the other. The embryos were kept (and survived) for 4–5 days after the operation."

Weiss and Matoltsy (1959) studied wound healing in embryos

after operations in ovo between the 4th and 17th days of incubation. Small lesions were made in the cornea and skin of the neck through holes, usually not more than 1 mm. in diameter, torn in the chorio-allantoic membrane. Some of the embryos operated on at the 5th day of incubation survived until the 17th day, those operated on later than the 5th day often survived for 4 days after the operation, at which time they were killed.

Matoltsy (1965) describes the procedure for operating through the chorio-allantoic membrane as follows: "After opening the egg, the vessels of the chorio-allantoic membrane are studied under the Zeiss operation microscope using a green filter. In many areas the large vessels run parallel and branch out into small vessels. A relatively large 'vessel-free' region, between parallel running large vessels, is selected for the site of the cut. The membrane is cut with iris scissors and the direction of the cut should be parallel with the direction of the adjacent large vessels. After cutting the membrane retracts and a round hole is formed. Further manipulations are elaborated through this hole. The success of the operation greatly depends on the degree of damage done to the chorio-allantoic membrane. The membrane should not be touched with forceps unnecessarily; it should be clamped only at one point when the cut is made. In case a vessel is ruptured, bleeding usually cannot be stopped, and in this case it is advisable to discard the egg and start a new operation.

"In some cases I did not find 'vessel-free' areas which were large enough to provide a hole through which an operation could be carried out conveniently. In such cases I attempted to cut small vessels to widen the hole. I found that bleeding did not occur in many cases if the small vessel was cut across by a rapid clip of the iris scissors.

"Even after several months of experience, I found that the rate of mortality is high. My studies revealed that mortality is the highest in embryos obtained after 9–13 days of incubation. In this age group I got an average survival rate of about 50 per cent. Younger and older embryos were less sensitive and survival varied between 70 and 90 per cent. In general, I found that the embryos die within 24 hours after an unsuccessful operation. If the embryos live more than 48 hours after the operation, the chances are good that they will continue to develop. Development of embryos is somewhat retarded after an operation; hatching usually occurs one or two days later than normally. The cut made through the chorio-allantoic membrane remains open throughout the entire period of development. It may shrink but will not close. I did not attempt to seal the holes of the chorio-allantoic membrane."

Chorio-allantoic grafting

The chick chorio-allantois with its extensive blood supply has proved to be a valuable site for the cultivation of isolated organs and tissues, and also tumours and viruses. Following the early development of the technique by Willier (1924), chorio-allantoic grafting has frequently been used for testing the self-differentiating capacities of isolated parts of the young embryo (reviews by Rudnick 1944, Rawles 1952, Waddington 1952). Grafts placed on the membrane become invaded by allantoic blood capillaries and may continue to grow for periods of up to 10 days. Thus much larger and more complex structures (e.g. whole limbs) can be grown by this method than is possible by isolating organs in vitro. On the other hand a greater variety of experiments, e.g. with different nutrient media, are possible in vitro, and the development of the organ can be more closely observed.

Some grafts have marked effects on the development of particular organs of the host embryo. Following an early observation by Danchakoff (1916) that adult spleen tissue grafted to the chorio-allantois caused marked enlargement of the host spleen, there have appeared in recent years a series of papers analysing the mechanism involved (e.g. Ebert 1951, 1954; Mun, Kosin and Sato 1959; Solomon 1963). Levi-Montalcini (1952) made the striking discovery that grafting pieces of certain mouse tumours to the chorio-allantois resulted in hypertrophy of the neurones of the host spinal and sympathetic ganglia, an observation which has subsequently led to the isolation of trophic substances. Van Alten and Fennell (1959) have examined the effects on the embryo following grafting of duodenum, skin, brain, liver and spleen.

Eggs that have been incubated for 8 days are in the best condition for receiving grafts to the chorio-allantois. Each egg is candled and a window (p. 55) cut in the shell over a bifurcation of a large chorio-allantoic blood vessel. The exposed shell membrane is moistened with chick saline (p. 4) to reduce its tendency to stick to the underlying chorio-allantois and is then cut away. This operation requires great care because the chorio-allantois lies very close against the shell membrane and is easily damaged. As soon as the shell membrane is opened the chorio-allantois usually drops slightly creating a space which will take the graft. If the space is not sufficient a small hole should be made in the large end of the egg to let the air out of the air sac; the contents of the egg will then sink further.

Grafts of limb buds from 3-day embryos, or eye primordia from 2-day embryos, are good for classroom work. The donor embryo with part of its surrounding blastoderm should be removed from the yolk (p. 82) and transferred to a watch glass of saline under the dissecting microscope. The parts required for transplanting are then cut away and transferred with a pipette to the host chorio-allantois. Any saline transferred with the graft should be removed; the transplant must settle on the membrane and not float. It is best to place the transplant on a well vascularised region between bifurcating blood vessels. Hamburger (1960) recommends gently lacerating the surface of the membrane with a sharp needle without rupturing it; a slight haemorrhage seems to facilitate incorporation of the grafts. Finally the opening in the shell is covered, and incubation of the egg continued with the window upwards, and without turning.

The grafts must be removed before the 19th day of development of the host. After this the chorio-allantois degenerates preparatory to hatching. Large grafts become opaque, and may be very irregular in external shape whilst containing well formed internal structures. They must be fixed and cleared before their structure can be seen properly. For limbs and other grafts of skeletal elements from chick embryos, the Lundvall technique for staining cartilage in situ gives excellent results.

1. Fix in Bouin's fluid or 10% formaldehyde for 1–2 days.
2. Wash in several changes of 70% alcohol. (After Bouin's fixation add 2% NH_4OH to the alcohol and continue washing until the yellow colour has completely disappeared.)
3. Remove skin and fatty tissue.
4. Stain in methylene blue (0·25 mg. per 100 cc. of 70% alcohol with 3% HCl by volume), or in toluidine blue (same solution) for 2–3 days. This will overstain.
5. Differentiate in 70% alcohol for about 48 hours.
6. Dehydrate in 95% and absolute alcohol for 3–4 hours. All stain should now be lost from the soft tissues, leaving only the cartilage stained.

7. Transfer to a mixture of 3 parts methyl salicylate and 1 part benzyl benzoate. In this the specimen will clear completely and may be stored.

In recent studies of growth on the chorio-allantois of grafts composed of embryonic epidermis and dermis that had been separated and then recombined, Rawles (1963) found that the feather germs failed to elongate normally unless the graft, after it had become attached to the membrane (i.e. after 12–18 hours), was kept submerged in fluid (15 parts albumen to 1 part balanced salt solution, thoroughly shaken and decanted). As the host embryo could not tolerate large additions of the fluid at any one time, small amounts were added daily just sufficient to keep the graft covered. Gradually this caused the chorio-allantois to rise to the level of the shell, and in order to provide space for more fluid a small chamber of wax was constructed over the shell opening. Development of the graft could then continue until the 19th day of incubation of the host, and the feathers and scales differentiated normally.

Parabiosis
Embryos of 9 to 12 days incubation can be joined parabiotically by means of vascular connections between their chorio-allantoic membranes. The technique, first described by Hašek (1953), consists essentially in cutting windows in two eggs, and opposing the bared chorio-allantoic membranes, with some kind of bridge material between them to encourage vascular interpenetration. Hasek used chick embryos of 24 to 36 hours incubation to form the bridge. In the modification of the method by Billingham, Brent and Medawar (1956), later used also by Chaytor (1963), the bridge consisted of a thick lens-shaped disk of clotted plasma and embryonic fragments, made by adding one drop of a dense suspension of chopped up heart and skeletal muscle from a 10–11 days embryo, to two or three drops of adult chicken plasma, and mixing them on a siliconed glass surface; when clotting had occurred the firm jelly could be prised off with a scalpel and stored in saline until required for use.

Windows of 0·8–1·2 cm. diam. were cut (p. 55) through the shell and shell membranes of two eggs, and placed in opposition with the clot between them. The eggs were sealed together with paraffin wax, care being taken not to let the wax make contact with the chorio-allantoic membranes. A blood link between the two circulations was found to be established after 50–72 hours.

Chaytor used the method to study the effects on growth of the liver of parabiosis between embryos of different age; he was successful in joining 9- and 12-day eggs and incubating them for a further few days. Billingham *et al.* were concerned to maintain the paired embryos for a much longer period in order to test them for acquired tolerance to homografts some time after hatching. The embryos were joined at 10 days, and the paired eggs were turned during subsequent incubation (though there is probably little advantage to be gained by doing this—see p. 53). A few of the embryos hatched successfully and survived into adult life, but a large proportion died between the 15th and 17th days of incubation.

Moore (1965), in studies on the blood-vascular migration of haemopoietic cells, has simplified the parabiosis technique. He uses a special drill to cut accurately a 6 mm. diameter circular hole in the shell and shell membranes of each egg. The chorio-allantoic membranes bulge through the holes sufficiently to make contact with each other when the eggs are brought together; no bridging material is necessary. The eggs are sealed together with ceresin wax, and a blood link between the two embryos forms after about 24 hours. The method can be used for eggs of 6–11 days incubation, and some of the parabiosed embryos survive until hatching.

EMBRYOS EXPLANTED WITH THE YOLK

Several studies have been made of embryonic development following the transference of the entire egg contents to dishes or beakers. Assheton (1896) and Romanoff (1943b) found that to obtain growth of previously unincubated embryos, it was necessary to prevent the yolk floating to the surface of the albumen (e.g. by depressing it with a heavy glass ring), particularly if the sac of thick albumen which normally surrounds the yolk at this stage had been broken. Their embryos developed for up to about 2 days. Vollmar (1935) obtained development for a much longer period starting from eggs incubated 1–2 days. The egg contents were tipped into small hemispherical dishes and incubated in a saturated atmosphere; the best embryos continued development up to 16 days.

Schmidt (1937) studied the effect of replacing part or all of the albumen in the cultures with saline. When the albumen was diluted

with $\frac{1}{4}$–$\frac{1}{3}$ of its volume of Ringer or other saline the embryos (explanted at 1–2 days incubation) developed for 4–6 days. Some growth
could be obtained with as little as 5–20% albumen in the saline, but
none if the albumen were omitted entirely. The addition of glucose
to the saline had some growth promoting effect but considerably less
than that of even small amounts of albumen. After dialysis of albumen
neither the protein fraction nor the dialysate supported growth
separately, but they would do so when recombined. Schmidt concluded that whole albumen had an important growth-stimulating
effect on the early embryo.

For most experiments on chick embryos there is little advantage
in culturing the embryo with the whole yolk. The embryo is scarcely
more accessible, either for observation or operation, than in ovo,
and the amount of development that can be expected is much less.

EMBRYOS EXPLANTED WITHOUT THE YOLK

Culturing on vitelline membrane

In the method of New (1955) the blastoderm is explanted ectoderm downwards on a piece of vitelline membrane stretched across
a glass ring in a watch glass, and this is housed in a petri dish lined
with wet cotton wool to maintain humidity (the arrangement of the
petri dish culture chamber is the same as that for mouse and rat
embryos—see Fig. 4A, p. 25). A little thin albumen introduced
beneath the vitelline membrane provides a nutrient medium. The
importance of the membrane is that it allows normal expansion of
the blastoderm, resulting in a well-formed area vasculosa and better
growth and development of the embryo than can be obtained by
other explantation techniques. The thin albumen, besides being easy
to obtain, also has considerable bacteriostatic properties which reduce
the risk of infection.

Glass rings of internal diameter 28 mm., made from 2–3 mm.
glass rod are a useful size. Larger rings can be used, but freeing
correspondingly greater areas of vitelline membrane from the yolk
introduces extra technical difficulties. Smaller rings allow less expansion of the blastoderm and less embryonic development.

Sufficient sterile water or saline should be introduced into the
petri dish culture chambers to cover the whole floor of the dish, but
not so much that there is a risk of it slopping over into the watch

glass. If the culture is to be examined by reflected light the outside of the watch glass can be painted black, but it is usually more convenient to leave the glass unpainted and to cut a hole in the cotton wool under it, so that transmitted light can be used.

The blastoderm should be explanted aseptically (p. 3). The egg is wiped with 70% ethanol and opened by tapping round the broad end with the handle of a scalpel or other convenient instrument. The yolk tends to float in the albumen with the blastoderm uppermost, so to avoid damage to the blastoderm it is best to tilt the egg and tap only on the under surface, at the same time rotating it. The optimum size for the opening is about 3 cm. diameter; if the opening is too large the contents start to pour out uncontrollably; if it is too small there is difficulty in removing completely the thick albumen, which is then a nuisance in the later stages of the explantation. If a pair of blunt forceps is passed down into the egg between yolk and shell, the thick albumen can be seized at the bottom and pulled out of the egg in one mass. The yolk is then tipped into a wide dish containing sufficient Panett and Compton saline (p. 5) to cover it completely; 3·5 cm. is a convenient depth. The thin albumen is poured into a container and kept for use as nutrient medium.

The yolk is gently turned in the saline until the embryo is uppermost, and the chalazae and any traces of thick albumen still adhering to the vitelline membrane are removed with blunt forceps. A watch glass is placed in the dish ready to receive the blastoderm, and the vitelline membrane is then cut with scissors round the equator (Fig. 14A). The cut edge of the membrane is grasped with a pair of fine forceps in each hand, and gently peeled off the surface of the yolk. With care the circle of membrane can be obtained almost completely free of yolk and with the blastoderm attached to it. The membrane is pulled through the saline to the watch glass and placed in it with the blastoderm side uppermost. It is convenient to place the glass ring on top of the membrane at this stage to keep it from drifting, and the watch glass with contents can then safely be transferred to the petri dish.

Subsequent stages are illustrated in Fig. 14B–D. Saline is pipetted off until the surface is level with the ring. If the free edges of the vitelline membrane are now folded inwards over the ring they stay in position, held by surface tension. Gentle pulling on the membrane gives a fairly flat surface, but it should not be pulled so tight that the blastoderm is distorted. Any small wrinkles left in the membrane at this stage can be ignored, as they tend to disappear shortly after the preparation has been returned to the incubator.

The saline under the vitelline membrane is now replaced by thin albumen. This can most easily be done, not by attempting to lift the ring, but by gently pushing it aside with the tip of the pipette.

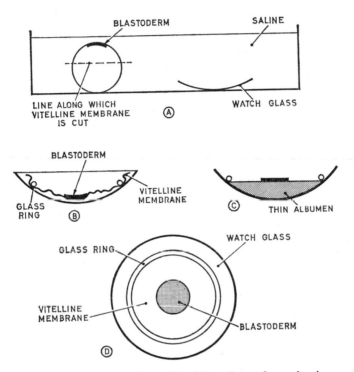

Figure 14. Explanting the chick blastoderm for culturing on vitelline membrane. A. Stage preparatory to peeling off vitelline membrane and blastoderm. B. Contents of watch glass after removal from dish of saline. C. Completed preparation. D. Completed preparation from above.

Next the edge of the vitelline membrane is trimmed with scissors and most of the saline on its upper surface is removed. The blastoderm should appear thoroughly moist, but it is most important not to leave a pool of fluid over it which will hinder respiration, or the embryo will fail to develop. For the same reason great care should be taken to avoid puncturing the vitelline membrane, because if the albumen can leak through to the upper surface and cover the blastoderm the preparation is useless.

It sometimes happens that during the manipulation, part of the blastoderm edge becomes loosened from the vitelline membrane. It will readily reattach itself on further incubation, provided it is pressed close against the membrane by surface tension. To ensure this, plenty of albumen should be added under the membrane; this causes it to bulge upwards, and any saline tending to float the blastoderm edge away from the membrane now drains off and can be removed with a fine pipette. Reattachment should be complete after 3–4 hours in the incubator and the excess albumen can then be removed and a few drops of saline added above the membrane.

A large proportion of embryos explanted at primitive streak, head process or early somite stages develop well when cultured in this way on vitelline membrane. In a series of experiments involving blastoderms explanted at late primitive streak or head process stage, over 90% were found to reach the 10-somite stage, about 75% developed a functional blood circulation, and 20% went on to early limb bud stages. The embryos were of normal size and, up to the 20-somite stage, developed at about the normal rate (primitive streak to 20 somites in 32 hours), but development of the amnion was usually much retarded. Mortality increased rapidly after 20 somites and no embryos developed further than early limb bud stages (30–40 somites).

Very young blastoderms (pre-streak or early streak stages) are only lightly attached to the vitelline membrane and tend to be left behind when the membrane is peeled off the yolk. To avoid this it is better, in explanting these early stages, only to free the edges of the circle of vitelline membrane from the yolk by pulling it, and then to use a broad spatula to lift off the remainder together with the blastoderm and some underlying yolk. The yolk may subsequently be gently scraped away with small (e.g. cataract) knives and pipetted off with the saline.

Alternatively, the vitelline membrane can be removed from the yolk without the blastoderm, and the blastoderm dissected away from the yolk and transferred separately to the membrane to reattach. If this is done, care must be taken that the blastoderm is replaced on the vitelline membrane with its ectoderm surface against the "yolk" surface of the membrane. Placed on the "albumen" surface of the

membrane, or with its endoderm against the membrane, the blastoderm does not expand normally (New 1959).

Vakaet (1962) has successfully cultured very young blastoderms
including pre-incubation stages. He recommends (1964) storing the
eggs for 4–5 days at laboratory temperature before use; this allows
some development of the germ wall and margin of overgrowth, and
increases the chances of the blastoderm adhering to the vitelline
membrane during explantation.

Applications of the vitelline membrane technique

The method of culturing on vitelline membrane has proved applicable to many studies on the young embryo. It has been used successfully for tracing morphogenetic movements after carbon marking
(e.g. Vakaet 1962) and by cinematography (e.g. De Haan 1963a, b);
for studying induction by grafted tissues (e.g. Mulherkar 1958); for
experiments involving excision of parts of the embryo or blastoderm
(e.g. New 1959, Bellairs 1963); for investigating the action of
teratogenic and other substances (e.g. O'Dell and McKenzie 1963,
Billett, Collini and Hamilton 1965); for analysing the mechanisms
of sub-blastodermic fluid formation (New 1956, Jurand and Tuft
1961) and expansion of the blastoderm across the vitelline membrane
(New 1959, Spratt 1963); and for studying phagocytosis by the blastoderm (Bellairs and New 1962).

Expansion of the blastoderm is brought about by the outward
movement of the cells at the blastoderm edge, and after excision or
grafting experiments it sometimes happens that the tension created
in the blastoderm by these cells pulls the wound open and prevents
it from healing, until eventually the blastoderm becomes a narrow
ring of tissues surrounding a large hole. This can be avoided by
delaying expansion, by releasing the blastoderm edge from the
vitelline membrane at the time of the operation, and then following
the procedure for unattached blastoderms (p. 78). Reattachment is
not complete for about 3 hours, and during this time small wounds
close. For larger wounds it may be necessary to release the blastoderm edge a second time, or to trim it off (Bellairs 1963).

In making cultures of isolated parts of the area pellucida, De
Haan (1963c) found it helpful to chill the blastoderm to 4°C before
operating. This reduced the stickiness of the tissues and their tendency to curl after cutting.

Studies on the effect of teratogenic substances in vitro have

usually been made on embryos returned to the incubator very soon
after the teratogen has been added to the culture medium. Billett,
Collini and Hamilton (1965) point out that unless the compound
diffuses quickly into the embryonic tissues this procedure may lead
to errors of interpretation, for it may take several hours for a toxic
concentration to build up. Thus a teratogen added at the primitive
streak stage may not reach a concentration in the embryo high
enough to be effective until the head fold stage; the conclusion
which might then be drawn that "this substance is harmless to the
primitive-streak embryo" would obviously not be justified. Billett
et al. eliminate this possible source of error by allowing the cultures
to remain cold ($15°C$) in a humid chamber for about 16 hours after
the agent has been added. Control experiments, without addition of
teratogen, have shown that the period of cold storage itself has little
effect, and provided adequate precautions are taken to keep the surface of the blastoderm moist, 90% of the control embryos develop
normally when returned to the incubator.

To obtain good optical definition for filming the morphogenetic
movements of heart formation, De Haan (1963a) transferred the
ring, vitelline membrane and blastoderm from the standard watch
glass culture to an agar clot (equal parts of thin albumen and saline,
with 1% agar and 1% glucose) 1 mm. deep, in a small tissue-culture
cup with an optically flat bottom (Fig. 15B). A drop of a suspension
of iron oxide particles was pipetted onto the blastoderm, and these
adhered to the endoderm and could be used for tracking movements
in that layer. Then the blastoderm was submerged under a layer of
light mineral oil (Surgeon's Products, Inc., Baltimore, Md.) to prevent evaporation and maintain optical clarity, and allowed to develop
on a thermostatically controlled microscope warm stage in 5% CO_2
and 95% O_2. Time lapse films were taken at magnifications of $\times 20$
to $\times 32$ with long exposures at low levels of illumination through a
critically adjusted sub-stage condenser. Development was followed
between Hamburger and Hamilton Stages 4 to 10.

Some variants of the standard method of supporting the vitelline
membrane have also been devised. Hell (1964) has successfully used
glass cups of internal diameter 20 mm. and depth 4 mm., with a
ground rim and flat bottom. A little thin albumen is placed in the
cup, and the vitelline membrane with blastoderm is drawn over it
so that the membrane overlaps the rim all round. No fixing ring is
necessary.

Nicolet and Gallera (1963) explanted the vitelline membrane with the blastoderm *downwards*, using two glass rings to support the membrane over albumen in a watch glass (Fig. 15A). They found that the amnion developed better under these conditions.

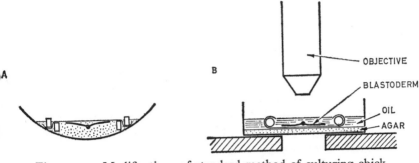

Figure 15.   Modifications of standard method of culturing chick blastoderms on vitelline membrane. A. Blastoderm suspended from vitelline membrane held by two glass rings (Nicolet and Gallera 1963). B. For filming embryonic development, blastoderm and vitelline membrane placed on agar and covered with oil (De Haan 1963a).

Menkes (1964) recommends a method (which he attributes to V. I. Sorokin of Moscow) in which the vitelline membrane is transferred from egg to culture dish on a ring of filter paper. The egg is opened, the thick albumen carefully removed, and the paper ring placed on the vitelline membrane so that it encircles the blastoderm. The paper adheres to the vitelline membrane, and if the membrane is now cut round the ring, paper, membrane and blastoderm can be lifted off the yolk together. The ring with its attached vitelline membrane is then placed on a nutrient agar clot with the blastoderm uppermost. Paper rings of internal diameter 20 mm. and external diameter 35 mm. are suitable, or smaller rings can be used. The nutrient medium can be made according to the method of Spratt (p. 82) or with pure egg albumen. This technique has been used in studies on the formation of axial organs in the embryo (Menkes and Miclea 1962, and earlier papers) and has proved valuable for filming embryonic development.

Culturing on plasma and agar clots
    Embryos of primitive streak stage or a few somites can develop to 20- or 30-somite stages on the surface of plasma or nutrient agar

clots. The plasma clot method was first adapted for chick embryos by Waddington (1932). The petri dish culture chamber and method of preparing the clot are the same as those described for rat embryos (p. 34). In the agar clot method, developed by Spratt (1947a), the culture chamber is similar, but the clot is made of nutrient agar.

Spratt (1947a) gives the following method for making nutrient agar clots:

(i) Ringer-albumen: The albumen from one unincubated egg is added to 50 ml. chick Ringer solution in a 500 ml. stoppered flask, and shaken vigorously for about 1 minute.

(ii) Ringer-agar: 0·13–0·15 gm. is added to 30 ml. Ringer solution in a small flask and gently brought to the boil over a small flame. Frequent agitation is necessary during the heating to prevent sticking to the agar.

When the Ringer-agar has cooled to about 40°–45°C, 20 ml. of the Ringer-albumen is added and the flask gently shaken to mix the two. About 2 ml. of the medium is poured into each watch glass, where it gels in about 30 minutes–1 hour.

The final NaCl concentration in this medium is 149 mM. (Spratt 1955). Howard (1953) examined the effect of varying the NaCl concentration and found that the embryos developed best when the total molarity of the medium was equivalent to 123 mM. NaCl, a figure similar to that indicated by the freezing point of albumen. Spratt (1955) agreed with this and reduced the NaCl accordingly. Yolk extract can be added to the albumen medium, and Spratt and Haas (1960a) particularly recommend it for pre-incubation blastoderms, but yolk extract without albumen is unsatisfactory (Spratt 1947b).

To explant the blastoderm the egg is opened and the thick albumen removed (p. 76). The vitelline membrane is cut round the blastoderm, either in the egg, or after the yolk has been transferred to a petri dish. Blastoderm and attached vitelline membrane are then transferred on a broad spatula to the surface of the clot in the culture chamber, a little saline having first been placed on the clot to help free the blastoderm from the spatula.

One difficulty of explanting a blastoderm from a yolk in a petri dish is that the flattening of the yolk greatly increases the tension in the vitelline membrane, which is then liable to split and tear the blastoderm as soon as the scissors are inserted. To minimise this risk, the yolk should first be arranged so that the blastoderm is in the centre of the upper surface, and then several cuts be rapidly made in the membrane at points all round the edge; this allows yolk to flow out and release the tension.

An alternative method of explanting the blastoderm is to place both the yolk and the watch glass containing the plasma or agar clot, in a dish of saline. The blastoderm and its attached piece of vitelline membrane can then be pulled with forceps through the saline from yolk to clot. This is perhaps the easiest method, if sufficient saline is available.

The explant is placed on the clot with the blastoderm uppermost. Excess yolk is then gently scraped from the blastoderm with cataract knives under a dissecting microscope, great care being taken not to damage the area pellucida. Next the blastoderm must be freed from the vitelline membrane. It is attached to the membrane only by its edge and can be released by gently working round the edge with a cataract knife; the membrane is then discarded. Finally the blastoderm is turned endoderm surface downwards and all saline pipetted off so that it lies flat on the clot. It is then ready to be returned to the incubator. (Spratt and Haas (1960a) recommend explanting pre-incubation blastoderms *ectoderm* surface downwards to reduce inhibition of endodermal cell movements during subsequent development.)

The blastoderm does not expand normally over the surface of a clot, and this is probably the main reason why embryos cultured on clots do not grow as well as on vitelline membrane. A higher proportion fail completely, and those that develop are usually abnormally small. Young blastoderms rarely form an adequate area vasculosa or functional blood circulation, and there is also some evidence (Waddington 1952, Vakaet 1962) that the morphogenetic movements of the primitive streak stages are abnormal.

Nevertheless the method has been used in a variety of studies on regulative mechanisms, morphogenetic movements and physiological requirements of the early embryo (e.g. references to earlier work in Waddington 1952, and Romanoff 1960, and more recent papers by Spratt and Haas 1960a, b, 1961, 1962). Klein, McConnell and Riquier (1964) have obtained improved embryonic development by incubating the cultures in high concentrations of oxygen.

Wolff and Simon (1955) made clots (of embryo extract and agar) with a convex surface, by allowing them to set between two watch glasses. These authors considered that such clots provided conditions which resembled more closely those in the egg. Simon (1956a, 1956b, 1960) used this method in studying parabiotic unions between two or more explanted blastoderms, and the migration of primordial germ cells.

Other methods

The first cultures of chick embryos in vitro were made by McWhorter and Whipple (1912) who explanted blastoderms into drops of nutrient medium suspended from coverslips, as in the standard hanging drop technique of tissue culture; this method was also used by Sabin (1917, 1919) and Patten and Kramer (1933). The hanging drop method may have some advantages in facilitating observations under high magnification, but the amount of embryonic development obtained is much less than in cultures on vitelline membrane or clots.

Spratt (1963) has recently made the interesting observation that blastoderms will expand over a polypore filter disk (composed of cellulose ester filaments) floating in a liquid medium of egg extract, and he reports that the rate of expansion is almost normal. At present this is the only method known for obtaining normal blastoderm expansion in vitro, except by explanting on to vitelline membrane.

STAGES IN THE NORMAL DEVELOPMENT OF
THE CHICK

The following illustrated table of normal development of the chick is an abbreviated version (abbreviated mainly by omission of many of the stages after Stage 20) of the table of Hamburger and Hamilton (1951), also published in "Lillie's development of the chick" (Hamilton 1952). The numbering of the photographs corresponds with the numbering of the stages.

I. Before laying:
   1. *Maturation and fertilisation:* found in the oviduct above the isthmus.

   2. *Early cleavage:* up to about the thirty-two-celled stage found in the isthmus of the oviduct during the formation of the shell-membrane.

   3. *Later cleavage:* formation of periblast and entoderm, etc., found in the uterus up to time of laying.

II. After laying:

   Stage 1. Pre-streak: Prior to the appearance of the primitive streak. An "embryonic shield" may be visible, due to the accumulation of cells toward the posterior half of the blastoderm.

   Stage 2. Initial streak: A rather transitory stage in which the primitive streak appears as a short, conical thickening, almost as broad as long ($0 \cdot 3$–$0 \cdot 5$ mm. in length), at the posterior border of the pellucid area. Usually obtained after 6–7 hours of incubation.

   Stage 3. Intermediate streak: (12–13 hrs.) The primitive streak extends from the posterior margin to approximately the centre of the pellucid area. The streak is relatively broad throughout its length, and is flared out where it touches the opaque area. No primitive groove.

D

Stage 4. *Definitive streak:* (18–19 hrs.) The primitive streak has reached its maximal length (average length = 1·9 mm.). The primitive groove, primitive pit, and Hensen's node are present. The area pellucida has become pear-shaped and the streak extends over two-thirds to three-fourths of its length.

Stage 5. *Head-process:* (19–22 hrs.) The notochord or head-process is visible as a rod of condensed mesoderm extending forward from the anterior edge of Hensen's node. The head fold has not yet appeared.

Stage 6. *Head fold:* (23–25 hrs.) A definite fold of the blasto-derm anterior to the notochord now marks the anterior end of the embryo proper. No somites have yet appeared in the mesoderm lateral to the notochord. This is a transitory stage, since the head fold and the first pair of somites develop rather closely in time.

Stages 7 to 14 are based primarily on the numbers of pairs of somites which are clearly visible. The number of somites appear to be the simplest criterion for staging this phase of development, and it is sufficiently accurate for practical purposes. A stage is assigned to every third pair of somites which is added; embryos with in-between numbers of somites are designated by adding a + or − sign to the appropriate stage. Thus, stage 7 designates an embryo with one pair of somites; stage 7+ = two pairs; stage 8− = three pairs; stage 8 = four pairs; etc.

Stage 7. *One somite:* (23–26 hrs.) This is actually the second somite of the series; number one is not yet clearly defined. Neural folds are visible in the region of the head.

Stage 8. *Four somites:* (26–29 hrs.) Neural folds meet at level of mid-brain. Blood islands are present in posterior half of blastoderm.

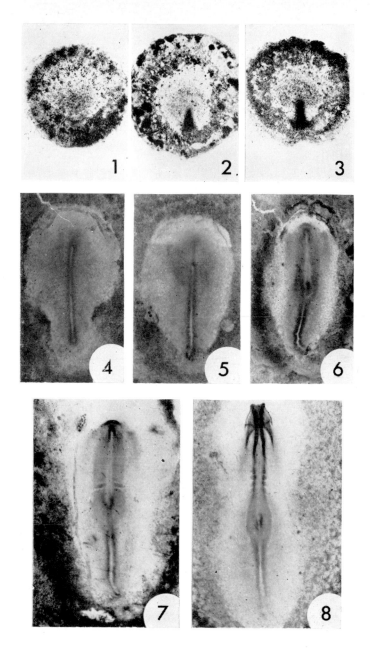

PLATE 3

 Stages 1–3. ×9. Stages 4–8. ×11.

Plates 3–7: Stages in the normal development of the chick embryo (Hamburger and Hamilton 1951).

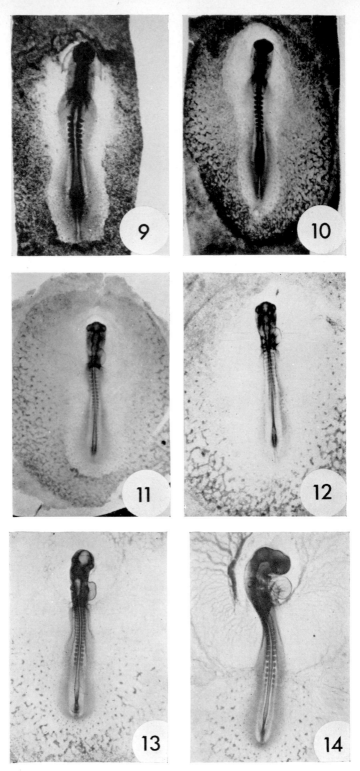

PLATE 4
Stage 9. ×12. Stages 10–14. ×7.

Stage 9. *Seven somites:* (29–33 hrs.) Primary optic vesicles are present. Paired primordia of heart begin to fuse.

Stage 10. *Ten somites:* (33–38 hrs.) The first somite is becoming dispersed; it is not included in the counts for subsequent stages. First indication of cranial flexure. Three primary brain vesicles are clearly visible. Optic vesicles not constricted at bases. Heart bent slightly to right.

Stage 11. *Thirteen somites:* (40–45 hrs.) Slight cranial flexure. Five neuromeres of hind-brain are distinct. Anterior neuropore is closing. Optic vesicles are constricted at bases. Heart bent to right.

Stage 12. *Sixteen somites:* (45–49 hrs.) Head is turning onto left side. Anterior neuropore closed. Telencephalon indicated. Primary optic vesicles and optic stalk well established. Auditory pit is deep, but wide open. Heart is slightly S-shaped. Head fold of amnion covers entire region of fore-brain.

Stage 13. *Nineteen somites:* (48–52 hrs.) Head is partly to fully turned onto left side. Cranial and cervical flexures make broad curves. Distinct enlargement of telencephalon. Slight narrowing of opening to deep auditory pit. No indication of hypophysis. Atrio-ventricular canal indicated by constriction. Head fold of amnion covers fore-brain, mid-brain, and anterior part of hind-brain.

Stage 14. *Twenty-two somites:* (50–53 hrs.)
Flexures and rotation: Cranial flexure: axes of fore-brain and hind-brain form about a right angle. Cervical flexure a broad curve. Rotation of body back as far as somites 7–9. Behind this level, a slight flexure makes its appearance which will be referred to as "trunk flexure".
Visceral arches 1 and 2, and clefts 1 and 2 are distinct. Posterior arches not distinct.
Primary *optic vesicle* begins to invaginate; lens placode is formed. Opening of *auditory pit* constricted. *Rathke's pouch* can be recognised. Ventricular loop of *heart* now ventral to atrio-ventricular canal. *Amnion* extends to somites 7–10.

Beyond stage 14 the number of somites becomes increasingly difficult to determine with accuracy. This is due in part to the dispersal of the mesoderm of the anteriormost somites, and, in later stages, to the curvature of the tail. Total somite counts given for the following stages are typical, but sufficiently variable so as not to be diagnostic. For these reasons, the limb buds, visceral arches, and other externally visible structures are used as identifying criteria from stage 15 onward.

Stage 15. (*ca.* 50–55 hrs.)
Lateral body folds extend to anterior end of wing level (somites 15–17).
Limb primordia: prospective limb areas flat, not yet demarcated. Inconspicuous condensation of mesoderm in wing level.
Somites: 24–27.
Amnion extends to somites 7–14.
Flexures and rotation: Cranial flexure: axes of fore-brain and hind-brain form an acute angle. The ventral contours of fore-brain and hind-brain are nearly parallel. Cervical flexure a broad curve. The trunk is distinct. Rotation extends to somites 11 to 13.
Visceral arches: Visceral arch 3 and cleft 3 are distinct. The latter is shorter than cleft 2 and usually oval in shape.
Eye: Optic cup is completely formed; double contour distinct in region of iris.

Stage 16. (*ca.* 51–56 hrs.)
Lateral body folds extend to somites 17–20, between levels of wings and legs.
Limbs: Wing is lifted off blastoderm by infolding of lateral body fold. It is represented by a thickened ridge. Primordium of leg is still flat; represented by a condensation of mesoderm.
Somites: 26–28.
Amnion: extends to somites 10–18.
Flexures and rotation: All flexures are more accentuated than in stage 15. Rotation extends to somites 14–15.
Tail bud: A short, straight cone, delimited from blastoderm.
Visceral arches: Third cleft still oval in shape.
Fore-brain lengthened; constrictions between brain parts are deepened. Epiphysis indistinct or not yet formed

Stage 17. (*ca.* 52–64 hrs.)

Lateral body folds extend around the entire circumference of the body.

Limb buds: Both wing and leg buds lifted off blastoderm by infolding of the body folds. Both are distinct swellings of approximately equal size.

Somites: 29–32.

Amnion: Considerable variability, ranging from a condition in which posterior trunk and tail, from approximately somite 26, are uncovered, to complete closure except for an oval hole over somites 28–36. Intermediate stages, with an anterior fold covering as far back as somite 25, and a posterior fold covering part of the tail, are common.

Flexures and rotation: Cranial flexure is unchanged. Cervical flexure is more sharply bent than in preceding stages, but its angle is still larger than 90°. Trunk flexure is distinct in brachial level. Rotation extends to somites 17–18.

Tail bud bent ventrally. Its mesoderm unsegmented.

Epiphysis: A distinct knob. Indication of nasal pits.

Allantois: Not yet formed.

Stage 18. (*ca.* 3 days.)

Limb buds enlarged; leg buds slightly larger than wing buds. L/W of wing = 6 or <6 (L = length = anterior-posterior dimension as measured along the body wall; W = width = distance from body wall to apex).

Somites: 30–36; extend beyond level of leg bud.

Amnion: Usually closed; occasionally an oval hole in lumbar region.

Flexures and rotation: At the cervical flexure, the axis of the medulla forms approximately a right angle to the axis of the posterior trunk. The trunk flexure has shifted to the lumbar region. The rotation extends now to the posterior part of the body; hence the leg buds are no longer in the horizontal plane.

Tail bud is turned to the right, at about an angle of 90° to the axis of the posterior trunk.

Visceral arches: Maxillary process absent or inconspicuous. Fourth visceral cleft indistinct or absent.

Allantois: A short, thick-walled pocket; not yet vesicular.

Stage 19. (*ca.* 3–3½ days.)

Limb buds: Enlarged, symmetrical. Leg buds slightly larger and bulkier than wing buds. L/W of wing buds = 4–6.

Somites: 37–40; extend into tail; but the end of the tail which is directed forward is unsegmented.

Flexures and rotation: In the cervical flexure the axis of the medulla forms an acute angle with the axis of the trunk. The trunk flexure has nearly or entirely disappeared owing to the rotation of the entire body. The contour of the posterior part of the trunk is straight to the base of the tail. *Tail bud* curved, its tip pointing forward.

Visceral arches: The maxillary process is a distinct swelling of approximately the same length as the mandibular process. The first visceral cleft is an open narrow slit at its dorsal part. It continues into a shallow furrow. The second arch projects slightly over the surface. The fourth cleft is a fairly distinct slit at its dorsal part and continues ventrally as a shallow groove. It does not perforate into the pharynx as a true (open) cleft, but is, nevertheless, homologous to the other three clefts.

Allantois: A small pocket of variable size; not yet vesicular.

Eyes unpigmented.

Stage 20. (*ca.* 3–3½ days.)

Limb buds enlarged: leg buds are distinctly larger from now on than wing buds. The wing buds are still approximately symmetrical; the leg buds are slightly asymmetrical. L/W of wing = 3–3·9; L/W of leg = 3–2·3.

Somites: 40–43; tip of tail still unsegmented.

Flexures and rotation: Cervical flexure more accentuated than in stage 19. The bend in the tail region begins to extend forward into the lumbo-sacral region. Contour of mid-trunk a straight line. Rotation completed.

Visceral arches: Maxillary process distinct, equals or exceeds the mandibular process in length. Second arch projects over surface. Fourth arch less prominent and smaller than third arch. Fourth cleft shorter than third cleft; a narrow slit at its dorsal part, continuing into a shallow groove.

Allantois: Vesicular, variable in size; on the average of the size of the mid-brain.

Eye pigment. A faint grayish hue.

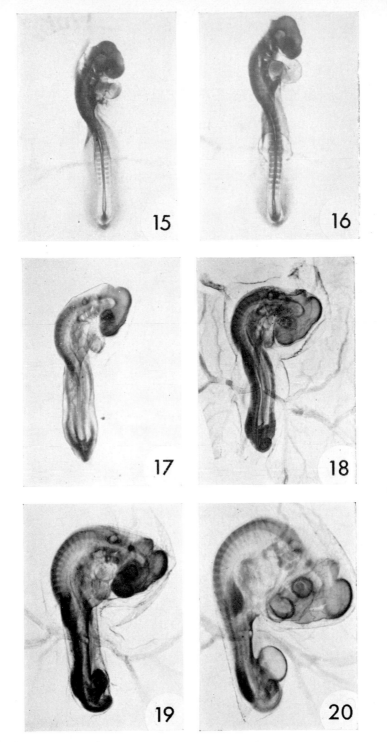

PLATE 5
Stages 15–20. ×7.

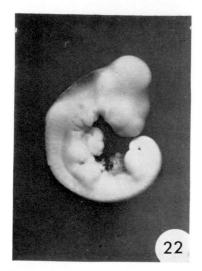

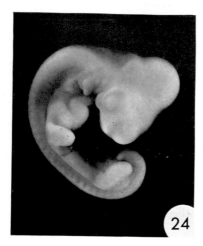

PLATE 6
Stages 22–26. ×6.

Stage 22. (ca. 3½–4 days.)
Limbs: Elongated buds, pointing caudally. The anterior and posterior contours are nearly parallel at their bases. L/W of wing = 1·5–2; L/W of leg = 1·3–1·8.
Somites: Extend to tip of tail.
Visceral arches: Maxillary process is definitely longer than mandibular process, extending approximately to the middle of the eye. The second arch extends distinctly over the surface and overlaps the third arch ventrally. Fourth arch distinct; fourth cleft visible as a slit.
Allantois: Variable in size; extends to head and may overlap the fore-brain.
Eye pigmentation: Distinct.

Stage 24. (ca. 4½ days.)
Limbs: Wing and leg buds distinctly longer than wide. Digital plate in wing not yet demarcated. Toe plate in leg bud distinct. Toes not yet demarcated.
Visceral arches: First visceral cleft a distinct curved line. Second arch longer ventrally and much wider than mandibular process. Third arch reduced and partly overgrown by second arch; 4th arch flattened. Both are sunk beneath the surface. Third visceral cleft is an elongated groove. Fourth visceral cleft reduced to a small pit.

Stage 26. (ca. 5 days.)
Limbs: Considerably lengthened. Contour of digital plate rounded. Indication of faint groove between second and third digit. Demarcation of the first three toes distinct.
Visceral arches: The second arch overlaps the third and fourth. The two pits representing the third and fourth visceral clefts no longer visible.

Stage 28. (ca. 5½–6 days.)
Limbs: Second digit and third toe longer than others, which gives the digital and toe plates a pointed contour. Three digits and four toes distinct. No indication of fifth toe.
Visceral arches: Mandibular process has lengthened and grown forwards. External auditory opening now very distinct.
Beak: A distinct outgrowth is visible in profile.

Stage 30. (*ca.* 6½–7 days.)

Limbs: The three major segments of wing and leg are clearly demarcated. Wing bent in elbow joint. Leg bent in knee joint. Distinct grooves between first and second digits. Contours of webs between first two digits and between all toes are slightly curved, concave lines.

Visceral arches: The mandibular process approaches the beak, but the gap between the two is still conspicuous.

Feather germs: Two dorsal rows to either side of the spinal cord at the brachial level. Three rows at the level of the legs; they are rather indistinct at thoracic level. None on thigh.

Scleral papillae: One on either side of choroid fissure; sometimes indistinct but never more than two.

Egg tooth distinct, slightly protruding. Beak more pronounced than in previous stage.

Stage 35. (*ca.* 8½–9 days.)

Limbs: Webs between digits and toes become inconspicuous. Phalanges in toes are distinct.

Feather germs: Mid-dorsal line stands out distinctly in profile view. At least four rows on inner side of each eye. New appearance of feather germs near mid-ventral line, close to sternum, and extending to both sides of umbilical cord.

Nictitating membrane has grown conspicuously and approaches the outer scleral papillae. Eyelids (external to nictitating membrane) have extended towards the beak and have begun to overgrow the eyeball. The circumference of the eyelids has become ellipsoidal.

Stage 40. (*ca.* 14 days.)

Beak: Length from anterior edge of nostril to tip of bill $= 4 \cdot 0$ mm.

Limbs: Length of third toe $= 12 \cdot 7 \pm 0 \cdot 5$ mm. Scales overlapping on inferior as well as superior surfaces of leg. Dorsal and ventral loci of cornification extend to base of exposed portion of claw. Entire plantar surface of phalanges is covered with well-developed papillae.

Stage 45. (*ca.* 19–20 days.)

Beak: Peridermal covering has been sloughed and beak is now shiny all over.

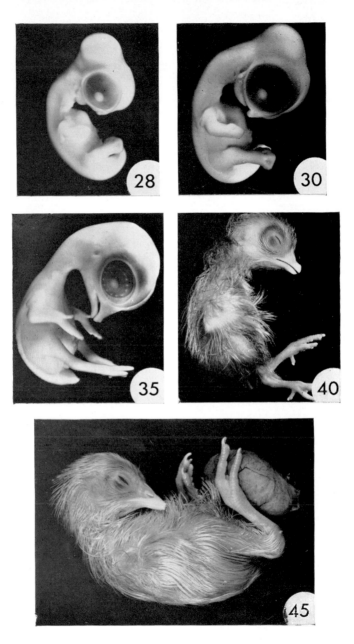

PLATE 7

Stages 28 and 30. ×2½.
Stage 35. ×2.
Stages 40 and 45. ×¾.

Third toe: Length = 20·5–22·0 mm.

Extra-embryonic membranes: Yolk sac is half-enclosed in body cavity. Chorio-allantoic membrane contains less blood and is "sticky" in the living embryo.

Stage 46. Newly hatched chick (20–21 days).

REFERENCES

ANCEL, P. (1958). Recherches sur l'action tératogène du refroidissement temporaire de l'œuf de poule au cours de l'incubation. *J. Embryol. exp. Morph.*, **6**, 335–45.

ANCEL, P. (1959). Recherches sur les malformations déterminées par le refroidissement temporaire de l'oeuf de poule et compatibles avec la vie des Poussins. *J. Embryol. exp. Morph.*, **7**, 330–4.

ASSHETON, R. (1896). An experimental examination into the growth of the blastoderm of the chick. *Proc. roy. Soc.*, **60**, 349–56.

BAROTT, H. G. (1937). Effect of temperature, humidity and other factors on hatch of hens' eggs and on energy metabolism of chick embryos. U.S. Department of Agriculture *Technical Bulletin*, **553**.

BELLAIRS, R. (1963). The development of somites in the chick embryo. *J. Embryol. exp. Morph.*, **11**, 697–714.

BELLAIRS, R. & NEW, D. A. T. (1962). Phagocytosis in the chick blastoderm. *Exp. Cell Res.*, **26**, 275–9.

BEVERIDGE, W. I. B. & BURNET, F. M. (1946). The cultivation of viruses and rickettsiae in the chick embryo. M.R.C. Special Report series, No. 256.

BILLETT, F. S., COLLINI, R. & HAMILTON, L. (1965). The effects of D- and L-threo-chloramphenicol on the early development of the chick embryo. *J. Embryol. exp. Morph.*, **13**, 341–56.

BILLINGHAM, R. E., BRENT, L. & MEDAWAR, P. B. (1956). Quantitative studies on tissue transplantation immunity. III. Actively acquired tolerance. *Phil. Trans. B.*, **239**, 357–414.

BURKE, E. (1925). A study of incubation. *Montana Agricultural Experiment Station Bulletin*, **178**.

CHAYTOR, D. E. B. (1963). The control of growth of the chick embryo liver studied by the method of parabiosis. *J. Embryol. exp. Morph.*, **11**, 667–72.

DANCHAKOFF, V. (1916). Equivalence of different hematopoietic anlages (by method of stimulation of their stem cells). *Amer. J. Anat.*, **20**, 255–327.

DeHAAN, R. L. (1959). Cardia bifida and the development of pacemaker function in the early chick heart. *Devl. Biol.*, **1**, 586–602.

DeHAAN, R. L. (1963a). Organisation of the cardiogenic plate in the early chick embryo. *Acta Embryol. Morph. Exp.*, **6**, 26–37.

DeHAAN, R. L. (1963b). Migration patterns of the precardiac mesoderm in the early chick embryo. *Exp. Cell Res.*, **29**, 544–60.

DeHAAN, R. L. (1963c). Regional organisation of pre-pacemaker cells in the
D*

cardiac primordia of the early chick embryo. *J. Embryol. exp. Morph.*, **11**, 65–76.

DEUCHAR, E. M. (1958). Experimental demonstration of tongue muscle origin in chick embryos. *J. Embryol. exp. Morph.*, **6**, 527–9.

DRACHMAN, D. B. & COULOMBRE, A. J. (1962). Method for continuous infusion of fluids into the chorioallantoic circulation of the chick embryo. *Science*, **138**, 144–5.

EBERT, J. D. (1951). Ontogenetic changes in the antigenetic specificity of the chick spleen. *Physiol. Zool.*, **24**, 20–41.

EBERT, J. D. (1954). The effects of chorio-allantoic transplants of adult chicken tissues on homologous tissues of the host chick embryo. *Proc. Nat. Acad. Sci. Wash.*, **40**, 337–47.

EYCLESHYMER, A. C. (1906–7). Some observations and experiments on the natural and artificial incubation of the egg of the common fowl. *Biol. Bull.*, **12**, 360–74.

FUNK, E. M. & FORWARD, J. (1960). The relation of angle of turning and position of the egg to hatchability of chicken eggs. *Poultry Sci.*, **39**, 784–5.

GRABOWSKI, C. T. (1956). The effects of excision of Hensen's node on the early development of the chick embryo. *J. exp. Zool.*, **133**, 301–44.

GRAU, C. R., FRITZ, H. I., WALKER, N. E. & KLEIN, N. W. (1962). Nutrition studies with chick embryos deprived of yolk. *J. exp. Zool.*, **150**, 185–95.

GRAU, C. R., KLEIN, N. W. & LAU, T. L. (1957). Total replacement of the yolk of chick embryos. *J. Embryol. exp. Morph.*, **5**, 210–14.

GRAU, C. R., WALKER, N. E., FRITZ, H. I. & PETERS, S. M. (1963). Successful development of chick embryos nourished by yolk-sac perfusion with calcium-low media. *Nature*, **197**, 257–9.

HAMBURGER, V. (1938). Morphogenetic and axial self-differentiation of transplanted limb primordia of 2-day chick embryos. *J. exp. Zool.*, **77**, 379–99.

HAMBURGER, V. (1960). *A manual of experimental embryology*. Revised ed. University of Chicago Press.

HAMBURGER, V. & HAMILTON, H. L. (1951). A series of normal stages in the development of the chick embryo. *J. Morphol.*, **88**, 49–92.

HAMILTON, H. L. (1952). *Lillie's development of the chick*. New York. Henry Holt.

HAŠEK, M. (1953). Vegetative hybridisation of animals by union of blood circulations during embryonic development. *Csl. Biol.*, **2**, 267–82.

HELL, A. (1964). Personal communication.

HOWARD, E. (1953). Some effects of NaCl concentration on the development of early chick blastoderms in culture. *J. cell. comp. Physiol.*, **41**, 237–54.

JURAND, A. & TUFT, P. (1961). A morphogenetic effect of beta-mercaptoethanol. Distribution of water in the embryo and distribution of water in the chick blastoderm. *Nature*, **191**, 1072–4.

KALTOFEN, R. S. (1961). Het keren der eieren van de hen tijdens het broeden als mechanische factor van betekenis voor de broeduitkomsten. *Thesis*. University of Utrecht.

KAUFMAN, L. (1938). Entwicklung und Wachstum von Hühnembryonen in frischen und in gelagerten Eiern. *Archiv für Geflügelkunde*, **12**, 65–77.

KEIBEL, F. & ABRAHAM, K. (1900). Normentafel zur Entwicklungsgeschichte des Huhnes (*Gallus domesticus*). In Keibel's *Normentafeln zur Entwicklungsgeschichte der Witbeltiere*. Gustav Fischer, Jena.

KENT, R. (1961). The development of the phagocytic activity of the reticuloendothelial system in the chick. *J. Embryol. exp. Morph.*, 9, 128–37.

KLEIN, N. W., GRAU, C. R. & GREEN, N. J. (1958). Yolk sac perfusion of chick embryos. Effects of various media on survival. *Proc. Soc. Exp. Biol. Med.*, 97, 425–8.

KLEIN, N. W., MCCONNELL, E. & RIQUIER, D. J. (1964). Enhanced growth and survival of explanted chick embryos cultured under high levels of oxygen. *Devl. Biol.*, 10, 17–44.

KÜNZEL, E. (1962). Die Entwicklung des Hühnchens im Ei. Paul Parey Verlag. Berlin. (Reprinted from *Zentralblatt für Veterinärmedizin*, 9, 371–96).

LANDAUER, W. (1961). The hatchability of chicken eggs as influenced by environment and heredity. *Monograph 1 of the Agricultural Experiment Station*, University of Connecticut, Storrs, Connecticut.

LEVI-MONTALCINI, R. (1952). Effects of mouse tumour transplantation on the nervous system. *Ann. N.Y. Acad. Sci.*, 55, 330–43.

MATOLTSY, A. G. (1965). Personal communication.

MAURICE, D. M. (1952). Electrical resistance and structure of the hen's egg. *Nature*, 170, 495.

MAURICE, D. M. & FIDANZA, A. (1952). Permeability of yolk of the hen's egg to bromine-82. *Nature*, 170, 546.

MCWHORTER, J. E. & WHIPPLE, A. O. (1912). The development of the blastoderm of the chick *in vitro*. *Anat. Rec.*, 6, 121–39.

MENKES, B. (1964). Personal communication.

MENKES, B. & MICLEA, C. (1962). Cercetări asupra formării organelor axiale. III. Posibilitățile de vindecare și reorganizare a mezodermului axial presomitic in urma disocierii mecanice. Formarea de somite supranumerare. *Studii Cerc. Baza Stiinte Timişoara*, 3–4, 203–28.

MOORE, M. A. S. (1965). Personal communication.

MOSCONA, A. (1959). Squamous metaplasia and keratinization of chorionic epithelium of the chick embryo in egg and in culture. *Devl. Biol.*, 1, 1–23.

MOSCONA, A. & CARNECKA3, Z. I. (1959). Etiology of keratogenic metaplasia in the chorioallantoic membrane. *Science*, 129, 1743–4.

MULHERKAR, L. (1958). Induction by regions lateral to the streak in the chick embryo. *J. Embryol. exp. Morph.*, 6, 1–14.

MUN, A. M., KOSIN, I. L. & SATO, I. (1959). Enhancement of growth of chick host spleens following chorio-allantoic membrane grafts of homologous tissues. *J. Embryol. exp. Morph.*, 7, 512–25.

NEEDHAM, J. (1931). *Chemical embryology*. Cambridge University Press.

NEEDHAM, J. (1950). *Biochemistry and morphogenesis*. Cambridge University Press.

NEEDHAM, J. (1959). *A history of embryology*. 2nd ed. Cambridge University Press.

NEW, D. A. T. (1955). A new technique for the cultivation of the chick embryo *in vitro*. *J. Embryol. exp. Morph.*, 3, 320–31.

NEW, D. A. T. (1956). The formation of sub-blastodermic fluid in hens' eggs. *J. Embryol. exp. Morph.*, **4**, 221–7.

NEW, D. A. T. (1957). A critical period for the turning of hens' eggs. *J. Embryol. exp. Morph.*, **5**, 293–9.

NEW, D. A. T. (1958). The hen's egg. *New Biology*, **26**, 7–29.

NEW, D. A. T. (1959). The adhesive properties and expansion of the chick blastoderm. *J. Embryol. exp. Morph.*, **7**, 146–64.

NICOLET, G. & GALLERA, J. (1963). Dans quelles conditions l'amnios de l'embryon de poulet peut-il se former en culture *in vitro*? *Experientia*, **19**, 165–6.

O'DELL, D. S. & McKENZIE, J. (1963). The action of aminopterin on the explanted early chick embryo. *J. Embryol. exp. Morph.*, **11**, 185–200.

OLSEN, M. W. & HAYNES, S. K. (1948). The effect of different holding temperatures on the hatchability of hens' eggs. *Poultry Sci.*, **27**, 420–6.

OLSEN, M. W. & KNOX, C. W. (1938). Early identification of fertility in hen's eggs. *Poultry Sci.*, **17**, 472–7.

OPPENHEIMER, J. (1955). Problems, concepts and their history. In *Analysis of Development*. (Willier, Weiss and Hamburger, eds.) Saunders Co., Philadelphia and London.

PASTEELS, J. (1935). Sur les mouvements morphogénétiques suscitant l'apparition de la ligne primitive chez les oiseaux. *C.R. Soc. Biol., Paris*, **120**, 1362–7.

PASTEELS, J. (1936). Analyse des mouvements morphogénétiques de gastrulation sur les oiseaux. *Bull. Acad. Roy. Belg. Classe Sci.*, **22**, 737–52.

PASTEELS, J. (1937). Études sur la gastrulation des Vertébrés méroblastiques. III. Oiseaux. IV. Conclusions générales. *Arch. Biol.*, **48**, 381–488.

PATTEN, B. M. & KRAMER, T. C. (1933). The initiation of contraction in the embryonic chick heart. *Amer. J. Anat.*, **53**, 349–75.

POLK, A., BUDDINGH, G. J. & GOODPASTURE, E. W. (1938). Experimental study of complement and hemolytic amboceptor introduced into chick embryos. *Amer. J. Path.*, **14**, 71–86.

PRICE, J. W. & FOWLER, E. V. (1940). Egg shell cap method of incubating chick embryos. *Science*, **91**, 271–2.

RAWLES, M. E. (1948). Origin of melanophores and their role in development of colour patterns in vertebrates. *Physiol. Rev.*, **28**, 383–408.

RAWLES, M. E. (1952). Transplantation of normal embryonic tissues. In "The chick embryo in biological research". *Ann. N.Y. Acad. Sci.*, **55**, 302–12.

RAWLES, M. E. (1963). Tissue interactions in scale and feather development as studied in dermal-epidermal recombinations. *J. Embryol. exp. Morph.*, **11**, 765–89.

ROMANOFF, A. L. (1931). Cultivation of chick embryo in opened egg. *Anat. Rec.*, **48**, 185–9.

ROMANOFF, A. L. (1943a). Assimilation of avian yolk and albumen under normal and extreme incubating temperatures. *Anat. Rec.*, **86**, 143–8.

ROMANOFF, A. L. (1943b). Cultivation of early chick embryo *in vitro*. *Anat. Rec.*, **87**, 365–8.

ROMANOFF, A. L. (1960). *The avian embryo.* New York. Macmillan Publishing Co.

ROMANOFF, A. L. & ROMANOFF, A. J. (1949). *The avian egg.* London, Chapman and Hall.

RUDNICK, D. (1944). Early history and mechanics of the chick blastoderm. A review. *Quart. Rev. Biol.,* 19, 187–212.

RYCHTER, Z., KOPECKY, M. & LEMEZ, L. (1955). A micromethod for determination of the circulating blood volume in chick embryos. *Nature,* 175, 1126–7.

RYLE, M. (1957). Studies on the influence of the embryonic environment on the post-hatching development of chickens. *J. exp. Biol.,* 34, 529–42.

SABIN, F. R. (1917). Origin and development of the primitive vessels of the chick and of the pig. *Contr. Embryol. Carneg. Inst. Wash. Publ.,* 226, 61–124.

SABIN, F. R. (1919). Studies in the origin of blood vessels and of red blood-corpuscles as seen in the living blastoderm of chicks during the second day of incubation. *Contr. Embryol. Carneg. Inst. Wash. Publ.,* 272, 213–62.

SCHMIDT, G. (1937). On the growth stimulating effect of egg white and its importance for embryonic development. *Enzymologia,* 4, 40–8.

SILVER, P. H. S. (1959). Embryonic growth relative to the vitelline membrane, and its role in determining the level of post-operative abnormalities, as measured in the chick. *J. Embryol. exp. Morph.,* 7, 564–71.

SILVER, P. H. S. (1960). Special problems of experimenting *in ovo* on the early chick embryo, and a solution. *J. Embryol. exp. Morph.,* 8, 369–75.

SILVER, P. H. S. (1962). *In ovo* experiments concerning the eye, the orbit, and certain juxta-orbital structures, in the chick embryo. *J. Embryol. exp. Morph.,* 10, 423–50.

SIMON, D. (1956a). Étude de la circulation dans les parabioses d'embryons de poulets explantés *in vitro.* *C.R. Soc. Biol., Paris,* 150, 415–7.

SIMON, D. (1956b). Étude de la circulation chez des embryons de poulet explantés *in vitro* après résection de divers territoires. *C.R. Soc. Biol., Paris,* 150, 11–15.

SIMON, D. (1960). Contribution a l'étude de la circulation et du transport des gonocytes primares dans les blastoderms d'oiseau cultivés *in vitro.* *Arch. Anat. Micr. et Morph. exp.,* 1, 93–182.

SOLOMON, J. B. (1962). A sex difference in the splenomegaly syndrome in chick embryos infected with adult spleen cells or blood. *Exp. Cell Res.,* 28, 151–7.

SOLOMON, J. B. (1963). Actively acquired transplantation immunity in the chick embryo. *Nature,* 198, 1171–3.

SPRATT, N. T. Jr. (1947a). A simple method for explanting and cultivating early chick embryos *in vitro.* *Science,* 106, 452.

SPRATT, N. T. Jr. (1947b). Development *in vitro* of the early chick blastoderm explanted on yolk and albumen extract saline-agar substrata. *J. exp. Zool.,* 106, 345–65.

SPRATT, N. T. Jr. (1955). Analysis of the organiser center in the early chick embryo. I. Localisation of prospective notochord and somite cells. *J. exp. Zool.,* 128, 121–63.

SPRATT, N. T. Jr. (1963). Role of the substratum, supracellular continuity, and differential growth in morphogenetic cell movements. *Devl. Biol.*, **7**, 51–63.

SPRATT, N. T. Jr. & HAAS, H. (1960a). Morphogenetic movements in the lower surface of the unincubated and early chick blastoderm. *J. exp. Zool.*, **144**, 139–57.

SPRATT, N. T. Jr. & HAAS, H. (1960b). Integrative mechanisms in development of the early chick blastoderm. I. Regulative potentiality of separated parts. *J. exp. Zool.*, **145**, 97–138.

SPRATT, N. T. Jr. & HAAS, H. (1961). Integrative mechanisms in development of the early chick blastoderm. II. Role of morphogenetic movements and regenerative growth in synthetic and topographically disarranged plastoderms. III. Role of cell population size and growth potentiality in synthetic systems larger than normal. *J. exp. Zool.*, **147**, 57–94, 271–93.

SPRATT, N. T. Jr. & HAAS, H. (1962). Integrative mechanisms in development of the early chick blastoderm. IV. Synthetic systems composed of parts of different developmental age. Synchronisation of developmental rates. *J. exp. Zool.*, **149**, 75–102.

SZÉKELY, G. & SZENTÁGOTHAI, J. (1962). Reflex and behaviour patterns elicited from implanted supernumerary limbs in the chick. *J. Embryol. exp. Morph.*, **10**, 140–51.

VAKAET, L. (1962). Some new data concerning the formation of the definitive endoblast in the chick embryo. *J. Embryol. exp. Morph.*, **10**, 38–57.

VAKAET, L. (1964). Personal communication.

VAN ALTEN, P. J. & FENNELL, R. A. (1959). The effects of chorioallantoic grafts on the developing chick embryo.
I. Studies on weight and histology of homologous and heterologous tissues.
II. Studies of adult antigens in the duodenum and spleen.
J. Embryol. exp. Morph., **7**, 459–75, 476–86.

VOLLMAR, H. (1935). Eine Methode zur Beobachtung der Entwicklung des Huhnembryo *in vitro*. *Z. Zellforsch.*, **23**, 566–700.

WADDINGTON, C. H. (1932). Experiments on the development of chick and duck embryos, cultivated *in vitro*. *Phil. Trans. Roy. Soc. B*, **221**, 179–230.

WADDINGTON, C. H. (1952). *The epigenetics of birds*. Cambridge University Press.

WALKER, N. E. & GRAU, C. R. (1963). Growth and development of chick embryos supplied with various concentrations of yolk. *J. Nutr.*, **79**, 205–10.

WEISS, P. & ANDRES, G. (1952). The fate of embryonic cells (chick) disseminated by the vascular route. *J. exp. Zool.*, **121**, 449–87.

WEISS, P. & MATOLTSY, A. G. (1959). Wound healing in chick embryos *in vivo* and *in vitro*. *Devl. Biol.*, **1**, 302–26.

WILLIER, B. H. (1924). The endocrine glands and the development of the chick. *Amer. J. Anat.*, **33**, 67–103.

WOLFF, E. & SIMON, D. (1955). L'explantation et la parabiose *in vitro* de blastoderms incubés d'embryons de Poulet. L'organisation de la circulation extra-embryonnaire. *C.R. Acad. Sci., Paris*, **241**, 1994–6.

ZWILLING, E. (1965). Personal communication.

CHAPTER 4

Reptiles

Less study has been given to the experimental embryology of reptiles than to any of the other vertebrate groups. A few methods have been devised for growing the embryos in culture and several studies have been made of the effect of excising or destroying parts of the embryo (Marcucci 1914a, b, Raynaud 1960, 1962c, d, 1963, Holder & Bellairs 1962, Maderson & Bellairs 1962, Dufaure 1964, Moffat & Bellairs 1964), but only one using vital marks to trace cell movements (Pasteels 1937). Clark and his collaborators (1956, 1957) have studied nitrogen excretion, Gordon (1960) water requirements, Yntema (1960) and Fox, Gordon & Fox (1961) effects of different temperatures, Dufaure (1961) and Raynaud & Pieau (1964) some effects of sex hormones, and Hubert (1964) the production of twin embryos by division of the early blastoderm. Needham (1931, 1950) gives references to a few earlier papers. But in general reptile experimental embryology is a subject with a future rather than a past.

Reasons for the comparative neglect of reptile embryos are not difficult to find. The embryos develop much more slowly than those of the chick or small laboratory mammals, and take considerably longer to reach equivalent stages; they can hardly be recommended therefore to those who like their results in a hurry. But the most serious problem is the difficulty of obtaining enough eggs of the required age. Reptiles rarely breed in captivity and the experimenter invariably has to rely on eggs found in the wild; these may occur singly or only in very small batches, and the stage of development may or may not be suitable for a particular experiment. In temperate climates breeding usually occurs only once a year, the eggs being laid in the spring and hatching in late summer. In the tropics the breeding season may be longer, and some species, particularly of the Crocodilia and Chelonia, lay clutches of 20–100 or more eggs (see Bellairs 1957); but finding the right eggs for particular experiments can still be a tiresome business. Perhaps the most urgent of all the problems of reptile embryology is the 'domestication' of at least one reptile species, so that embryos of a desired stage can be made available when required. Until this is done it is unlikely that the subject will advance at more than a reptilian pace.

However, thanks to the patience of a few dedicated herpetologists, at least a beginning has been made with the culturing of reptile embryos. Of the species studied so far the viviparous forms *Lacerta vivipara* and *Anguis fragilis* have received the most attention. In the following account of the techniques used the "D-H stages" of *Lacerta vivipara* refer to the table of Dufaure and Hubert (1961) on pages 110–16. Two other complete tables of reptile development have been published: Peter (1904) for *Lacerta agilis*, and Zehr (1962) for the garter snake *Thamnophis sirtalis*. The latter is only partially illustrated, but it contains useful information about the length of time required for the development of each stage in vivo, which the author has managed to obtain by removing embryos at intervals from the same snake. Keibel (1906) gives short illustrated tables of a few other reptile species, including a crocodile, the slow worm, the tuatara, the grass snake and the turtle *Trionyx*. Pasteels (1956–57) describes the early stages (up to the end of gastrulation) of the chelonians *Clemmys leprosa*, *Chrysemys picta* and *Pseudemys virginica*, and of the lizards *Chameleo bitaeniatus*, *Mabuia megalura* and *Chamaesaura anguinea*. Milaire (1957) gives details about some of the later stages of the last three of these, and of the chelonian *Emys orbicularis*.

EMBRYOS IN THE SHELL

Pasteels (1937) has studied gastrulation movements in the Algerian turtle *Clemmys leprosa*, using a method of vital staining in ovo similar to that employed for chick blastoderms (p. 64). This species normally lays 3–12 hard-shelled eggs during early July. Gastrulation is almost completed by the time of laying, so the eggs had to be taken from the maternal oviduct from late May onwards. Windows were cut in the shell and nile blue marks applied to the blastoderm with blocks of impregnated agar. Towards the end of gastrulation the blastoderm was found to be very close to the shell and great care had to be taken in opening the eggs at this stage. The resealed eggs were kept in a humid chamber at 25°–35°C. Development was very slow at the lower temperatures but appreciably faster at the higher.

The marks could be followed clearly for 24 hours but had completely disappeared after 3 days. The short life of the stain, combined with the slow rate of development, meant that morphogenetic movements could not be traced as far as in chick blastoderms; nevertheless Pasteels was able to elucidate the general pattern of movements during the later stages of gastrulation. He could not, however, study the early stages of endoderm formation by vital staining methods because of the very glutinous albumen and soft shell in eggs of this age.

Yntema (1964) describes methods of obtaining and operating on eggs of the snapping turtle *Chelydra serpentina* of North America. The laying season of this species, in the vicinity of Syracuse, New York, usually starts during the second week of June and lasts a week or two. Females about to lay can be collected most frequently in early morning or at dusk in ploughed or open areas near bodies of water inhabited by the turtles. The animals are palpated to confirm the presence of hard mature eggs, and are then killed and the eggs dissected out. Thirty to fifty eggs can be obtained from a 5 kg. female and these are incubated in a moist chamber. At 20°C the embryos develop about one somite per day and at 30°C about five somites per day, and the stage required for a particular experiment can be obtained by regulation of the temperature. Access to the embryo is gained by making a window in the shell and shell membranes, and operations can then be made on the embryo in ovo similar to those on chick embryos. After operations on the trunk region of embryos at stages between 4 and 18 somites about half the embryos survive, but the survival rate is lower after operations to the head region, particularly if the developing embryonic membranes are disrupted.

Yntema also considers that the painted turtle, *Chrysemys picta*, is a promising reptile for experimental embryology. It is widely distributed and withstands shipping and handling, and the embryos are suitable for microsurgical procedures. Its main disadvantage is that the female has relatively few eggs, usually less than ten.

EMBRYOS EXPLANTED WITH THE YOLK

The eggs of two lizards, *Lacerta vivipara* ($=Zootoca\ vivipara$) and *Anguis fragilis* (the slow-worm) have been successfully cultivated in vitro. Both these species are viviparous and have the advantage that from one pregnant female several embryos can be obtained all at the same stage of development. *Lacerta vivipara* usually contains five to seven fertile eggs and *Anguis fragilis* six to twelve or more. In Anguis the egg coverings (shell membrane and embryonic membranes) are thinner and the embryo can be seen more clearly, but the limb buds are only transient (Raynaud 1962a, 1962b); it seems also to have more exacting culture requirements.

The best general account of the natural history of *L. vivipara* and *A. fragilis* is by Smith (1964). Both animals are widely distributed in Europe; they can sometimes be obtained from dealers (p. 17) but otherwise must be caught in the wild. According to Bellairs (1965) "Lacerta is difficult to catch, especially in country with dense undergrowth; the only way is to stroll about till you see one, stalk it and pounce. With Anguis it is just a matter of finding them under trash, corrugated iron, stones, etc., and picking them up. We find that Lacerta v. is quite difficult to keep for very long in the laboratory— more so than some of the continental lacertids. It is very prone to mite infestation which may kill, presumably by virtue of being a vector for some disease organism, very quickly. It is also prone to go off food and needs a variety of food; mealworms, spiders, grasshopper, roaches, etc. The babies can with luck be reared on a mixture of Drosophila, green aphids and tiny spiders. Both babies and adults need individual attention and often coaxing to feed. I suspect that this species would do better in outdoor vivaria and that if one kept a lot one would need to maintain cultures of various bugs to provide a regular and copious food supply. Anguis, however, will live for years almost anywhere and feeds well on earthworms and slugs, especially the white Agrolimax. It is potentially a very good laboratory reptile."

The use of ether or chloroform to kill the pregnant females does not seem to affect the viability of the embryos (Holder & Bellairs 1962). The body of each female is slit open and the thin-walled oviducts with the eggs inside are removed and placed in a large Petri dish containing 0·6% sodium chloride. The oviducts are pulled away with fine forceps and the eggs released. The eggs do not have any shell and are ready for culturing without further dissection. They can be transferred individually to the culture chamber by means of a wide pipette.

Two methods of culture have been developed, Panigel's (1956) and Raynaud's (1959a, b), and will be described here in detail. In Panigel's method little or no provision is made for supplying water and nutrient materials to the embryo beyond that already stored in the egg itself. It seems to give good results with Lacerta but rather poor results with Anguis. The eggs of Anguis may be more highly adapted to viviparity and so require an external food source; certainly their thinner coverings bring foetal and maternal blood circulations closer together. In Raynaud's method, where greater provision is made for exchange of materials between embryo and culture medium, the eggs of Anguis develop very much better, but the technique has the disadvantage that the apparatus required is more elaborate. If contact with a large volume of nutrient medium is the essential feature of Raynaud's method, this might be provided by simpler apparatus.

Holder & Bellairs (1962) have shown that it is possible to operate successfully on embryos in Panigel cultures. This involves first cutting through the shell membrane and underlying embryonic membranes. Small haemorrhages are almost inevitable, but seem to have little effect on the embryo; the larger chorio-allantoic blood vessels should be avoided.

The embryonic membranes seem to harden a little after the eggs have been removed from the oviduct, and since this makes operating easier it is a good idea to leave the eggs in culture for at least 24 hours before making the initial incision.

If the hole in the membranes is left open the embryos tend subsequently to protude through it and to develop very abnormally. This can often be prevented by covering the hole with a small piece of sterilised cotton handkerchief, which soon adheres to the membranes and forms an effective seal (Plate 8.E).

Another problem, which has not yet been solved, is that constriction bands may develop in the embryonic membranes near the site of experimental injury. Removal of the tail, for example, is very often followed by auto-amputation by constriction bands of this kind (Bellairs 1965).

The eggs of Lacerta can be kept at 10°C for several days in a state of almost arrested development and normal growth will often recommence when the temperature is raised. This may be of practical importance in allowing specimens to be stored until a convenient time for operation. It does not seem to be successful with embryos younger than D-H stage 32 but preliminary experiments have shown that older embryos can withstand such storage for a fortnight or more. This may also apply, though it has not yet been demonstrated, to Anguis.

Panigel's culture method

Small petri dishes, lined with gauze or cotton wool, are heat sterilised. The gauze is moistened with sterile 0·6% NaCl in distilled water, and the eggs are placed on it with the embryo uppermost. To maintain the humidity of the cultures the petri dishes are transferred to a large glass-covered chamber containing wet cotton wool or a dish of water (Fig. 16). The cultures can be kept at laboratory temperatures or placed in an incubator at temperatures up to 30°C (28°C is good for *L. vivipara* eggs). In successful cultures, development continues for days or weeks without further treatment.

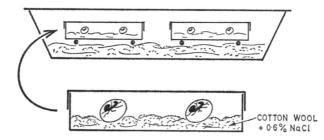

Figure 16. Panigel's culture method. The eggs are placed, embryo uppermost, on cotton wool or gauze soaked in 0·6% NaCl in a petri dish. The petri dish is then transferred to a larger chamber kept humid with wet cotton wool.

The progress of development can be inspected daily by transferring the petri dishes to a dissecting microscope and temporarily replacing the lid of each dish with a warmed (to prevent condensation) flat plate of glass. It is usually possible to tell if an embryo is alive by observing the flow of blood through the chorio-allantoic vessels, and in the later stages movements of the embryo can be seen. Moffat & Bellairs (1964) have found the addition of chick albumen to the saline (1 part to 4 of saline) useful in discouraging fungus infections, which are otherwise apt to develop after long periods in culture. Dufaure (1961, 1964) and Hubert (1964) have replaced the saline entirely by chick albumen; each egg is cultured, embryo uppermost, in a small dish of capacity 30 ml. containing sufficient albumen (no cotton wool) to bathe most of the egg but not to cover it; humidity is maintained by sealing a glass cover onto the dish with wax.

(i) *Lacerta vivipara*. Panigel describes the results from ten cultures of *Lacerta vivipara* embryos. One of these, maintained at 27°C, hatched after 17 days in culture; two others, maintained at laboratory temperatures (18°–22°C) hatched, one after 24 days and the other after one month. Of the remainder, none hatched, but many of them developed almost to hatching stage. Unfortunately, it is not clear at what stage any of these embryos were explanted.

TABLE 2

	Embryo No.	Duration and temperature (°C) of culture	Final Stage
5 sibling embryos explanted at D-H Stage 29	1	13 days at 21°–23°	D-H stage 32
	2	21 ,, at ,,	D-H stage 35
	3	40 ,, ,, ,,	Almost hatching
	4	11 days at 4°; then 1 day at 21°–23°	No development
	5	11 days at 4°; then 10 days at 21°–23°	D-H stage 31
6 sibling embryos explanted at D-H Stage 30	6	8 days at 30°	D-II stage 35
	7	9 ,, ,, 21°–23°	D-H stage 33
	8	23 ,, ,, ,,	D-H stage 37
	9	30 ,, ,, ,,	D-H stage 39
	10	9 ,, ,, 4°	No development
	11	23 ,, ,, ,,	D-H stage 30-31

TABLE 2. Survival of two hatches of sibling embryos of *Lacerta vivipara* cultured by Panigel's method (Maderson & Bellairs, 1962). "D-H stages" refer to the table of Dufaure & Hubert on pages 110–16.

A more detailed description of the results obtainable with Panigel's method has been provided by Maderson & Bellairs (1962) and Holder & Bellairs (1962). Table 2 shows the amount of development obtained from two batches of sibling embryos cultured at different temperatures. At 4°C development was arrested, but between 20°C and 30°C the embryos grew well, the rate of growth increasing with temperature. Other cultures of *Lacerta vivipara* embryos have given similar results. Even when good development is obtained, death just before hatching is common. At 33°–35°C the embryos die within 10 days.

(ii) *Anguis fragilis*. Holder & Bellairs have also studied the development of slow-worm eggs in Panigel cultures at room temperature (21°–23°C).

Out of six embryos explanted at "D-H stage 28", three were alive after 7 days, but none lived longer than 10 days or developed beyond "D-H stage 30". (Apart from the short table in Keibel (1906) no normal table of development has been made for the slow-worm, and the stages given here are obtained by comparison with the Dufaure and Hubert table for Lacerta (p. 114) and can be regarded only as approximate.)

Out of sixty embryos explanted at "D-H stage 32" or older, more than half survived for longer than 14 days. Two survived over 40 days but did not hatch. Only those on the point of hatching when explanted succeeded in hatching in culture. Oedema and abnormalities of development were common, and the embryos that survived for long periods in culture were much smaller than corresponding stages in vivo.

Raynaud's culture method
Anguis fragilis

Raynaud (1959a, b) has cultured slow-worm eggs in an assembly of small oval glass cups, each 12 mm. × 18 mm. with a hole at the bottom (Plate 8.A). The assembly is housed in a covered crystallising dish, containing liquid nutrient medium up to the level of the upper border of the oval cups (Fig. 17). The apparatus is heat sterilised and the medium is prepared sterile.

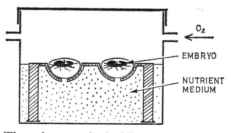

Figure 17. The culture method of Raynaud (1959a, b). The eggs are supported at the surface of liquid nutrient medium in a sealed crystallising dish. Oxygen is introduced through a side tube (see also Plate 8.A–D).

Sufficient oxygen (without CO_2) to fill the crystallising dish is introduced through a side tube, and is renewed every 24 hours. The cultures are incubated at 26°–27°C and the medium is changed every 4 or 5 days.

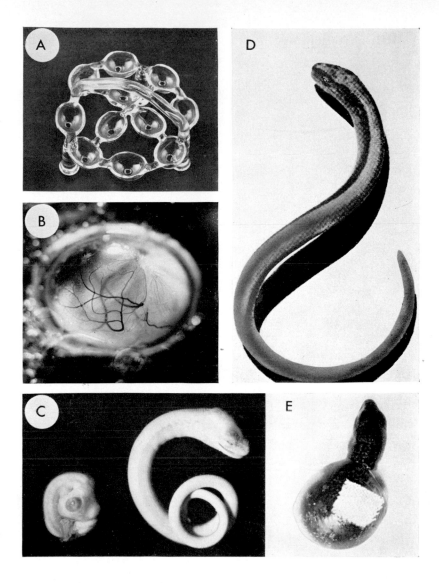

PLATE 8

    A–D. Culture of slow worm embryos (Raynaud 1959).

        A. Assembly of glass cups for supporting eggs. $\times \frac{1}{2}$.

        B. Living egg in culture. $\times 2$

        C. On the left, embryo as explanted, weight 65 mg.
           On the right, after 16 days in culture, weight 155 mg. $\times 3$.

        D. Embryo explanted in mid-development (weight about 90 mg.) and grown 16 days in culture; weight has increased to 447 mg. $\times 2$.

      E. *Lacerta vivipara* hatching in Panigel culture. The piece of handkerchief was applied to prevent prolapse after operation. (Moffat & Bellairs 1964). $\times 2\frac{1}{2}$.

In one experiment twelve eggs from the same slow-worm were divided into two batches of six, and one batch grown in each of the following media:

Medium A=One part Hanks solution (p. 5) to two parts albumen from hens' eggs; +neomycin.

Medium B=Medium A with 10–20% chick serum.

TABLE 3

Period in culture (days)	State of embryo	Weight (mg) of embryo in	
		Medium A	Medium B
11	Living	197	
,,	Dead	244	
,,	Living		308
16	Living	225	
,,	,,	303	
,,	Dead		435
,,	Living		310
,,	,,		447
19	Living	305	
,,	,,		329
,,	,,		446
20	Living	405	

TABLE 3. Growth of embryos of *Anguis fragilis* cultured by Raynaud's method (Raynaud, 1959b). At the time of explantation the embryos weighed 86–98 mg. See text for details of the media.

Embryonic development was already well advanced at the time of explantation, each embryo being about 37 mm. long and weighing 86–98 mg. In culture growth continued and the more successful embryos doubled in length and obtained a weight of nearly 450 mg. (Plate 8.D). Details are given in Table 3.

The results suggest that medium B promotes faster growth, but Raynaud states that this conclusion must be accepted with reserve, since other factors e.g. oxygenation or pH may have differed in the two sets of cultures. Both media gave well developed embryos comparable in length and weight with those grown to term in vivo.

In another experiment some eggs explanted at an earlier stage of development and grown in medium A did not develop so far. After 16 days they attained a weight of 155 mg. and a length of 51–55 mm. A small proportion survived for 26 days, reaching a weight of about 200 mg. The eggs became abnormally swollen, and histological examination of the embryos revealed abnormal dilation of the meso-nephric tubules.

Recently Raynaud (1964) has had good results with culture chambers designed to take single embryos, and has used them to measure the respiration of the growing embryo (Fig. 18). The

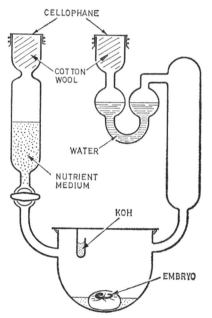

Figure 18.   A culture method devised by Raynaud which permits measurements on the respiration of individual embryos.

apparatus is made of pyrex glass and is heat sterilised before use. Sterile culture medium is introduced into the column on the left and sterile water into the two glass spheres on the right. The upper openings of the apparatus are covered with cotton wool and thick cellophane. The embryo is placed in the lower chamber and the lid is then sealed on with paraffin wax. This chamber contains a cell of KOH which absorbs the CO_2 given off by the embryo. Measurements of the CO_2 absorbed have shown that a young embryo produces about

1 ml. CO_2 in 24 hours. As oxygen is consumed, air enters through the cellophane, and the water levels in the glass spheres alter. The presence of this water is important for maintaining the humidity of the culture chamber; without it the surface of the egg dries rapidly. By means of the tap on the left-hand column, fresh medium can be allowed to flow into the culture chamber as required.

EMBRYOS EXPLANTED WITHOUT THE YOLK

Only three brief reports are available of attempts to culture explanted blastoderms and embryos without the yolk.

Bellairs (1951) used the plasma clot method of Waddington (p. 82) to culture the embryos of the snakes *Natrix natrix* and *Vipera berus*, and of the lizards *Lacerta vivipara* and *Anguis fragilis* incubated at 15°–20°C. The results for these four species were:

(i) *Natrix:* Ten blastoderms explanted at late cleavage stages failed to develop.

(ii) *Vipera:* One late embryo (> 30 somites) survived in culture for $4\frac{1}{2}$ days. During this time the embryo lengthened, and the allantois increased to about twice its original size and applied itself to the inner surface of the chorion.

(iii) *Lacerta.* Two blastoderms were explanted at the blastopore canal stage. Both survived, and in nine days the better one developed a neural plate, notochord, otic vesicles, somites and gut.

　　Four out of six embryos survived explantation at 20–30 somites (D-H stages 25–27) and the best continued growing for 10 days after transplantation at 4 days.

(iv) *Anguis:* Seven out of ten embryos survived explantation at 20–30 somites and the best lived 20 days. During the period in culture otic vesicles, nasal pits and nephric tubules developed, and the pharyngeal pouches disappeared.

Lutz and Dufaure (1960) explanted five *Lacerta vivipara* blastoderms at 5–7 somites (D-H stage 19) into a culture medium of Wolff and Haffen. They report that after 20 days at 20°–25°C three of the embryos had developed normally with recognisable optic and otic vesicles and viseral clefts. Histological examination showed primordial gonocytes in the genital crest of two of the embryos, and disseminated in the mesoderm near the mesonephros of the third.

Hubert (1964) obtained development of twin embryos from blastoderms of *Lacerta vivipara* that were explanted at D-H stage 4, divided into halves with a glass needle, and cultured on clots of agar, Tyrode saline and egg-extract.

These results indicate that reptile embryos explanted without the yolk sometimes undergo considerable development in vitro, but further studies will be necessary before the reliability of such techniques can be assessed.

STAGES IN THE NORMAL DEVELOPMENT OF
LACERTA (=ZOOTOCA) VIVIPARA
(Dufaure and Hubert, 1961)

The following table of normal stages is based on the study of 350 embryos obtained at intervals during gestation. The pattern of development shows little variation between different embryos, except in the time of closure of the neural groove and the dimensions of the pre-neurula embryo; neither of these criteria should be used therefore in staging embryos. The number of somites is a useful criterion, but until the 10-somite stage the somites are only visible from the ventral side of the embryo.

The text is a direct translation from Dufaure & Hubert's paper, except for a few of the stages where the description has been somewhat compressed. The photographs are all taken of embryos in their natural position. In the earlier stages the embryos are viewed dorsally; after torsion has occurred they are viewed laterally. The numbering of the photographs corresponds with the numbering of the stages in the text. Where some feature of the embryo can only be seen in histological section this is indicated by (h.s.). (The original paper also contains enlarged photographs of the limbs, which have not been reproduced here.)

Development, from fertilisation to birth (at Stage 40), normally takes about two months.

Stage 1. Beginning of segmentation: 1 central blastomere is completely isolated: 6 cleavage furrows radiate from it.

Stage 2. Disc of small blastomeres with about 20 cleavage furrows radiating from them.

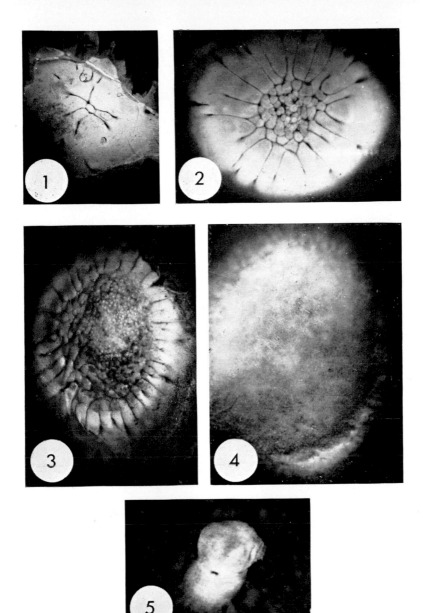

PLATE 9

Stages 1-4. ×18.   Stage 5. ×13.

Plates: 9-14 Stages in the normal development of *Lacerta vivaipar* (Dufaure and Hubert 1961).

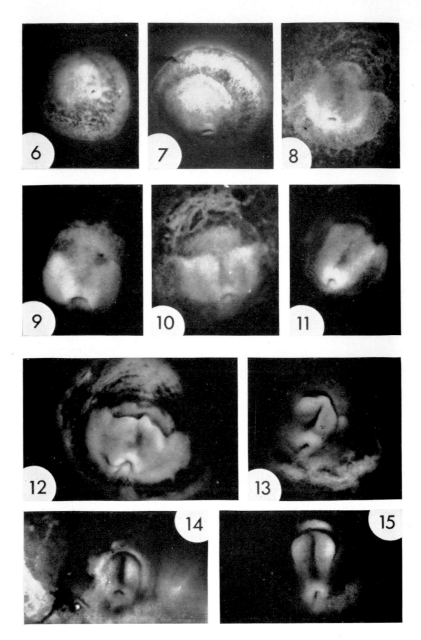

PLATE 10
Stages 6–15. ×11.

Stage 3. Embryonic disc contains blastomeres of three sizes. Large peripheral blastomeres encircle a zone in which cell division is more rapid at one "pole" than at the other.

Stage 4. Segmentation complete; embryonic disc composed entirely of very small blastomeres.

Stage 5. Embryonic shield becomes distinct. Formation of blastopore: it is rectangular and marks posterior region of shield. Large blastoporal plate forms an extension posterior to shield.

Stage 6. Reduction of the blastoporal plate. Extra-embryonic region divided into two concentric zones: the area pellucida and the area opaca. Blastoporal canal forming (h.s.).

Stage 7. Blastoporal plate integrated with embryonic shield. Dorsal lip of blastopore prominent and arched. Blastoporal canal clearly defined and closed ventrally (h.s.).

Stage 8. Head field distinct. Mesodermal crescent with horns directed anteriorly. Blastoporal canal open ventrally.

Stage 9. Mesoderm thickens forming two lateral "wings".

Stage 10. Median furrow indicates first stage of neural groove. Mesodermal "wings" reach head field.

Stage 11. Beginning of head fold.
Blastopore forms an inverted U.
Notochord distinct.

Stage 12. Head folds very distinct.
Neural folds forming.

Stage 13. Head fold becoming curved ("sickle-shaped").
Neural folds well formed and deep neural groove.

Stage 14. Formation of anterior amniotic fold; its lateral extensions almost reach level of blastopore.
Neural folds same size throughout their length.

Stage 15. Lateral body folds forming.
Beginning of fore gut.

Neural folds begin enlarging anteriorly to form brain.
Neural groove does not extend to the blastopore, which
is still distinct.

Between stages 5 and 15 the length of the embryo varies between
1 and 2 mm.

Stage 16.   Somites: 2 pairs.
Continued enlargement of anterior neural folds.
Elongation of trunk.
Neural groove reaches blastopore forming neurenteric
canal (h.s.).

Stage 17.   (Photographs 17a and 17b) Somites: 4 pairs.
Amniotic folds begin to extend over head.
Neural folds unite posteriorly.
Islets of Wolff appear in posterior extra-embryonic
region.

Stage 18.   Somites: 4 pairs.
Amnion completely covers head.

Stage 19.   (Photographs 19a and 19b) Somites: 6 pairs.
Amnion covers anterior half of embryo.
Two large sero-amniotic cavities extend on each side of
embryo.
Islets of Wolff very marked posteriorly.

Stage 20.   Somites: 7 pairs.
Neural folds close anteriorly.

Between stages 16 and 20 the length of the embryo varies between
1·5 and 2·2 mm.

Stage 21.   Somites: 10 pairs.
Amnion: Covers most of embryo, but a large opening
still present posteriorly.
Torsion: Head of embryo lies on its left side. Trunk still
unaffected.
Eyes: Primary optic vesicles forming.
Trunk region: Still largely open ventrally.
Length: 3 mm. ±0·1.

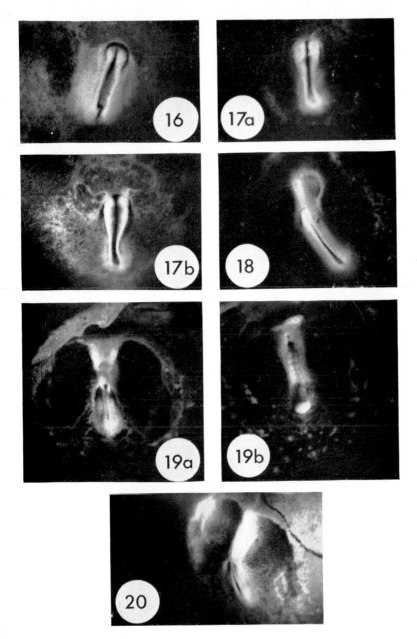

PLATE 11
Stages 16–20. ×13.

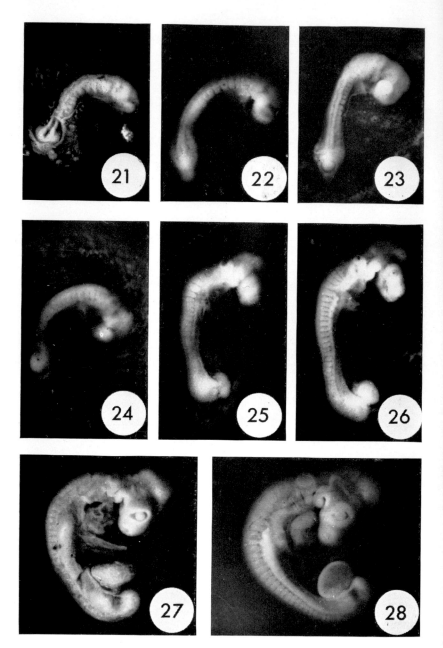

PLATE 12
Stages 21–28. ×13.

Stage 22. Somites: 10 pairs.
Torsion: Trunk now affected.
Posterior region: Tail bud forming.
Length: 3·2 mm. ±0·1.

Stage 23. Somites: 15 pairs.
Amnion: A small opening still present posteriorly.
Brain: Telencephalon, diencephalon, mesencephalon and rhombencephalon differentiated.
Neural folds: Meet in trunk and caudal regions.
Heart: Beginning to form.
Eyes: Primary optic vesicles completely differentiated.
Length: 3·5 mm. ±0·1.

Stage 24. Somites: 15 pairs.
Torsion: Reaches caudal region.
Neural tube: Closed throughout its length.
Trunk region: Lateral body folds approaching each other ventrally.
Length: 3·6 mm. ±0·1.

Stage 25. Somites: 18 pairs.
Amnion: Completely covers embryo.
Torsion: Entire length of embryo now lying on its left side.
Eyes: Secondary optic vesicles (optic cups) forming.
Ears: Auditory vesicles differentiated.
Visceral arches: Mandibular and hyoidean arches become distinct and hyo-mandibular cleft appears.
Allantois: Present as a small posterior vesicle.
Length: 4 mm. ±0·1.

Stage 26. Somites: 25 pairs.
Eyes: Secondary optic vesicles (optic cups) and lens differentiated.
Visceral clefts: Visceral clefts 1 and 2 begin to open.
Trunk region: Almost closed ventrally.
Length: 5 mm. ±0·2.

Stage 27. Somites: 33 pairs.
Eyes: Optic cups horseshoe shaped. Choroid fissure open.
Visceral clefts: 1 and 2 open.

Trunk region: Closed ventrally.
Nose: Olfactory rudiments beginning to differentiate.
Trigeminal nerve: Visible by transparence.
Limbs: First appearance of anterior and posterior limb
buds.
Length: 7 mm. $\pm$o·2.

Stage 28. Somites: 35 pairs.
Visceral clefts: The third begins to open.
Heart: Auricle and ventricle differentiated.
Length: 7·2 mm. $\pm$o·1.

Stage 29. Somites: 40 pairs.
Visceral clefts: 1, 2 and 3 open.
Limbs: Anterior limb buds o·25 mm. long.
Length: 8·8 mm. $\pm$o·2.

Stage 30. Somites: 50 pairs.
Limbs: Limb buds fringed longitudinally by a small
crest. Anterior buds o·5 mm. long.
Eyes: Lips of choroid fissure united. Optic cups spherical.
Pigmentation beginning.
Visceral cleft: Five clefts now open.
Ears: Endolymphatic canal differentiated.
Brain: Epiphyses, pineal body and paraphysis visible by
transparence.
Allantois: Extends to level of mesencephalon.
Length: 10 mm. $\pm$o·1.

Stage 31. Limbs: Limb buds flattened at extremities. Anterior buds
1 mm. long.
Eyes: Marked pigmentation.
Visceral clefts: 4 and 5 closed.
Penis: Rudiment present.
Length: 15·9 mm. $\pm$o·5.

Stage 32. Limbs: Paddle shaped. Anterior limbs 1·4 mm. long.
Visceral clefts: Two are still open.
Length: 17 mm. $\pm$o·2.

Stage 33. Limbs: Edge of digital plate sinuous. Three digits
beginning to differentiate. Anterior limbs 1·6 mm.
long.

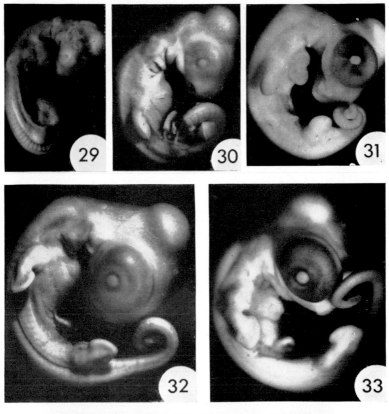

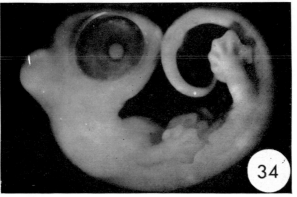

PLATE 13
Stages 29–34. ×12.

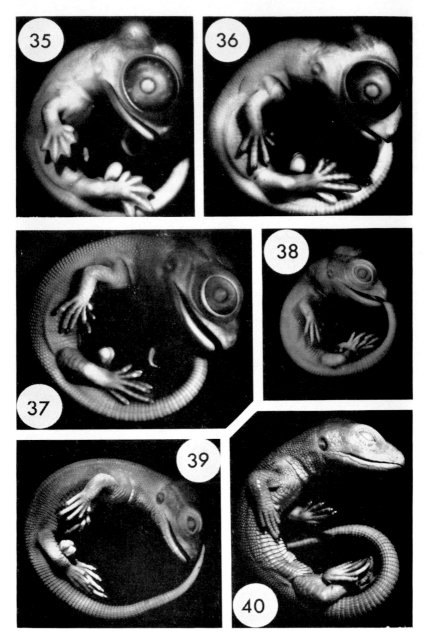

PLATE 14

Stages 35–37. ×7.   Stages 38–40. ×3½.

Eyes: Circular eyelids beginning to develop.
Mouth: Lower jaw forming.
Penis: Well formed and similar in both sexes.
Length: 19·2 mm. ±0·2.

Stage 34. Limbs: Five digits differentiated. Anterior limbs 2·2 mm. long.
Eyes: Several papillae visible.
Visceral clefts: All closed.
Nose: Nares formed.
Length: 20 mm. ±0·1.

Stage 35. Limbs: Anterior limbs 2·7 mm. long.
Eyes: Internal border of eyelids is indented.
Pineal eye: A circle of pigment visible.
Ear: Tympanum formed.
Pigmentation: Digits covered with points of pigment, particularly concentrated at the extremities. Head also covered with points of pigment.
Mouth: Lower jaw completely formed.
Length: 22 mm.

Stage 36. Limbs: Web between digits greatly indented. It disappears progressively from the external towards the internal digit and more rapidly in the anterior than in the posterior limbs. Rudiments of claws appearing, strongly pigmented. Anterior limbs 3·2 mm. long.
Scales: Beginning to differentiate on the body but not on the head.
Penis: Dimorphism between male and female now apparent.
Length: 23 mm. ±0·6.

Stage 37. Limbs: Web completely disappeared. Claws differentiated. Scales appearing on the paws. Anterior limbs 3·6 mm. long.
Eyes: Internal border of eyelids oval.
Pigmentation: Head heavily pigmented.
Scales: Body scales very marked.
Length: 2·5 mm. ±0·6.

Stage 38. Limbs: Annular rings very marked on digits. Anterior limbs 4 mm. long.

Eyes: Internal border of eyelids almost reaches lens.
Length: 26 mm. ±0·2.

Stage 39. Limbs: Pads of digits covered with incompletely differentiated scales. Anterior limbs 5·3 mm. long.
Eyes: Eyelids scaly.
Pigmentation: Pigment formation beginning in body scales.
Scales: Large scales differentiating on muzzle and lower jaw. Remainder of head still without scales.
Length: 35 mm. ±1.

Stage 40. Limbs: Scales completely differentiated and pigmented. Anterior limbs 6·7 mm. long.
Pigmentation: As present at birth.
Scales: Large scales differentiated on head.
Length: 40 mm. ±1.

REFERENCES

BELLAIRS, A. D'A. (1957). *Reptiles*. Hutchinson, London.
BELLAIRS, A. D'A. (1965). Personal communication.
BELLAIRS, R. (1951). Development of early reptile embryos *in vitro. Nature*, **167**, 687–8.
CLARK, H. & SISKEN, B. F. (1956). Nitrogenous excretion by embryos of the viviparous snake *Thamnophis s. sirtalis* (L). *J. exp. Biol.*, **33**, 384–93.
CLARK, H., SISKEN, B. & SHANNON, J. E. (1957). Excretion of nitrogen by the alligator embryo. *J. cell comp. Physiol.*, **50**, 129–34.
DUFAURE, J. P. (1961). Action des hormones sexuelles sur les pénis des embryons de lézard vivipare (*Zootoca vivipara*). *C.R. Acad. Sci., Paris*, **253**, 1130–1.
DUFAURE, J. P. (1964). Survie et développement d'embryons de lézard vivipare (*Lacerta vivipara* Jacquin) privés de la région moyennes du corps à un stade précoce. *C.R. Acad. Sci., Paris*, **259**, 1211–14.
DUFAURE, J. P. & HUBERT, J. (1961). Table de développement du lézard vivipare: *Lacerta* (*Zootoca*) *vivipara* Jacquin. *Arch. Anat. micr. Morph. exp.*, **50**, 309–27.
FOX, W., GORDON, C. & FOX, M. J. (1961). Morphological effects of low temperature during embryonic development of the garter snake, *Thamnophis elegans*. *Zoologica*, **46**, 57–71.
GORDON, R. E. (1960). The influence of moisture on variation in the eggs and hatchlings of *Anolis c. carolinensis* Voigt. *Natural History Miscellanea*, No. **173**, 1.
HOLDER, L. A. & BELLAIRS, A. D'A. (1962). The use of reptiles in experimental embryology. *Brit. J. Herpetology*, **3**, 54–61.

HUBERT, J. (1962). Étude histologique des jeunes stades de développement embryonaire du lézard vivipare (*Lacerta vivipara* Jacquin). *Arch. d'Anat. micr. Morph. exp.*, **51**, 11–26.

HUBERT, J. (1964). Essais de fissuration de l'oeuf de lézard vivipare (*Lacerta vivipara* Jacquin). *C.R. Soc. Biol. Paris*, **158**, 523.

INUKAI, T. (1927). Beiträge zur Entwickelungsgeschichte der Reptilien. *J. Coll. Agric. Sapporo*, **16**, 125–301.

KEIBEL, F. (1906). Die Entwickelung der äusseren Körperform der Wirbeltierembryonen, insbesondere der menschlichen Embryonen aus den ersten 2 Monaten. In *Handbuch der vergleichenden und experimentellen Entwicklungslehre der Wirbeltiere*. Erster Band. Zweiter Teil. Gustav Fischer, Jena.

LUTZ, H. & DUFAURE, J. P. (1960). Culture d'embryons et d'organes du lézard vivipare (*Lacerta vivipara*). *C.R. Acad. Sci., Paris*, **250**, 2456–8.

MADERSON, P. F. A. & BELLAIRS, A. D'A. (1962). Culture methods as an aid to experiments on reptile embryos. *Nature*, **195**, 401–2.

MARCUCCI, E. (1914a). Gli arti e la coda della *Lacerta muralis* regenerano nello stadio embrionale? *Boll. Soc. Nat. Napoli*, **27**, 98–101.

MARCUCCI, E. (1914b). Anche nella *Lacerta muralis* si può inibire la rigenerazione della coda. *Boll. Soc. Nat. Napoli*, **27**, 249–56.

MILAIRE, J. (1957). Contribution a la connaissance morphologique et cytochimique des bourgeons de membres chez quelques reptiles. *Arch. Biol. Paris*, **68**, 429–512.

MOFFAT, L. A. & BELLAIRS, A. D'A. (1964). The regenerative capacity of the tail in embryonic and post-natal lizards (*Lacerta vivipara* Jacquin). *J. Embryol. exp. Morph.*, **12**, 769–86.

NEEDHAM, J. (1931). *Chemical embryology*. Cambridge University Press.

NEEDHAM, J. (1950). *Biochemistry and morphogenesis*. Cambridge University Press.

PANIGEL, M. (1956). Contribution à l'étude de l'ovoviviparité chez les reptiles: gestation et parturition chez le lézard vivipare *Zootoca vivipara*. *Ann. Sci. Nat. (Zool.)*, **18**, 569–668.

PASTEELS, J. J. (1937). Études sur la gastrulations des vertébrés méroblastiques. *Arch. Biol., Paris*, **48**, 105–84.

PASTEELS, J. J. (1956–57). Une table analytique du développement des reptiles. *Ann. Soc. roy. zool. Belg.*, **87**, 217–41.

PETER, K. (1904). Normentafel zur Entwicklungsgeschichte der Zauneidechse (*Lacerta agilis*). In Keibel's *Normentafeln*, **4**, Jena.

RAYNAUD, A. (1959a). Une technique permettant d'obtenir le développement des oeufs d'orvet (*Anguis fragilis* L.) hors de l'organisme maternel. *C.R. Acad. Sci., Paris*, **249**, 1715–17.

RAYNAUD, A. (1959b). Développement et croissance des embryons d'orvet (*Anguis fragilis* L.) dans l'oeuf incubé in vitro. *C.R. Acad. Sci., Paris*, **249**, 1813–15.

RAYNAUD, A. (1960). Essais de destruction par irradiation localisée au moyen des rayons X, des ébauches hypophysaires de l'embryon d'orvet (*Anguis fragilis* L.). *C.R. Acad. Sci., Paris*, **251**, 2416–18.

E

RAYNAUD, A. (1962a). Les ébauches des membres de l'embryon d'orvet (*Anguis fragilis* L.). *C.R. Acad. Sci., Paris*, **254**, 3449–51.

RAYNAUD, A. (1962b). Étude histologique de la structure des ébauches des membres de l'embryon d'Orvet (*Anguis fragilis* L.). *C.R. Acad. Sci., Paris*, **254**, 4505–7.

RAYNAUD, A. (1962c). Une technique de décapitation du jeune embryon d'Orvet (*Anguis fragilis* L.). *C.R. Acad. Sci., Paris*, **255**, 2829–31.

RAYNAUD, A. (1962d). Le développement de l'embryon d'orvet (*Anguis fragilis* L.) décapitè a un stade précoce. *C.R. Acad. Sci., Paris*, **255**, 3041–3.

RAYNAUD, Λ. (1963). Le développement de la glande thyroiide chez l'embryon d'orvet (*Anguis fragilis* L.) décapité a un stade précoce. *C.R. Acad. Sci., Paris*, **257**, 2538–41.

RAYNAUD, A. (1964). Personal communication.

RAYNAUD, A. & PIEAU, C. (1964). Les canaux de Wolff de l'embryon d'orvet (*Anguis fragilis* L.). *C.R. Acad. Sci., Paris*, **258**, 4850–3.

SMITH, M. (1964). *The British amphibians and reptiles*. 3rd ed. Collins, London.

YNTEMA, C. L. (1960). Effects of various temperatures on the embryonic development of *Chelydra serpentina*. *Anat. Rec.*, **136**, 305–6.

YNTEMA, C. L. (1964). Procurement and use of turtle embryos for experimental procedures. *Anat. Rec.*, **149**, 577–86.

ZEHR, D. R. (1962). Stages in the normal development of the common garter snake, *Thamnophis sirtalis sirtalis*. *Copeia*, No. **2**, 322–9.

CHAPTER 5

Amphibia

Many amphibia will live and breed readily in the laboratory and the embryos are not difficult to culture. The eggs are a convenient size, are often available in very large numbers, and will survive a wide variety of microsurgical and other operations. With such advantages it is not surprising that amphibians have for long been favourite animals for embryological study, and that a large proportion of the classic demonstrations of epigenetic processes have been made, at least in the first instance, with these embryos.

One anuran, the clawed toad *Xenopus laevis*, and one urodele, the axolotl *Ambystoma mexicanum* will be discussed here in some detail, as being excellent animals for a wide range of laboratory and class work. Some account will also be given of the curious amphibian *Eleutherodactylus*, whose embryos have special advantages for certain types of study, although they are not yet widely available. Other species will only be described briefly.

This is not to say that the clawed toad or the axolotl will meet all requirements. Particular experiments may demand other animals. The local species, if they breed at convenient times, may provide a useful supply of eggs. But Xenopus and the axolotl have great advantages which are not common among other amphibia. Xenopus will yield fertile eggs at any time of year, and almost at any required hour, in response to gonadotrophic hormone injections; and the animals are very easy to feed and maintain in the laboratory, both as adults and as larvae. The axolotl is rather more trouble to feed, and its breeding is not so easily stimulated, but with careful handling it is possible to obtain eggs at most times of year and the young can be reared to maturity without difficulty. A colony of axolotls can be bred through several successive generations without need to introduce fresh stock. Furthermore the axolotl lays much larger eggs than Xenopus and, unlike many other urodeles, lays several hundred at a time.

Both Xenopus and the axolotl are widely used in research laboratories.

THE CLAWED TOAD (*Xenopus laevis*)

The anuran *Xenopus laevis*, like its close relative the South American *Pipa*, is amphibian by classification but not by mode of life. Provided water is available it remains fully aquatic after, as well as before, metamorphosis, and the adult retains several structures associated with an aquatic existence, including an elaborate system of lateral line organs. Its popular name derives from the presence on each of the long hind legs of three small black horny claws. These claws help the animal to get out of its skin, which is regularly shed, pulled over the head and then eaten (Elkan 1957).

A full grown Xenopus is about 10 cms. long. The skin is brown with a mottled pattern on the back, and pale yellow to white on the ventral side. The animal is capable of considerable changes of colour, varying between pale yellow and dark brown, and has proved useful in studying the influence of the pituitary on colouration. The internal anatomy is very like that of the common frog, *Rana temporaria*, apart from the lack of a tongue and some differences in the skeleton. The adult breathes through lungs, and will drown if it cannot reach the water surface.

The natural home of *Xenopus laevis* is in lakes, ponds and swamps over a wide area of southern Africa. It is remarkably catholic in its tastes and is found living happily in water of low or high pH, brackish or fresh, clear or muddy, permanent or temporary. If the water dries up the toads dig themselves in until the next rainy season, or migrate overland.

The toads are very sensitive to both amphibian and mammalian pituitary hormones, and the reliability with which the females lay eggs in response to injections of chorionic gonadotropin has proved valuable for human pregnancy testing, though this is now being replaced by other methods.

Xenopus has been the subject of a very large number of studies. References to many of the earlier publications are given in Nieuwkoop and Faber (1956) and in the large compilation by Zwarenstein, Sapeika and Shapiro (1946) with its supplement by Zwarenstein and Burgers (1955).

Keeping Xenopus in the laboratory

The following account contains many of the recommendations of Nieuwkoop and Faber (1956) and Elkan (1957).

One of the advantages of Xenopus is that at no stage in its life does it require elaborate living accommodation. The only essential is an aquarium with a large volume of water, at least 10 litres per adult animal. The water should be kept slowly running, or changed at frequent intervals, and maintained at a temperature of about 20–25°C, though the animals will tolerate temperatures of 10–28°C.

Xenopus is capable of jumping considerable distances out of the water, and the aquarium should be covered over, e.g. with wire netting. There must be a space between the cover and the water surface, so that the animals can come up to breathe, and if running water is used care must be taken that a space will still be left even if the normal outlet becomes blocked and the water rises. The animals are very excitable and should be disturbed as little as possible. Some stones, tiles, or other objects behind which they can shelter, will increase their comfort.

Any large tank which fulfils these requirements should suffice, but Elkan gives details of a tank specially designed for Xenopus.

The adults need only be fed twice a week. Minced beef (e.g. heart) or horsemeat, or chopped beef liver are the most convenient foods, but earthworms, tadpoles or *Enchytraeus* worms (p. 16) can be added as available and will be readily taken. The meat should be as lean as possible; fat will always be rejected and left floating on the surface. It is sufficient just to tip the food into the water; the animals will take it rapidly and no hand feeding is necessary. The toads do not swim towards food, so when minced meat is being fed it is a good idea to distribute it fairly evenly over the tank. 100 gms. of meat per week is sufficient for 50 toads.

Xenopus is a fairly hardy animal but is subject to a few parasites. Fungal infection is the commonest cause of trouble, and is best avoided by keeping the water clean and well aerated. If the water is static a few ml. of a saturated solution of sea salt, added to the aquarium each time the water is changed, discourages fungus.

Pieces of the tapeworm *Cephalochlamys namaquencis* are frequently found extruded with the Xenopus eggs, but this parasite appears to have little harmful effect. The trematode *Diplostomulum xenopi* is more serious. It lives in the pericardial sac for long periods without, at first, affecting the health of the host; then fairly suddenly the toad comes to the surface in obvious distress and dies within a few hours. No cure is at present available.

Sometimes the toads suffer from a paralysis of the limbs, of cause unknown. The hind legs are first affected, then, in more serious cases the fore-legs as well. Such animals can no longer swim to the surface to breathe and will drown unless transferred to shallow water. But if kept in a shallow dish they often survive. Food may be refused by an affected animal for several weeks but in the end, especially if tempted with a live earthworm, it will begin feeding again and will recover completely.

For further information on the diseases of Xenopus see Reichen-bach-Klinke and Elkan (1965).

Induced breeding

Xenopus toads reach sexual maturity in 6–9 months but are not at their best for breeding purposes until 2 years. The sexes can be distinguished by the cloacal valves of the female which are absent in the male (Plate 15).

In the wild the breeding season is September–December and egg laying follows a rise in temperature. Eggs appear about 8–10 hours after the temperature has passed a certain critical level, which in the full breeding season is about 21°C. A similar management of the temperature can induce laying in the laboratory, but it is much simpler to inject gonadotrophin, which will yield fertile eggs at any time of year.

A convenient method of handling Xenopus while injecting is to catch it in a net, where it usually makes for one of the corners and can be held there firmly. Injection is then made through the net into the dorsal lymph sac, piercing the skin of the thigh and the septum between the lymph sacs of the thigh and the back. (Injection via the thigh is recommended because the skin heals better there.) The amount of hormone to be injected varies with the reproductive condition of the animals and on the particular preparation of hormone used. Gurdon (1964) recommends the following doses. If the animals are ready to breed (as indicated in the male by the presence of "nuptial pads"—black discolourations along the flexor side of the forearms, and in the female by the swollen abdomen indicating many mature eggs) they need only be given one injection about 8 hours before the eggs are required; 75 i.u. of chorionic gonadotrophic hormone (p. 7) to the male and 150 i.u. to the female. If the animals are not so ready to breed two injections of hormone are given. Two days before the eggs are required the male is injected with 50–100 i.u., and on the following day the female receives 30 i.u.; about 8 hours before the eggs are required the male is injected with 150–300 i.u.

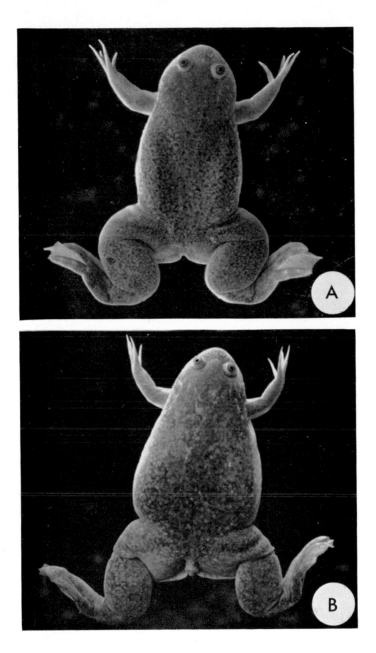

PLATE 15

The clawed toad (*Xenopus laevis*)

A: Male. B: Female. $\times \frac{2}{3}$.

PLATE 16

The Axolotl (*Ambystoma mexicanum*)

A. Black and white axolotls, neotenous forms. A mature black individual and a half-grown white one. ×⅔.
B. Cloacal region of male. ×½.   C. Cloacal region of female. ×¾.   D. Metamorphosed form. ×⅗.
(A from Newth (1959); B, C and D from Brunst (1955).)

and the female with 300–600 i.u. All the injections are given in
0·5–1·0 ml. of 0·7% (w/v) NaCl in water.

The males and females soon pair, sometimes within a few
minutes of the last hormone injection, and remain together in
amplexus. If the usual time interval of 8 hours between injection and
egg laying is inconvenient it can be lengthened by temporarily
lowering the temperature. Curtis (1964) delays spawning 2–3 hours
by adding ice to the aquarium containing the injected animals, to
give a temperature of about 11°C; if the toads are injected at 6 p.m.
the eggs are then at the blastula stage at 9 a.m. the following morning.
Care must be taken that the temperature does not fall below 9°C
except for periods of a few minutes.

Xenopus toads are liable to eat their own eggs, and it is important
that any non-pairing individuals be removed from the breeding tank
as soon as possible, and those in amplexus as soon as they have
finished spawning. Spawning may continue for up to 24 hours, and
a single pair will lay several hundreds or even thousands of eggs.

Often some of the eggs are infertile, but Curtis (1964) finds that
even when the toads are induced to spawn as frequently as every
7–14 days, for periods of 6–8 months at a time, nearly all the layings
contain a large proportion of fertile eggs. If the fertility of either the
males or the females shows any sign of failing, he gives them an
injection of 100 i.u. of serum gonadotrophin and a rest for a fortnight, and finds this method of reviving the animals works well.

Sometimes a female that has not spawned for a long period produces a batch containing many infertile eggs; this is probably the
result of an accumulation of overripe eggs in the animal, and is not
repeated in subsequent spawnings.

Rearing Xenopus

The eggs are fertilised as they are laid and are attached individually to plants or other objects. Cell division begins immediately after
fertilisation, the blastula stage is found 4–7 hours later, and hatching
occurs after 2 days. Details of development are given on pp. 125–52.

The aquarium should be large enough to allow one litre of water
for every three larvae that it is intended to rear, and should be
equipped with an aeration pump. Good aeration is essential, and
care should also be taken that the water is free of chlorine and copper
ions (p. 165). Elkan considers that growing larvae benefit if the
sodium chloride concentration of the water is raised to 0·2% to

compensate for the amount they excrete. Bright light must be avoided, as it interferes with larval development.

The newly hatched larvae immediately suspend themselves from plants, or from the water surface, by a mucous thread secreted by glands situated in the place of the future mouth. For two days they live on stored yolk, and then a mouth is formed and they require feeding. The larvae combine feeding with breathing, filtering out particles of food from the respiratory current passing through the branchial apparatus. In the natural state they live on small planktonic algae and protozoa. In aquaria they are easy to feed because they will thrive on powdered dried nettle (*Urtica dioica*), powdered alfalfa leaf, dried yeast, powdered liver, or a liquid extract from fresh nettles. The powders must be very fine; they should be squeezed through a bag of fine cloth into the water until it is slightly turbid. The powdered food sold by chemists under the name of "Complan" is another excellent food for Xenopus larvae. The larvae are fed once a day, and the amount of food should be such that the water is cleared before the next feeding. If plant food is used there is no need to change the water for the first few weeks; in fact it is better not to, because the young larvae are very susceptible to damage, and are best left undisturbed. Removal of excrement is also unnecessary.

During metamorphosis, which takes place between weeks 4–8, the larvae stop feeding, become very sluggish and keep to the bottom of the tank. They should be transferred to shallow water to save them from drowning. Feeding is resumed before metamorphosis is complete, but the animals are now carnivorous and require small worms such as *Enchytraeus* and *Tubifex* (pp. 16–17), or *Daphnia*, or very finely shredded liver. The volume of water should soon be increased to 3 litres per young toad, and the animals can gradually be brought on to an adult diet. Juvenile and adult animals should regularly receive extra vitamin D and calcium in order to prevent skeletal abnormalities and brittleness of the bones; this can conveniently be given in the form of small quantities of bone meal and cod liver oil added to the shredded meat.

STAGES IN THE NORMAL DEVELOPMENT OF
XENOPUS LAEVIS

The "Table of Normal Development of *Xenopus laevis* (Daudin)" 1956, edited by Nieuwkoop and Faber, contains a wealth of information on the development of the different organs and organ systems of Xenopus. The table of "stages", which is reproduced here in abbreviated form, is only a part of the whole work and for a more complete picture the original should be consulted.

Nieuwkoop and Faber's illustrations are here reproduced in entirety, Figs. 19–28, and the numbering corresponds with the numbering of the stages in the text.

The ages given are approximate and apply to development in the laboratory at 22—24°C.

Features easily visible externally are listed under "External", others under "Internal".

From Stage 11 onwards the internal development of each stage is described in the following sequence:

Ectodermal derivatives
Skin, nervous system, olfactory organ, eye and ear (except middle ear), neural crest.

Mesodermal derivatives
Skeleton, musculature, heart and blood circulation, pronephros, mesonephros and ducts, reproductive system (including germ cells).

Entodermal derivatives
Oro-pharyngeal cavity with visceral pouches (including filter apparatus and operculum), lungs and trachea, thyroid, alimentary tract with glands and diverticula.

CLEAVAGE

Stage 1. Age 0 hours; length 1·4–1·5 mm.

External: One cell stage, shortly after fertilisation. Pigmentation darker ventrally than dorsally.

Internal: Germinal vesicle disappeared. Clear animal-vegetal and dorso-ventral polarity. Well-defined cortical layer and layer of subcortical plasm, mainly located in animal half of egg. Thickness of cortical and subcortical layers decreasing in animal-vegetal and dorso-ventral polarity.

Stage 2. Age $1\frac{1}{4}$ h.; length 1·4–1·5 mm.

External: First cleavage groove has not yet reached vegetal pole.

Stage 2. Age $1\frac{1}{2}$ h.; length 1·4–1·5 mm.

External: Advanced two cell stage. First cleavage groove has reached vegetal pole.

Internal: Formation of very thin partition wall between the two blastomeres; blastomeres not equal size. First plane of cleavage more or less coinciding with plane of bilateral symmetry.

Stage 3. Age 2 h.; length 1·4–1·5 mm.

External: Advanced four cell stage. Second cleavage groove has reached vegetal pole. In animal view dorsal blastomeres usually smaller than ventral ones; the latter darker than the former.

Internal: Cleavage cavity present for the first time, mainly located in animal half of egg. Partition walls between the four blastomeres.

Stage 4. Age $2\frac{1}{4}$ h.; length 1·4–1·5 mm.

External: Advanced eight cell stage. Dorsal micro- and macromeres usually smaller than ventral ones; dorsal micromeres less pigmented than ventral ones.

Internal: Pigmented cortical layer and subcortical plasm penetrating over about $\frac{1}{5}$ of egg radius along third cleavage furrow.

Stage 5. Age $2\frac{3}{4}$ h.; length 1·4–1·5 mm.

External: Advanced sixteen cell stage. Macromeres entirely separated by cleavage grooves. Dorsal micromeres distinctly smaller and less pigmented than ventral ones.

Internal: Cleavage cavity about as large as a micromere, located slightly eccentrically towards dorsal side.

St. 1 — Animal view (An.)
Magnification 24x

St. 1 — Dorsal view (Dors.)

St. 1 — Ventral view (Ventr.)

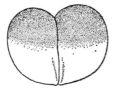

St. 2 — Ventr.

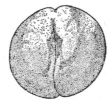

St. 2 — An.

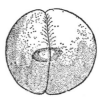

St. 2 — An.

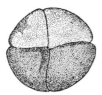

St. 3 — An.

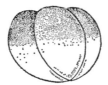

St. 3 — Dorso-lateral view (Dors. lat.)

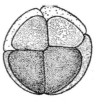

St. 4 — An.

St. 5 — Dors.

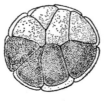

St. 5 — An.

St. 4 — Dors.-lat.

Figure 19.

Stage 6. Age 3 h.; length 1·4–1·5 mm.
External: Advanced thirty-two cell stage. Distinction between dorsal and ventral micromeres as in preceding stage.
Internal: Cleavages still nearly synchronous. Blastomeres roughly arranged in four rows of eight.

Stage 6½. Age 3½ h.; length 1·4–1·5 mm.
External: Morula stage. In animal view about 6 micromeres along meridian. About 48 blastomeres.
Internal: Synchronism of cleavages gradually lost; animal blastomeres in advance with respect to vegetal ones. Blastomeres still arranged in single layer around cleavage cavity.

Stage 7. Age 4 h.; length 1·4–1·5 mm.
External: Large-cell blastula stage. In animal view about 10 micromeres along meridian.
Internal: Tangential cleavage; formation of double-layered embryo. Pregastrulation movements noticeable for the first time: slight epibolic extension of animal.

Stage 8. Age 5 h.; length 1·4–1·5 mm.
External: Medium-cell blastula stage. Surface not yet entirely smooth. Gradual transition in cell size from animal to vegetal pole.
Internal: First appearance of intercellular spaces between outer and inner cell material. First indication of distinction between animal, marginal and vegetal areas in inner cell material. Outer cell layer single, inner cell material 1–4 cells thick.

Stage 9. Age 7 h.; length 1·4–1·5 mm.
External: Small-cell blastula stage. Border between marginal zone and vegetal field distinct. Animal cells smaller at dorsal than at ventral side.
Internal: *Blastocoel* has attained its full size; inner surface smooth.

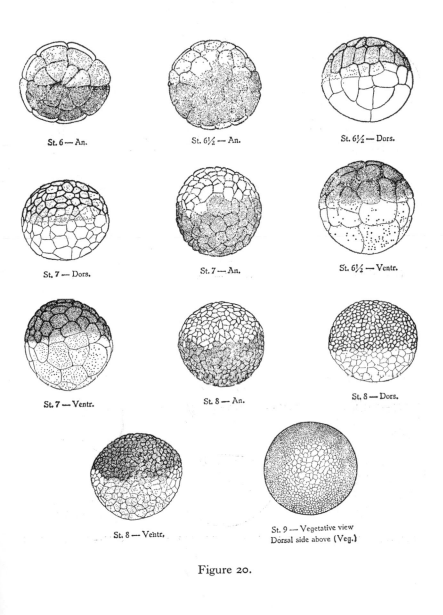

St. 6 — An.

St. 6½ — An.

St. 6½ — Dors.

St. 7 — Dors.

St. 7 — An.

St. 6½ — Ventr.

St. 7 — Ventr.

St. 8 — An.

St. 8 — Dors.

St. 8 — Ventr.

St. 9 — Vegetative view
Dorsal side above (Veg.)

Figure 20.

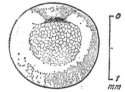

St. 10 — Veg.

Two forms
St. 10½ — Veg.

St. 12 — Veg.

St. 11½ — Veg.

St. 11 — Veg.

St. 12½ — Post.-dors.

St. 13 — Posterio-dorsal view (Post.-dors.)

St. 14 — Post.-dors.

St. 15 — Post.-dors.

St. 14 — Lateral view (left side) (Lat.)

St. 15 — Anterior view (Ant.)

Figure 21.

GASTRULATION

Stage 10. Age 9 h.; length 1·4–1·5 mm.
External: Initial gastrula stage. First indication of blastopore only by pigment concentration. (No formation of groove.)
Internal: Formation of bottle-necked cells in outer cell layer in area of future blastopore groove. Beginning of formation of *mesodermal mantle* at dorsal side by rolling-in of presumptive prechordal plate mesoderm around inner blastopore lip.

Stage 10½. Age 11 h.; length 1·4–1·5 mm.
External: Crescent-shaped blastopore stage. Ventral border of future yolk plug indicated by pigment concentration.
Internal: Invagination of short slit-shaped *archenteron* over 10–15°. Epibolic extension of *presumptive ectoderm*, particularly of its inner, sensorial layer, and reduction of vegetal area. First contact between prechordal part of archenteron roof and most caudal portion of sensorial layer of ectoderm.

Stage 11. Age 11¾ h.; length 1·4–1·5 mm.
External: Horse-shoe-shaped blastopore stage; diameter more than ⅖ of diameter of egg (<50° of circumference).
Internal: *Mesodermal mantle* extending to 30–40° above equator on dorsal side, to 20–30° above equator on lateral side, and approximately to equator on ventral side.
Invagination of *archenteron* extended to lateral side; archenteron still slit-shaped, extending dorsally over 40–50°.

Stage 11½. Age 12½ h.; length 1·4–1·5 mm.
External: Large yolk plug stage. Blastopore groove closed ventrally. Diameter of yolk plug about ⅓ of diameter of egg. Yolk plug not yet quite circular.
Internal: First indication of *neural plate* in sensorial layer of ectoderm.
Mesodermal mantle extending dorsally to 20–30° from animal pole, ventrally not beyond equator.
Archenteron extending over 80–90°, still slit-shaped.

Stage 12. Age 13¼ h.; length 1·4–1·5 mm.
External: Medium yolk plug stage. Diameter somewhat less than ¼ of diameter of egg. Yolk plug circular.
Internal: *Neural* and *epidermal* areas clearly distinguishable anteriorly.

Archenteron extending over more than 90°; first indications of widening.

Stage 12½. Age 14¼ h.; length 1·4–1·5 mm.

External: Small yolk plug stage. Future position of neural plate and median groove indicated by darker pigment lines. Yolk plug usually ovoid, variable in size.

Internal: *Mesodermal mantle* has reached its definitive extension at dorsal side close to animal pole, at lateral and ventral sides to 40–50° from animal pole; first indication of *notochord* formation. *Archenteron* extending up to animal pole and much widened.

Stage 13. Age 14¾ h.; length 1·5–1·6 mm.

External: Slit-blastopore stage. Caudal part of median groove formed.

Internal: Presumptive *somite mesoderm* double-layered.
Archenteron extended to about 10° ventral to animal pole. *Blastocoel* rapidly decreasing in size.

Stage 13½. Age 15½ h.; length 1·5–1·6 mm.

External: Initial neural plate stage. Neural plate clearly delimited.

Internal: First indication of formation of *neural crest* zone in margin of anterior half of neural plate.
Archenteron widened and extended to definitive position at about 45° ventral to animal pole; first formation of *liver* diverticulum.

NEURULATION

Stage 14. Age 16¼ h.; length 1·5–1·6 mm.

External: Neural plate stage. Initial elevation of neural folds. Cerebral part of neural plate bent downwards, with median elevation at rostral end of median groove. Blastopore always slit-shaped.

Stage 15. Age 17½ h.; length 1·5–1·6 mm.

External: Early neural fold stage. Anterior part of neural plate roundish. Neural folds distinct, except medio-rostrally; initial formation of sharp inner ridges on neural folds in rhomben-cephalic region. Presumptive cement gland faintly circumscribed.

Internal: Presumptive *eye* rudiments beginning to sink in. First symptoms of segregation of *neural crest* from thickening and narrowing *neural plate*.
Clearly discernible *myocoel*.
Blastocoel disappeared or greatly reduced.

Stage 16. Age 18¼ h.; length 1·5–1·6 mm.
External: Mid neural fold stage. Anterior part of neural plate rectangular; neural plate sharply constricted in the middle. Darkly pigmented eye rudiments present. Inner ridges on neural folds forming angle of about 90° with neural plate in rhombencephalic region.
Internal: Left and right *heart* rudiments beginning to fuse.

Stage 17. Age 18¾ h.; length 1·5–1·6 mm.
External: Late neural fold stage. Anterior part of neural plate oblong triangular, angles formed by eye rudiments. Neural folds approaching each other from blastopore up to anterior trunk region.
Internal: *Eye* rudiments showing first signs of lateral evagination. In anterior half of embryo *neural crest* material located at lateral edges of neural plate; in caudal half sharp delimitation of *neural crest* material from neural plate.
First indications of *somite* segregation.

Stage 18. Age 19¾ h.; length 1·5–1·6 mm.
External: Neural groove stage. Anterior part of neural plate narrow, more or less club-shaped. Parallel neural folds in trunk region very close to each other (not yet touching).
Internal: *Eye* evaginations with slit-shaped cavities. First segregation of mes- and rhombencephalic *neural crest*.
Anterior 3–4 *somites* in process of segregation.

Stage 19. Age 20¾ h.; length 1·5–1·6 mm.
External: Initial neural tube stage. Neural folds touching each other except for inconstant openings at anterior and posterior end and behind nucal region. Considerable lateral extension of brain. Lateral outline of embryo still convex.
Internal: *Neural crest* segregated into 4–5 cell masses; beginning of lateral migration.
Segregation of anterior 4–6 *somites*. Presumptive *heart* rudiment a single median mesodermal thickening.

Stage 20. Age 21¾ h.; length 1·7–1·8 mm.
External: Neural folds fused, suture still present. The two eye rudiments showing through dumb-bell-shaped; eyes hardly protruding. Beginning of stretching of embryo. Lateral outline flat.
Internal: *Brain* subdivided into *arch-* and *deuterencephalon*. Massive *neural crest* extending anteriorly approximately to anterior border of eye rudiments; in trunk region *neural crest* still in contact with suture of closing neural tube.

Anterior 6–7 *somites* segregated.

First indications of 1st and 2nd *visceral pouches* in pharyngeal wall.

Stage 21. Age 22½ h.; length 1·9–2·0 mm.

External: Suture of neural tube completely closed. Delimitation of frontal field by pigment lines. Beginning of protrusion of eyes. Primary eye vesicles showing through in the form of two separate, obliquely placed oval protruberances.

Internal: *Ear placode* visible for the first time as thickening of sensorial layer of ectoderm.

Segregation of *maxillary* and *mandibular* portions of *mesectoderm*. Anterior 8–9 *somites* segregated. First indication of *pronephros* rudiment.

Stage 22. Age 24 hr. (=1 day); length 2·0–2·2 mm.

External: Distinct protrusion of eyes. Initial groove forming dorso-laterally between jaw- and gill-areas. Lateral and ventral outlines of embryo slightly concave. Anal opening displaced to ventral side.

Internal: Segregation of *brain* into *pros-*, *mes-* and *rhombencephalon*. Primary *eye vesicles* in broad contact with epidermis.

Segregation of *hyal* portion of *mesectoderm*. Anterior 9–10 *somites* distinct. Formation of *blood islands* indicated in mesoderm behind liver diverticulum.

Stage 23. Age 1 day, ¾ h.; length 2·2–2·4 mm.

External: Jaw- and gill-areas completely separated by groove.

Internal: Segregation of *prosencephalon* into *tel-* and *diencephalon*. First appearance of *olfactory placodes* as thickenings of sensorial layer of ectoderm.

Segregation of 1st *branchial* portion of *mesectoderm*. Approximately 12 *somites* segregated. Beginning of segregation of *nephrotomes*.

First contact of ectoderm and entoderm in 1st *visceral pouch* (formation of *mandibular arch*); 3rd *visceral pouch* indicated.

Stage 24. Age 1 d., 2¼ h.; length 2·5–2·7 mm.

External: Eyes protruding less far laterally than gill-area. Ventral outline of embryo nicked. Tail bud discernible. Initial motor reactions to external stimulation.

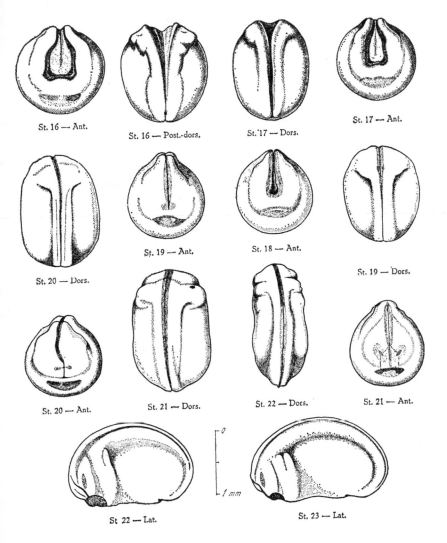

St. 16 — Ant.

St. 16 — Post.-dors.

St. 17 — Dors.

St. 17 — Ant.

St. 20 — Dors.

St. 19 — Ant.

St. 18 — Ant.

St. 19 — Dors.

St. 20 — Ant.

St. 21 — Dors.

St. 22 — Dors.

St. 21 — Ant.

St 22 — Lat.

St. 23 — Lat.

0

1 mm

Figure 22.

Internal: 15 *somites* segregated; *axial mesenchyme* becoming liberated from somites.

Stage 25. Age 1d., 3½ h.; length 2·8–3·0 mm.
External: Eyes protruding equally far or further laterally than gill-area. Gill area grooved. Invagination of ear vesicle indicated by pigment spot. Beginning of fin formation.
Internal: 16 *somites* segregated. *Head somite* 1 diminishing.
4th *visceral pouch* indicated.

MUSCULAR MOVEMENTS

Stage 26. Age 1 d. 5½ h.; length 3·0–3·3 mm.
External: Ear vesicle protruding. Pronephros distinctly visible. Fin somewhat broadened at dorso-caudal end of body. Myotomes showing through for the first time. Beginning of spontaneous movements.
Internal: First indications of *olfactory lobe* formation in antero-lateral portion of telencephalic wall; beginning of evagination of *pineal body*.
Head somite 1 disintegrated; 17 *somites* segregated. *Wolffian duct* rudiment extended to level of trunk somite 3.
First contact of ectoderm and entoderm in 2nd *visceral pouch* (formation of *hyoid arch*).

Stage 27. Age 1 d., 7¼ h.; length 3·4–3·7 mm.
External: Fin translucent. Tail bud formation accentuated in lateral outline.
Internal: 19 *somites* segregated.
First contact of ectoderm and entoderm in 3rd *visceral pouch* (formation of 1st *branchial arch*).

Stage 28. Age 1 d., 8½ h.; length 3·8–4·0 mm.
External: Fin broadened and distinctly divided into outer trans-parent and inner translucent band.
Internal: *Ear* vesicle detached from epidermis.
20–22 *somites* segregated. First formation of *endocardial* tube and beginning of formation of *pericardial* cavity. 1st *nephrostome* funnel clearly indicated, the following two just distinguishable.

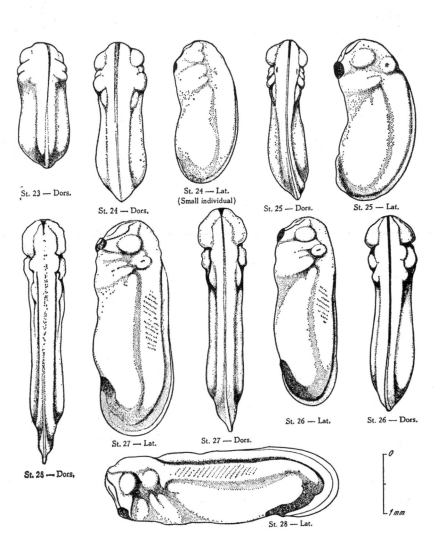

St. 23 — Dors.

St. 24 — Dors.

St. 24 — Lat.
(Small individual)

St. 25 — Dors.

St. 25 — Lat.

St. 27 — Lat.

St. 27 — Dors.

St. 26 — Lat.

St. 26 — Dors.

St. 28 — Dors.

St. 28 — Lat.

0

1 mm.

Figure 23.

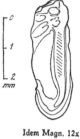

Idem Magn. 12x

St. 29/30 — Lat.

St. 31 — Lat.

St. 32 — Lat..

St. 33/34 — Lat.

St. 35/36 — Lat.

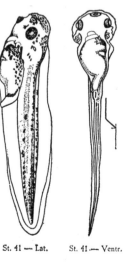

St. 42 — Lat.   St. 41 — Lat.   St. 41.— Ventr.   .St. 40 — Lat.
(Small ind.)

St. 39 — Lat.
(Small ind.)

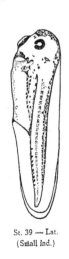

St. 37/38 — Lat.

Figure 24.

Stage 29/30. Age 1 d., 11 h.; length 4·0–4·5 mm.
External: Fin transparent up to the base over its whole length. Grey
   eye cup showing through for the first time. Tail bud distinct.
Internal: *Eye* vesicle envaginated, but central portion still convex.
   Head somites 2 and 3 much reduced; 24–25 *somites* segregated,
   segregation reaching tail. *Pericardial* cavity surrounding *endocardial* rudiment on lateral and ventral sides.

Stage 31. Age 1 d., 13½ h.; length 4·2–4·8 mm.
External: Tail bud equally long as broad.
Internal: Thin layer of *nerve fibres* extending over 70% of length of
   spinal cord. Nasal pit indicated. *Neural crest* of spinal cord entirely
   withdrawn from neural tube.
   Segregation of 2nd *branchial* portion of mesectoderm. 22–23
   post-otic *somites*. 1st pair of *aortic arches* completed, and beginning of paired *dorsal aortae* formed. 1st *nephrostome* funnel
   completed.

Stage 32. Age 1 d., 16 h.; length 4·5–5·1 mm.
External: Length of tail bud about 1½ × breadth.
Internal: Cavity of primary *optic vesicle* disappeared except for
   region near optic stalk; margins of optic cup, forming *choroid
   fissure*, touching each other. First appearance of rudiments of
   ductus endolymphaticus.
   About 26 post-otic *somites* formed. 2nd *nephrostome* funnel completed.
   First contact of ectoderm and entoderm in 4th *visceral pouch*
   (formation of 2nd *branchial arch); 5th visceral pouch* indicated;
   paired *lung rudiments clearly visible.*

Stage 33/34. Age 1 d., 20½ h.; length 4·7–5·3 mm.
External: Length of tail bud about twice its breadth. Melanophores
   appearing, dorsally on the head and laterally in a row extending
   from just below the pronephros backwards. Beginning of heart
   beat.
Internal: Appearance of *Rohon-Beard* cells at trunk levels of spinal
   cord. Nearly spherical *lens* rudiment detached from ectoderm.
   Sensorial rudiments of *auditory* vesicle indicated.
   About 32 postotic *somites* formed. 3rd *nephrostome* completed.
   Thyroid rudiment clearly discernible.

HATCHING

Stage 35/36. Age 2 d., 2 h.; length 5·3–6·0 mm.

External: Stomodeal invagination roundish. Formation of two gill rudiments. Melanophores appearing on back. Length of tail bud about 3 × breadth. Beginning of hatching.

Internal: Beginning of differentiation of pars optica retinae (=visual part of *retina*); cavity of optic stalk obliterated; *lens* cavity fully developed.

About 36 post-otic *somites* formed. 4th, 5th and dorsal part of 6th *aortic arches* completed; paired *dorsal aortae* united as median *dorsal aorta;* medial *postcardinals* united behind cloaca.

First contact of ectoderm and entoderm in 5th *visceral pouch* (formation of 3rd *branchial arch*). Horizontal ridge separating primary *liver* cavity from *tracheal* cavity; dorsal *pancreas* rudiment indicated; *neurenteric canal* occluded.

Stage 37/38. Age 2 d., 5½ h.; length 5·6–6·2 mm.; length of tail with fin about 1·8 mm.

External: Both gill rudiments nipple-shaped, a branch of the anterior one indicated. Posterior outline of proctodeum straight, forming very obtuse angle with ventral border of tail myotomes.

Internal: *Rohon-Beard* cells appearing in anterior tail levels of spinal cord.

About 40 post-otic *somites* formed. *Wolffian ducts* and rectal diverticula communicating; entire *pronephros* functional.

The two ventral *pancreas* rudiments discernible.

Stage 39. Age 2 d., 8½ h.; length 5·9–6·5 mm.; length of tail with fin maximally 2·6 mm.

External: Opening of stomodeal invagination transversely elongated. Outlines of proctodeum and tail myotomes forming angle of about 135°.

Internal: Roots of *vagus* nerve distinct.

About 43 post-otic *somites*. 6th *aortic arch* completed with *ductus Botalli* and *pulmonary artery*.

Contact between ectoderm and entoderm obliterated in 1st and 2nd *visceral pouch* (1st visceral pouch representing rudiment of *middle ear* and *Eustachian tube*).

Stage 40. Age 2 d., 18 h.; length 6·3–6·8 mm.

External: Mouth broken through. Outlines of proctodeum and tail myotomes forming angle of 90°. Beginning of blood circulation in gills.

Internal: Nuclei of central *lens* fibres degenerating; inner *corneal* layer formed.

About 45 post-otic *somites*. The various parts of *cranium* and *visceral skeleton* well distinguishable as mesenchymatous condensations. *Hepatic vein* present; left *omphalomesenteric vein*, receiving *subintestinal vein*, has lost connection with heart and has broken into capillaries in liver.

Oral plate ruptured and 3rd and 4th *visceral pouches* perforated; 6th *visceral pouch* indicated. *Tracheal* cavity separated from *gastro-duodenal* cavity. The three *pancreatic* rudiments fused.

Stage 41. Age 3 d., 4 h.; length 6·6–7·5 mm.

External: Formation of a left-rostral and a right-caudal furrow in yolk mass; torsion of interjacent part about 45°*; formation of conical proctodeum. Formation of fin rostral to proctodeum.

Internal: First *motor neurons* enlarging at edge of grey matter in tail region of spinal cord. First indications of formation of *semicircular canals*.

Ductus Botalli and 1st *aortic arch* absent; right *omphalomesenteric vein* has lost connection with heart and has broken into capillaries in liver.

Beginning of segregation of primordial *germ cells* from dorsal entoderm.

Appearance of *filter* rudiments along caudal margin of 3rd visceral arch.

Stage 42. Age 3 d., 8 h.; length 7·0–7·7 mm.

External: Torsion of intestine about 90°; proctodeum connected with yolk mass by short horizontal intestinal tube. Beginning of formation of opercular folds.

Internal: *Rods* and *cones* distinguishable in *eye*.

Head somites 1 and 2 disappeared. Beginning of chondrification of *visceral skeleton* and *palatoquadrate*.

5th *visceral pouch* perforated; *filter* rudiments appearing along caudal margin of 4th and 5th visceral arches.

---

*The torsion of the intestine is indicated by diagrams added to the illustrations of Stages 41 to 45.

Stage 43. Age 3 d., 15 h.; length 7·5–8·3 mm.

External: Torsion of intestine about 180°. Lateral line system becoming visible externally.

Internal: First signs of *choroid plexus* formation in pros- and rhomb-encephalic roof. Latero-cranial sensorial rudiment of ear vesicle split into rudiments of *crista anterior* and *macula utriculi*.

Beginning of chondrification of *cranium*. Anterior and posterior *valves* capable of closing atrio-ventricular aperture of *heart*. Continuous *mesonephric* rudiment formed.

Long *intestinal* loop formed, reaching anteriorly as far as liver.

Stage 44. Age 3 d., 20 h.; length 7·8–8·5 mm.

External: Appearance of tentacle rudiments. Coiling part of intestine showing S-shaped loop; torsion about 360°. Blood-circulation in gills usually ceased. Gills smaller.

Internal: *Head somite* 3 disappeared. Lateral *postcardinal veins* indicated; *posterior vena cava* established.

FEEDING

Stage 45. Age 4 d., 2 h.; length 8–10 mm.

External: Intestine spiralised in ventral aspect, showing 1½ revolutions. Operculum partly covering gills, edge still straight. Beginning of feeding.

Internal: *Motor neurons* standing out in posterior trunk region of spinal cord.

Partition wall between *atria* completed. 3–4 pairs of *mesonephric* units discernible in mesonephric rudiment. Paired *genital* ridges formed.

Rudiments of *filter* processes on inner surface of operculum.

Stage 46. Age 4 d., 10 h.; length 9–12 mm.

External: Intestine showing 2–2½ revolutions. Hindlimb bud visible for the first time. Xanthophores appearing on eye and abdomen.

Internal: Cells of *Purkinje* differentiating in *corpora cerebelli*. Some *spinal ganglion* cells enlarging and equalling *Rohon-Beard* cells in tail region.

Complete chondrification of *visceral skeleton*. First mesenchymal accumulation of *forelimb* rudiment. 4–5 *mesonephric* units distinguishable.

Oesophagus free of yolk. Food appearing in intestinal tract.

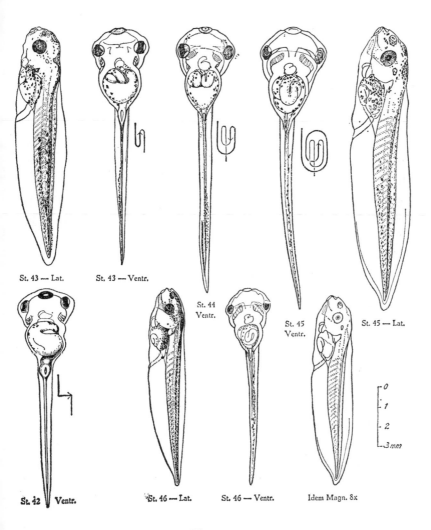

St. 43 — Lat.   St. 43 — Ventr.

St. 44
Ventr.

St. 45
Ventr.   St. 45 — Lat.

St. 42 Ventr.

St. 46 — Lat.   St. 46 — Ventr.   Idem Magn. 8x

0
1
2
3 mm

Figure 25.

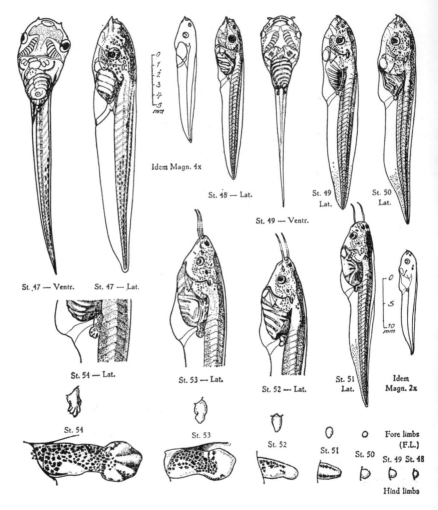

St. 47 — Ventr.   St. 47 — Lat.

Idem Magn. 4x

St. 48 — Lat.

St. 49 — Ventr.

St. 49
Lat.

St. 50
Lat.

St. 54 — Lat.

St. 53 — Lat.

St. 52 — Lat.

St. 51
Lat.

Idem
Magn. 2x

St. 54

St. 53

St. 52

St. 51

St. 50

Fore limbs
(F.L.)

St. 49 St. 48

Hind limbs

Figure 26.

Stage 47. Age 5 d., 12 h.; length 12–15 mm.

External: Edge of operculum forming quarter of a circle. Intestine showing 2½–3 revolutions. Hindlimb bud more distinct.

Internal: *Head somite* 4 disappeared and *trunk somite* 1 reduced. 6–8 *mesonephric* units segregated, central lumen in oldest units.

Stage 48. Age 7½ d.; length 14–17 mm.

External: Forelimb bud visible for the first time. Hindlimb bud semicircular in lateral aspect. Shining gold-coloured abdomen.

Internal: *Trunk somite* 1 disappeared. Medial *postcardinals* fused as *interrenal vein* as far as junction with posterior vena cava; *lateral postcardinals* completed, opening into interrenal vein at level of cloaca. First 6–8 pairs of *mesonephric tubules* coiling; 2–3 pairs communicating with Wolffian ducts.

Yolk completely disappeared from *alimentary canal*.

Stage 49. Age ca. 12 d.; length 17–23 mm.

External: Hindlimb bud somewhat longer, distal outline still circular, no constriction at base. Forelimb bud distinct. Melanophores appearing on dorsal and ventral fins.

Internal: *Semicircular canals* with ampullae completed; *macula lagenae* located in separate diverticulum of sacculus.

10–12 pairs of functional *mesonephric* units and 6–8 pairs of *glomeruli* formed.

Follicle formation starting in *thyroid* gland.

Stage 50. Age ca. 15 d.; length 20–27 mm.

External: Forelimb bud somewhat oval-shaped in dorsal aspect. Hind-limb bud longer than broad, constricted at base, distal outline somewhat conical.

Internal: Cells of lateral *motor columns* beginning to differentiate at lumbar levels of *spinal cord*. *Brachial ganglia* with a few large cells. *Forelimb* and *hindlimb nerves* entering limb rudiments. *Choanae* perforated.

Beginning of differentiation of mesenchyme in *hindlimb* bud; paired *pelvic girdle* rudiment indicated. About 20 pairs of *glomeruli*, and open *nephrostomes* in *mesonephros*. Complete *gonadal* rudiments formed.

Beginning of colloid formation in *thyroid* follicles.

Stage 51. Age a. 17 d.; length 28–36 mm.

External: Forelimb bud oval-shaped in lateral aspect. Hindlimb bud conical in shape, length about 1½ × breadth.

Internal: Cells of lateral *motor columns* beginning to differentiate at brachial levels of *spinal cord*.
Forelimb rudiment segregated into rudiments of *shoulder girdle* and *forelimb*. Number of *glomeruli* augmented to 40–50.
Typhlosole formed in *duodenum*.

Stage 52. Age ca. 21 d.; length 42–56 mm.
External: Forelimb bud irregularly conical. Hindlimb bud showing first indication of ankle constriction and first sign of flattening of foot.
Internal: Lumbar ganglia with a few large cells. *Dorsal column* ("dorsal horn") beginning to appear at postbrachial levels of *spinal cord*.
Chondrification completed in 4th to 9th *vertebral arches*. *Femur* rudiment procartilaginous, *tibia* and *fibula* mesenchymatous. Beginning of sexual differentiation of *gonads*.
5 complete revolutions in outer and in inner spiral of *intestinal* helix.

Stage 53. Age ca. 24 d.; length 50–60 mm.
External: Fore- and hindlimbs in paddle stage. Hindlimb without foot somewhat longer than broad; 4th and 5th toe indicated.
Internal: *Purkinje* layers fusing in dorsal midline. *Dorsal column* extending into prebrachial levels of *spinal cord*.
Shoulder girdle divided into *scapular* and *coracoidal* portions.

Stage 54. Age ca. 26 d.; length 58–65 mm.
External: All four fingers indicated. Length of hindlimb without foot nearly twice its breadth; all five toes indicated, the 2nd only very slightly.
Internal: *Dorsal column* extending throughout trunk levels and over short distance into postsacral levels of *spinal cord*.
Chondrification completed in 1st and 2nd pairs and caudally down to 10th pair of *vertebral arches*. Chondrification of hindlimb advanced up to *tibiale* and *fibulare*. First signs of atrophy in *pronephros*.
Up to 7 revolutions in outer and in inner spiral of *intestinal* helix.

Stage 55. Age ca. 32 d.; length 70–80 mm.
External: Hand pronated about 90°; free parts of fingers about

equally long as broad. Length of hindlimb without foot about 3 × breadth; length of cartilages of 4th and 5th toe about 4 × breadth.

Internal: All major muscles of *thigh* and *leg* present with both origins and insertions. First meiotic division in *ovary*.
Single row of *maxillary tooth germs* developed.

Stage 56. Age ca. 38 d.; length 70–100 mm.

External: Elbow and wrist clearly indicated; length of free parts of fingers 3 to 4 × breadth. Length of cartilages of 4th and 5th toe about 6 × breadth.

Internal: *Coracoid* slightly ossified perichondrally; *scapula, procoracoid* and *coracoid* chondrified. Chondrification of *forelimb* up to phalanges, which are still blastematous; ossification extended to forearm. Skeleton of *hindlimb* completely chondrified, ossification extended distally to *tibiale* and *fibulare*.
Urinary bladder forming distinct pocket on ventral side of cloaca.

Stage 57. Age ca. 41 d.; length 75–105 mm.

External: Angle of elbow more than 90°; fingers stretched out in forelimb atrium, their length about 7 × breadth.

Internal: Left and right halves of *pelvic girdle* in contact with each other. *Oocytes* beginning their major growth period.
Closure of *branchial clefts* beginning. Beginning of *metamorphosis* in alimentary canal; *oesophagus* mucosa peeling off and first signs of histolysis in *duodenum*.

(Stage 58 —. Forelimbs in process of eruption, elbow piercing skin; angle of elbow about 90° and fingers folded in forelimb atrium.)

Stage 58. Age ca. 44 d.; length 80–110 mm. (ultimate length of larva).

External: Forelimbs broken through. Guanophores appearing on abdomen and thighs (adult skin areas). All three claws present on hind limb.

Internal: Metamorphosing *skin* of forelimb area caudally continuous with metamorphosing skin of trunk.
Tip of *tail* beginning to atrophy. *Arm* and *hand musculature* differentiated. *Pronephros* no longer functional.
Extensive histolysis in *duodenum*.

Stage 59. Age ca. 45 d.
External: Stretched forelimb reaching down to base of hindlimb.
Tentacles beginning to shrivel up. Guanophores appearing near
base of forelimb (adult skin area); anterior border of adult skin
area on abdomen not yet sharp; appearance of irregular dark
spots on back.
Internal: *Lymph sacs* beginning to develop underneath metamorphosing skin areas. Intercellular *melanin* deposits underneath
epidermis, around blood vessels and between muscle fibres of
tail. New generation of *mesonephric tubules* formed in reorganisation process. First meiotic division in *testis*.
Second row of *tooth germs* formed. Histolysis in non-pyloric part
of *stomach*, and *pancreas*.

Stage 60. Age ca. 46 d.
External: Distal half of fingers of stretched forelimb extending
beyond base of hindlimb. Adult skin area of base of forelimb
covered with guanophores; anterior border of adult skin area on
abdomen sharper, reaching up to heart. Openings of gill chambers
still wide.
Internal: Well defined stratum corneum formed on *upper jaw*.
Appearance of *horn papillae* in the other adult skin areas.
Chondrification of dorsal *perichordal tube* extending vertebrally
down to 12th pair and intervertebrally down to 11th pair of
vertebral arches. Complete differentiation of *hindlimb musculature*.
Third row of *tooth germs* formed.

Stage 61. Age ca. 48 d.
External: 4th arterial arch seen just in front of adult skin area of
forelimb. Forelimb at level of posterior half of heart. Fins
considerably reduced. Tentacles considerably shortened, mostly
curved backwards. Openings of gill chambers considerably
narrowed.
Internal: Metamorphosis of *adult skin* areas completed. *Spinal
ganglion* 8 descended to level well posterior to root of ganglion 9,
and nearly all of ganglion 9 posterior to lumbar level of spinal
cord.
Atrophy of *fins* and posterior tail *notochord*.
Middle ear cavity shifted to position somewhat cranial to eye.
First signs of degeneration of *filter* apparatus. Histolysis in
pyloric part of *stomach* and in *ileum*.

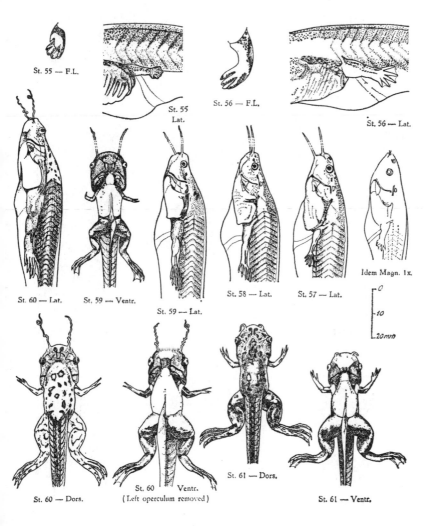

St. 55 — F.L.

St. 55
Lat.

St. 56 — F.L.

St. 56 — Lat.

St. 60 — Lat.   St. 59 — Ventr.

St. 59 — Lat.

St. 58 — Lat.   St. 57 — Lat.

Idem Magn. 1x.

St. 60 — Dors.   St. 60   Ventr.
(Left operculum removed)

St. 61 — Dors.

St. 61 — Ventr.

Figure 27.

F

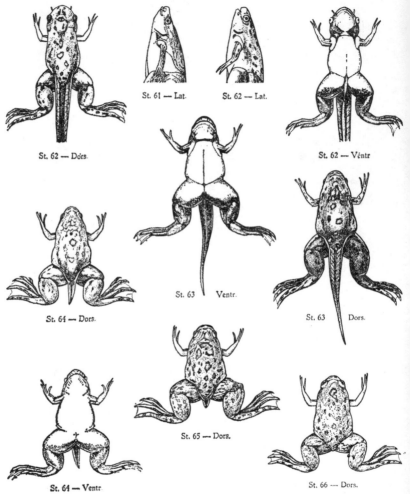

St. 61 — Lat.   St. 62 — Lat.

St. 62 — Dors.

St. 62 — Ventr

St. 64 — Dors.

St. 63   Ventr.

St. 63   Dors.

St. 64 — Ventr.

St. 65 — Dors.

St. 66 — Dors.

Figure 28.

Stage 62. Age ca. 49 d.
External: Head still somewhat broader than cranial part of trunk.
3rd arterial arch ("larval aorta") seen at distance of its own
diameter in front of adult skin area of forelimb. Opening of
operculum reduced to curved slit. Forelimb at level of middle
of heart. Thymus gland somewhat protruding. Ventral fin disappeared from abdomen.
Internal: Lower *eyelid* forming. Areas of *larval skin* on head beginning to shrivel.
Signs of atrophy in *notochord* over entire length of tail; degenera-
tive hypertrophy of mesenchymatous *perichordal tube* and
vertebral arches of tail. Portion of *Wolffian duct* between pro- and
mesonephros disappeared.
Middle ear situated below caudal margin of eye. Number of
intestinal revolutions reduced to about 2 in outer and 2 in inner
spiral; epithelium of *oesophagus*, non-pyloric part of *stomach*,
duodenum and *ileum* reconstituted to more or less continuous
layer (that of non-pyloric part of stomach already differentiating).

Stage 63. Age ca. 51 d.
External: Head narrower than trunk. Corner of mouth at level of
posterior border of eye. Operculum closed. Forelimb at level of
anterior half of heart. Tail still slightly longer than body. Tentacles mostly disappeared. "Larval aorta" and thymus gland no
longer externally visible.
Internal: Root of *spinal ganglion* 9 just posterior to ganglion 7.
Cartilage of 13th pair of *vertebral arches* and cartilage of anterior
ventral *perichordal tube* degenerating. In tail entire notochord
shrivelling; beginning of actual degeneration of *muscle segments*
(still 49 post-otic muscle segments distinguishable). *Ductus
caroticus* disappeared.
Gill slits closed. *Operculum* a shapeless mass. *Intestinal* helix
making only $1\frac{1}{2}$ irregular revolutions. Histolysis in *colon*.

Stage 64. Age ca. 53 d.
External: Adult skin areas joined almost everywhere, borderlines
still clearly visible. Length of tail (from anus) $\frac{1}{3}$ of body length.
Corner of mouth well behind eye.
Internal: Root of *spinal ganglion* 7 anterior to ganglion 6.
Entire cartilage formation of ventral *perichordal tube* converted

into loose connective tissue, and cartilage of lateral *perichordal tube* in process of resorption. Only about 14 postotic *muscle segments* distinguishable. 4th *aortic arch* (adult aorta) larger than 3rd (larval aorta). *Pronephros* completely disappeared. Primordia of *Müllerian ducts* developing.

Epithelium of pyloric portion of *stomach* and of *colon* reconstituted; new glandular elements in *oesophagus, duodenum* and *ileum*.

Stage 65. Age ca. 54 d.

External: Tail length about $\frac{1}{10}$ of body length. Borderlines between adult skin areas partly disappeared.

Internal: *Spinal ganglion* 8 situated at posterior end of lumbar area of spinal cord.

Intervertebral joints formed. *Notochord* and *somites* disappeared in tail region. Adult *abdominal vein* established.

Openings and proximal portions of *pharyngo-tympanic ducts* fused.

Stage 66. Age ca. 58 d.

External: Border lines between adult skin areas disappeared. Tail only a very small triangle, no longer visible from ventral side.

Internal: Dorsal root of *spinal ganglion* 9 at level of ganglion 7.

Reorganisation of *mesonephros* not yet completed.

Typhlosole disappeared; *intestine* making single loop.

THE AXOLOTL (*Ambystoma mexicanum*)

The axolotl is a neotenous urodele which in its natural home in the cold water lakes of the Mexican mountains spends its entire life in the larval state, becoming sexually mature and reproducing without at any time leaving the water or completing metamorphosis. Although the animal has much in common with any other urodele amphibian, it also has many peculiarities associated with its neotenous and permanently aquatic existence. Its limbs are well formed, but are short and project horizontally in a position better adapted for swimming than for support. A powerful tail and feathery external gills are present throughout life. The skeleton is only lightly ossified, the vertebrae are amphicoelous, and the body is surrounded by a thick layer of segmented muscle, as in fish. Lungs are developed but are little used, most respiratory exchange taking place through the gills and skin.

Full grown, the axolotl is 20–30 cm. in length and, in the commonest form, is coloured grey speckled with small indefinitely outlined black spots (Plate 16A).

Deuchar (1957) provides a very readable and informative general account of the axolotl. The animal's first official zoological name was given by Wagler in 1830. He named it *Siredon pisciformis*, thinking that it was related to a type of newt called "siren" which belongs to the Perennibranchiates, a group of amphibia which do not metamorphose. However, in 1856, some axolotls which had been imported from Mexico to the Jardin des Plantes in Paris started to breed, and to the astonishment of all concerned some of their young went through all the changes characteristic of metamorphosis. They lost their gills and fin, shed their larval skin, changed colour and emerged on land as a form which strongly resembled salamanders of the genus *Ambystoma*. Axolotls were therefore promptly renamed *Ambystoma mexicanum*, and this has led to some splendid confusion. According to the rules of priority in zoological nomenclature *Siredon pisciformis* is the correct name, but this gives a completely false idea of the animals' classificatory position since they are obviously Ambystomids. Most zoologists now use *Ambystoma mexicanum*, which is much the better name, though Brunst (1955) who has had much experience with axolotls, uses *Ambystoma mexicanum* for the adult and *Siredon mexicanum* for the larva. "Amblystoma" has sometimes been used instead of "Ambystoma"; this is a spelling error and has nothing whatever to recommend it.

Axolotls are valuable animals for embryological studies, and are used in many laboratories, particularly in Europe. Unlike many other urodeles which may only lay one or a few eggs at a time, an axolotl lays 300–1100 in a single clutch and will readily breed in the laboratory. The embryos are hardy enough to withstand many experimental procedures, and the large size of the embryonic cells facilitates histological and cytological studies. Dark and white individuals can be obtained, which is helpful in grafting experiments where it is desired later to identify the graft. (Small white axolotls placed under a low power binocular microscope are also excellent for demonstrating blood circulation in the gills.) Axolotls have great powers of regeneration, particularly the larvae, which will regenerate after amputation limbs, tail, gills, parts of the head and even some internal organs, completely and rapidly. Information is also now available on their genetics (Humphrey 1959, 1962; Briggs and Humphrey 1962).

No table of normal development has yet been prepared for the axolotl, but the embryonic stages are very similar to those of other *Ambystoma* species and it is sufficient for most purposes to use Harrison's table for *A. maculatum*. This table is published in Hamburger 1960, and Rugh 1962.

Keeping axolotls in the laboratory

The care and breeding of axolotls has been described by Brunst (1955) and the following owes much to his useful paper.

The best temperature is about 20°C. The animals are very resistant to low temperatures, and can live for some time under a thick layer of ice, but cannot tolerate very warm water. They can conveniently be kept in wide 4–5 litre bowls, two thirds full of tap water (see p. 165 for purifying tap water). In each such bowl it is possible to keep many young animals, or 3 or 4 animals six months old, or 1 or 2 older animals. If the axolotls are kept in deeper water in tanks, it should be continuously aerated. Bowls and tanks should be covered with wire mesh, otherwise the animals are apt to jump out and die.

Feeding is only necessary on two or three days each week. The best food is good quality beef or lamb (not pig) liver or muscle (e.g. heart) without bones, fat, tendons or other connective tissue. A convenient procedure is to divide the meat into portions of the size required for a single feeding, and then wrap these in strong waxed paper and keep them frozen until required. Frozen meat can be cut with a knife into thin slices about 3 mm. in thickness and for full grown axolotls strips about 4–5 mm. broad and 30–40 mm. long should be cut from these slices. Axolotls will usually not take meat from the bottom of the bowl, and they must be fed by hand, a strip of meat being held in long forceps in front of the animal's mouth. Some animals, if they are not very hungry, react very slowly and patience may be necessary. Moving the meat about makes it more attractive. An occasional change of diet to earthworm, fish, tadpoles or newborn mice stimulates appetite.

The axolotls should be fed at least two or three times on each feeding day, with an interval between each meal.

The proper size of the piece of meat is important. If it is too small the animal will be hungry and will soon start to bite the limbs of any other sharing its bowl. If the piece is too large the animal may regurgitate it within the next hour and again be left hungry.

The water must be changed in the bowls almost every day, and particularly a few hours after feeding. Fresh water from a cold tap should not be added just before feeding because the lower temperature causes loss of appetite. Cool water also causes defaecation, and it is very important after a day in which the water has been changed to remove from the bowls, with a large pipette, all faecal matter and uneaten food. Once a week the bowls should be scrubbed clean of any algae which have started to grow on the walls.

If at any time one of the animals appears sick it should immediately be isolated. Little is known about the diseases of axolotls (but see Reichenbach–Klinke and Elkan 1965 for amphibian diseases in general) and they are usually fatal.

Healing of wounds occurs best at low temperatures and wounded animals should be kept for several days in a refrigerator just above freezing, and without food. Under such conditions healing occurs quickly and without any infections.

Breeding

Axolotls are often sexually mature at 12–18 months, but the best age for breeding is 2 or 3 years. They are not much good after 6 years though some will live in the laboratory for 10–15 years.

Maturity in the male is indicated by marked enlargement of the lateral margins of the cloaca (Plate 16.B). The maturity of the female may be better indicated by the plumpness of the body which results from the increased size of the ovaries and oviducts. In the laboratory the animals usually breed between November and May, and much more rarely from June to October.

Unfortunately there is no way of inducing breeding in the axolotl as simple and reliable as that for *Xenopus*, and whatever method is used failure must be expected in at least half the attempts. A sudden change of temperature sometimes seems to be effective; the animals can either be left in a refrigerator for a few days and then transferred to water at 30°C, or transferred from room temperature to water at 10°C. Another recommendation often made is that the males and females be kept separate until eggs are wanted. Billett (1964) describes the following procedure used at the Middlesex Hospital Medical School: "Ideally the animals are kept in isolation, but where this is not possible they are kept in groups of 2 or 3 of the same sex. During the season pairs of animals are mated when fertilised eggs are required. Previously isolated males and females often display vigorous mating behaviour when brought together. Success is usually indicated when the male lays spermatophores some hours after mating. Some 12 to 24 hours after this, fertilised eggs may be expected from the female. We find that most females will attach their eggs to glass rods held vertically in the tank by means of corks. Almost certainly the main stimulus to mating is the bringing together of the isolated male and female. The animals are also stimulated by lowering the water temperature—this often happens during the routine cleaning of the tanks and can of course be achieved with chunks of ice. It is probably not advisable to drop the temperature suddenly by more than about 5 degs. C, and we try to avoid dropping it below 10°C."

Brunst recommends placing the male and female in a large aquarium, not less than 25 cm. × 30 cm. × 40 cm., filled to the top with water. The bottom of the aquarium is covered with 1 cm. or more of clean sand or gravel which serves to keep the spermatophores deposited by the male upright and facilitate their transfer to the cloaca of the female. Many water plants such as *Elodea* or *Valisneria* should also be placed in the aquarium; usually the female will attach the eggs to the plants. The eggs can then be very easily removed from the aquarium together with the plants, without disturbing the female which can continue laying. Oxygen from the plants is also beneficial to the eggs.

The breeding aquarium should be disturbed as little as possible. Often the male will show courtship behaviour a few hours after being placed with the female. He swims round her and elevates his tail, making writhing movements with it. One to twenty spermatophores are usually deposited on the floor of the tank during the night. Each consists of a transparent base of jelly, pyramidal in shape, secreted by the glands of the cloaca, and capped by an opaque white mass of spermatozoa.

The female picks up one of the spermatophores and transfers it to her cloaca. Soon after, she begins to spawn, and may continue spawning over a period of two days although most of the eggs appear within 24 to 36 hours. Between 100 and 1100 eggs are laid, with the number commonly around 500. A good female will spawn two or three times a year. The eggs are normally fertilised as they pass through the cloaca but often some are infertile; eggs removed from the oviducts are always infertile.

Induced ovulation and artificial fertilisation

Ovulation can be stimulated by intramuscular injection of gonado-trophin—Fankhauser (1963) recommends 180–220 i.u. of F.S.H.—or by implantation of frog pituitaries (p. 166). Eggs can then be removed from the oviducts and artificially fertilised. Brunst gives the following method:

1. It is necessary to prevent the female from depositing her eggs for some time (up to a few hours, if possible) by disturbing her constantly whenever she becomes quiet. This will result in the accumulation of more eggs in the lower ends of the ducts.

2. The female is killed by decapitation and a fine wire is run down the cord to stop reflex movements. The oviducts are exposed and the ducts torn open, beginning at their caudal ends, with two pairs of fine forceps. The eggs can be removed with forceps alone. Toward the cephalic end of the duct the egg membranes are poorly formed and the eggs cannot be handled by the forceps without being broken. Such eggs are few in number, however.

3. The eggs should be placed one layer thick on two or three sheets of filter paper soaked in aquarium water and put in a flat-bottomed dish which can be covered tightly. Several such dishes should be used, and each one covered after a short time to prevent

F*

drying of the jelly of the eggs while others are being collected. (The eggs should be removed from the oviducts as quickly as possible, but they may then stand for a half-hour or even longer if drying of the jelly is prevented.)

4. If the male is to be killed, the same method as used for the female should be employed. If the male is to be kept alive (this is illegal except under a vivisection licence in some countries, including the United Kingdom), 5 cc. of 10% urethan is injected intraperitoneally and when the animal is completely quiet, a small lateral incision 1–2 cm. in front of the hind leg is made and peritoneal fluid and blood carefully absorbed from the region of the exposed vas deferens. The vas deferens is cut with fine scissors and the seminal fluid either sucked from this opening with a fine pipette or collected with a pipette as it flows into the peritoneal cavity. If the male has been killed instead of anaesthetised, the vas deferens should be cut at its caudal end, held with forceps to stop escape of the contents, and the entire duct or as much of it as possible removed. It is then transferred to the dish prepared for making the sperm suspension, and cut into short pieces from which the seminal fluid is stripped by pressure with the forceps.

5. The sperm suspension is made in 10% Holtfreter saline (p. 4), pond water, or tap water which has been tested and found harmless. The contents of each vas deferens are suspended in 10 ml. of water or saline. The suspension is stirred to break up clumps of spermatozoa, then pipetted in a thin layer or film over the surface of the eggs, adding only a small quantity at a time so that it does not run off. More can be added later if the amount of suspension permits.

6. The dishes are allowed to stand covered for 15–20 minutes. Water is then added to the level of the eggs without flooding them; after a few minutes they are transferred to large dishes with a volume of water adequate for the number of eggs. At room temperature the first cleavage divisions should appear in from 7 to 9 hours. The layer of eggs can then be detached from the filter paper, the eggs cut apart with needles, and the infertile ones discarded.

7. The time allowed to elapse between killing the female and adding the suspension of sperm should be kept down to an hour or less for best results. The sperm suspension should be prepared immediately before using (the eggs can stand for a longer time without harm). Neither the eggs nor the sperm suspension should be con-

taminated with blood, or with urethan or other anaesthetic if such is used. 25 to 70 per cent fertilisation may be expected.

Rearing axolotls

The eggs, whether fertilised naturally or artificially, require plenty of oxygen, and overcrowding must be avoided. Tap water is an adequate medium, provided it does not contain excess chlorine or copper ions (p. 165). The eggs can be put either into shallow dishes, about 60 to 70 per litre of water, or into small aquaria containing plenty of plants (preferably *Elodea*) and equipped with an aeration pump. They should not be allowed to accumulate in the breeding tank during laying, but should be removed every few hours, disturbing the laying female as little as possible. Dead eggs or embryos are readily distinguished from the living by their light greyish colour, and at later stages by their inactivity.

The rate of development varies with temperature. At normal room temperatures the embryos have tails, and some are moving, about 5 days after laying. Hatching occurs at around 9–12 days and the young axolotls then become very active and grow quickly. If they are well fed they grow to over 30 mm. in length 3 weeks after hatching, and are over 150 mm. by 5 months. If, however, the animals have insufficient or incorrect food they vary greatly in size and many are much smaller than this.

For the first week after hatching the axolotls live on the yolk stored in the intestine. After this they need feeding. Nauplius larvae of the brine shrimp *Artemia salina* are an ideal first food, but small *Daphnia*, or pieces of small *Tubifex* or *Enchytraeus* worms may also be used (pp. 14–17).

Larger larvae are fed *Daphnia* or *Tubifex*, or pieces of earthworms. *Artemia* or *Enchytraeus* alone constitute an insufficient diet as is shown by the appearance of oedema and small haemorrhages in the skin (Fankhauser 1963). Eventually feeding with beef or lamb's liver is necessary, particularly if the animals are to be brought to breeding condition as quickly as possible. Young larvae should be fed daily, but after several months feeding may be reduced to alternate days. Brunst has found that by placing only a small quantity of liver in an aquarium with many young axolotls, and replacing it if necessary at hourly intervals, the animals can sometimes be taught to feed themselves. This is much easier than individual hand feeding which is the only alternative.

Metamorphosis

Metamorphosis of axolotls has never been known to occur in nature and it occurs spontaneously only very rarely under laboratory conditions. In other amphibia metamorphosis is under the control of the thyroid gland, and it can be induced in axolotls by implanting extra thyroid glands, or by injecting or feeding certain pituitary hormone preparations, thyroid hormone, or various other iodine compounds (see Deuchar 1957). Humphrey and Burns (1939) joined larvae of axolotls to larvae of *Ambystoma punctatum*, so that in each pair of animals the blood systems were united (parabiosis), and found that the axolotls then metamorphosed at the same time as their parabiotic partners. It seems likely that either the axolotl thyroid is in some way deficient, or that the tissues of axolotl larvae are much less sensitive to thyroid hormone than those of most other amphibia, but the explanation is still far from complete.

ELEUTHERODACTYLUS

The various species of *Eleutherodactylus* are distributed through-out the Caribbean and adjacent mainlands. They are among those few amphibia in which the aquatic larval stage has been entirely omitted. Although the adults are mostly small (length 2–4 cm.) the eggs are large (3–5 mm. diam. with a yolk about 2–3 mm. diam.). They are surrounded by several concentric jelly layers and are laid in small clutches of separate eggs in damp situations. Cleavage is holoblastic, but embryonic development proceeds much faster at the animal pole, so that the embryo appears to be on top of the egg, superficially resembling a fish or chick embryo more than a typical amphibian (Fig. 29). There are no tadpole-like mouth parts or coiled gut. The only complete aortic arches ever to be formed are the carotid and systemic. The gill clefts are never open and in some species there are no traces of external gills. The embryo develops a short, highly vascular tail with very large dorsal and ventral fins; presumably this has a respiratory function and is an amphibian substitute for the chorio-allantois of amniotes; it is completely resorbed around the time of hatching.

Eleutherodactylus deserves to be very much better known among embryologists than it is at present. Besides the interest of its unusual form of development—a "non-amphibious amphibian"—it has several features which make it potentially of great value for experimental embryology. Among the most important of these is its very rapid development. Comparison of Table 4 (p. 164) with the tables of other amphibia shows that Eleutherodactylus develops in a few days many of the structures which usually require several weeks. The juvenile toad at hatching is only about 5·0 mm. long, and in serial

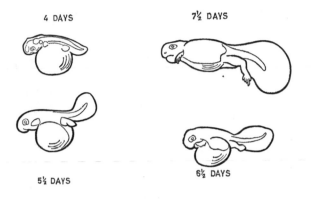

4 DAYS   7½ DAYS

5½ DAYS   6½ DAYS

0 1 2 3 4 5 mm

Figure 29.   *Eleutherodactylus* embryos (Hughes 1962).

sections occupies no more than one or two 3 × 1 in. slides. It has been shown to be valuable in several neuro-embryological studies (Hughes, 1959, 1962, 1964a, b, c), a particularly useful feature being the exceptionally small number of cells in the spinal cord. The final number of cells in each ventral horn of Eleutherodactylus is about 400, as compared with 1200 in *Xenopus* and 26,000 in man. The embryos survive removal of large parts of the brain, even if this involves injury to the buccal cavity, because unlike other larval amphibia, Eleutherodactylus larvae do not use the mouth for feeding. The quiescent (non-swimming) nature of the tadpole is a great advantage in studying the development of limb movements. Furthermore, although the eggs are normally terrestrial, the fact that they will develop in water makes it a simple matter to treat them with substances in solution, as in the experiments of Lynn (1948) and Lynn and Peadon (1955) with thyroxin and thyroid inhibitors.

The eggs can easily be grown and observed in culture. A Petri dish lined with wet filter paper forms a convenient culture chamber, a few drops of water being added from time to time to keep the paper thoroughly moist. The outermost jelly layer of the eggs is usually contaminated with soil or other debris and hinders observation of the embryo. It is not difficult, however, to remove it with forceps under a dissecting microscope. This does not affect development of the embryo which can then be studied in great detail through the perfectly clear and transparent inner jelly layers. Between the jelly and the embryo is a layer of fluid, and during the early stages of development the embryo slowly rotates in this fluid by ciliary action.

For studying the effect of a particular chemical substance on development the most convenient method is to grow the eggs in a solution of the substance. Whole eggs immersed in water develop into normal toads but at a retarded rate. If the vitelline membrane and all the jelly layers are removed, however, the immersed eggs develop into normal toads at nearly the normal rate (Lynn, 1948). When the embryos reach the stage at which hatching would normally occur, as indicated by tail resorption and attempts to engulf air, provision must be made for them to leave the water, as by tilting the culture dish. Once air-breathing is established the young toads will usually climb up the side of the dish.

Hughes (1962) has devised a technique for limb grafting operations on *E. martinicensis*. His studies have been made in Jamaica, where this species usually begins to breed a day or two after the beginning of the spring and autumn rains. Each female lays a clutch of 10–20 eggs. The outer jelly coverings of the egg are not difficult to remove but the innermost is very tough. "To broach this structure and avoid damage to the embryo is the main hazard in operative procedure; only if the membrane is cut when still under tension will it tear sufficiently widely to allow the embryo to escape. If the membrane is merely punctured, the capsular fluid escapes and the soft embryo is then closely wrapped in a tough and wrinkled investment which can only be removed with great difficulty. The earliest time at which living embryos can be removed undamaged from their envelopes is about 4 days, the stage of early limb buds. Before this period, the yolky endodermal mass becomes distorted by its own weight when deprived of support. In later stages of development, the embryo assists in freeing itself from the ruptured envelope, the inner layer of which afterwards resembles a wrinkled coagulum. It is removed from the dish, together with the gelatinous outer layers.

"The embryo is now gently laid on its side in a pool of its own capsular fluid. To graft limb-buds from one position to another, the bud is severed at its base with a pair of fine forceps scissors, and placed near its new position. . . . The graft is manoeuvred into position as soon as possible after incision of the host in order to take advantage of the surrounding blood-clot in holding the transplant. . . . During the operation, the embryo shows little activity. Surface tension in the film of fluid over its upper moist surface both checks movement, and holds the graft in place. Within an hour after the operation Holtfreter saline containing 1 : 500,000 sulphathiazole (or better, chloramphenicol) is cautiously added from a fine pipette to the liquid surrounding the embryo. Both the time and the extent of this irrigation need to be regulated by experience. If the embryo remains too dry, blood vessels over the yolk may undergo statis; if saline is added too early or incautiously the graft may float away.

"From time to time, more Holtfreter is pipetted into the dish and after a further hour the embryos may be fully immersed. Generally speaking, the proportion of grafts which immediately adhere to the host is upwards of 60 per cent of those attempted. This figure is appreciably higher where a forelimb is at once replaced in position after amputation."

"Within a day after transplantation of an embryonic limb, the wound has healed. It is then advisable progressively to dilute the Holtfreter saline in the dish with distilled water. A small ciliate, some 40μ in length, may infect the embryos; they multiply more rapidly in saline than in water. Dying embryos are usually surrounded by a dense cloud of these Protozoa. Once a few are noticed within the dish, the water should be changed frequently. In general resistance to infection increases with the age of the embryo; in eggs within their envelope, the outer layer remains free of fungal hyphae only so long as the embryo within is alive."

Table 4 shows the rate of development of *E. martinicensis* as given by Hughes (1962). Other species in which embryonic development has been described are *E. nubicola* (Lynn, 1942), *E.guentheri* (Lynn and Lutz 1946a), *E. nasutus* (Lynn and Lutz, 1946b), *E. portoricensis* (Gitlin, 1944) and *E. ridordii* (Goin, 1947, Lynn, 1948, Hughes, 1959).

No species of Eleutherodactylus has yet been successfully reared to the adult in the laboratory, but Goin (1947) obtained eggs from adults of *E. ricordii* kept in cages with damp sphagnum, and Hughes (1962) found that *E. martinicensis* would readily deposit eggs in boxes of dampened straw placed in its natural breeding grounds. In captivity the adults will readily feed on *Drosophila* or other small flies. There seems reason to hope that with further study of the environ-

TABLE 4. Development of *Eleutherodactylus martinicensis* at c. 30°C (Hughes, 1962).

		Length of hind limbs (mm.)
0	Laying.	
4 hours	1st Cleavage. Cleavages on dorsal surface follow at intervals of 40–45 minutes.	
7 ,,	1st furrow on ventral surface.	
14 ,,	Early gastrula.	
24 ,,	Fluid accumulates in upper third of egg.	
52 ,,	Neural folds. Rotation begins within egg envelope.	
60 ,,	Closed fore brain and neural tube.	
64 ,,	Straight tail-bud. Hind-limb area raised above embryo surface.	
70 ,,	Tail spatulate.	
72 ,,	Three brain vesicles.	
74 ,,	Tail bends to one side.	
84 ,,	Circulation begins.	
4 days	First signs of body pigment. Early limb-buds.	
4½ ,,	Eye pigment. Rotation ceases.	
5 ,,	First signs of otoliths	0·7
5½ ,,	Circulation well established	1·0
6 ,,	Pigment cells migrating over yolk	1·5
6½ ,,		2·0
7 ,,	Large otoliths	
7½ ,,	Pigment over most of abdomen	3·0
8 ,,		
8½ ,,		4·0
9 ,,	Xanthophores first appear over dorsal surface of head	
9½ ,,	Egg-tooth appears	5·0–5·5
11½ ,,	Xanthophores over general body surface	6·5
13½–14½ days	Hatching.	

mental requirements of these animals it will soon become possible to maintain and breed them in any laboratory.

OTHER AMPHIBIA

Many amphibia will survive in captivity for months or even years. Several will breed in the laboratory, though their readiness to do so varies very much from species to species. In addition to *Xenopus* and the axolotl, the Spanish salamander (*Pleurodeles waltlii*) and the Japanese newt (*Triturus pyrrhogaster*) have been kept in permanent breeding colonies. Others can be kept long enough to provide fertile eggs for several successive years.

The fully aquatic species are the most convenient to house; the others, if they are to be kept beyond the breeding season when they are normally aquatic, will require an "aquaterrarium" with access to water in one part of the enclosure and damp soil, rocks, etc., in another. Water from a pond or stream in which there is plenty of plant life is usually the best, but tap water is adequate provided it is free of chlorine and copper ions. Excess chlorine can be eliminated by allowing the water to stand for two or three days in shallow open containers, or more quickly by bubbling air through the water. According to Fankhauser (1963) de-chlorination can be accomplished more efficiently by passing the water through charcoal filter beds, or by adding a few milligrams per litre of sodium thiosulphate. "The presence of even small amounts of chlorine can be detected by mixing a few ml. of a saturated solution of ortho-tolidine (3,3′ dimethylbenzidene) with 50–60 ml. of water, which will turn a greenish-yellow colour. The copper may be removed by chelation with versene (50 mg./l.)." Rose (1960) has investigated the optimum conditions for the culture water for growth of frog tadpoles. Whatever the source of the water, it will soon become foul with faeces and decaying particles of food, and must be changed frequently.

Normal room temperatures of around 15°–20°C are suitable for most amphibia, but usually no harm will result from a drop in temperature even for a few days. Few amphibians, however, will feed below 7°C (Lester 1957).

All adult amphibians are carnivorous. The terrestrial animals can often be fed on mealworms, pieces of earthworms, *Drosophila* or other insects. The aquatic forms may be fed on *Tubifex*, pieces of earthworms, beef liver or heart. The food will not be taken unless it is either alive and moving, or waved in front of the animal's mouth. Urodele larvae also are carnivorous; when newly hatched they will usually take *Artemia* larvae or small *Daphnia*, and as they grow larger they can be given adult *Artemia* and *Daphnia*, *Tubifex*, *Enchytraeus* or small amphibian larvae (pp. 14–17). Most Anuran larvae are vegetarian and can be fed with boiled spinach or lettuce which they will rasp away with their horny teeth (*Xenopus* larvae, however, are filter feeders—p. 124). Terrestrial juvenile (recently metamorphosed) anurans and urodeles can conveniently be fed with

Drosophila, particularly the non-flying mutants of *D. melanogaster* such as "vestigial-wing" (p. 16).

Fertilisation in the Anura is external, the male grasping the female from the back (amplexus) and shedding sperm over the eggs as they are laid. In the Urodela fertilisation is internal. After elaborate courtship behaviour, which may or may not include a period of amplexus, the male extrudes one or more spermatophores, consisting of a small conical mass of jelly capped by a capsule of sperm. The spermatophore is usually deposited on the bottom of the pond or aquarium, and the female crawls over it and picks it up with the lips of her cloaca. The spermatozoa remain alive and functional within the female at least for several months.

It is very important that developing embryos and larvae of Amphibia be given adequate space and oxygen if they are to grow normally. Rugh (1962, p. 52) recommends a ratio of 1 egg to 2 ml. of water, with a maximum of 25 eggs to 50 ml. in each dish. As the embryos develop into tadpoles the ratio must be changed, so that there is at least 5 ml. of water for each young larva. At this stage the larvae are best transferred to tanks containing water not more than 3 cm. deep, so that the surface exposed to the air is large in proportion to the volume. Both embryos and larvae are very sensitive to anaerobic conditions. Artificial aeration may not be necessary, but aquatic plants such as *Elodea* should be provided.

Induced breeding

In many amphibia breeding can be induced, but the ease with which this can be done varies greatly from one species to another. *Xenopus* and *Discoglossus* readily ovulate and lay eggs at most times of the year in response to injection of mammalian gonadotrophin. Toads of the genus *Bufo* can also be induced in this way to breed during the winter and spring, though the response is more reliable if either frog or toad pituitary glands are injected (Rugh 1962, p. 99).

Other anurans do not in general respond to mammalian hormones, but many can be induced to ovulate by injection of amphibian pituitaries, and the eggs are then squeezed out of the oviducts by hand (stripping) and fertilised artificially. The technique is described in detail by Hamburger (1960) and Rugh (1962). The pituitary glands are dissected from frogs which are healthy, sexually mature and in pre-breeding condition. Female glands are twice as potent as male. The number of glands necessary varies with the season. For

Rana pipiens, Rugh recommends 4–5 female glands per recipient animal during the autumn and winter, 2–3 female glands during the spring. The glands are drawn with a little water into the barrel of a syringe, a large bore needle is then attached, and the glands are injected into the lower abdominal cavity of the recipient female. As the glands pass through the needle they should break up into a fine suspension ready for quick absorption. At room temperature most of the eggs are shed from the ovaries within 48 hours and can be obtained by stripping, without killing the animal. The palm of the hand is placed over the back of the frog with the fingers encircling its body just posterior to the fore limbs, and the animal's hind legs bent forwards. By a gentle squeezing of the hand in the direction of the cloaca the eggs will then be forced out. If only liquid or jelly oozes out, the frog should be tested again after a further 24 hours, and if there are still no eggs a further pituitary injection should be given.

The males need not be injected. Functional spermatozoa can be secured simply by macerating the testes from a sexually mature male in 10–20 ml. of 10% Holtfreter solution (p. 4), and leaving them for a few minutes to become active. The suspension is divided between 2–3 large petri dishes so that the bottom of each dish is just covered. The eggs are squeezed directly from the female into the petri dishes and should be spread out so that all are in contact with the sperm suspension. After 5–10 minutes the eggs are rinsed and then allowed to stand submerged in clear water. The jelly membranes will swell slowly. Eggs remain viable in the oviduct for several days if the females are kept at 10°–15°, and it is therefore possible to obtain eggs from the same female on several successive days by removing only a portion of her eggs each day.

Rugh (1962) lists the following from the more common amphibia that have responded to pituitary treatment in the manner just described.

Ambystoma tigrinum	*Desmognathus fuscus*
Bombinator pachypus	*Discoglossus pictus*
Bufo americanus	*Eurycea bislineata*
Bufo arenarum	*Gryinophilus porph.*
Bufo calamita	*Hyla aurea*
Bufo d'Orbignyi	*Hyla crucifer*
Bufo fowleri	*Leptodactylus ocellatus*
Bufo vulgaris	*Pseudobranchus striatus*

Rana aurora	*Rana vulgaris*
Rana catesbiana	*Rhyacotriton olympicus*
Rana clamitans	*Stereochilus marginatum*
Rana esculenta	*Triton cristatus*
Rana japonica	*Triturus pyrrhogaster*
Rana nigricauda	*Triturus torosus*
Rana palustris	*Triturus viridescens*
Rana pipiens	*Xenopus laevis*
Rana temporaria	

Ovulation in urodeles can usually be induced by injecting amphibian pituitaries, and often by injection of mammalian hormones (see Hamburger 1960, p. 33). The general practice for obtaining fertile eggs outside the breeding season is to inject only the females, and to rely for fertilisation on the presence of functional spermatozoa in the spermatheca. But artificial fertilisation is also possible, and Hamburger gives the following method. "The eggs cannot be stripped but must be recovered from the oviduct. Prepare a number of petri dishes laid out with moist filter paper (moist chambers) and clean microscope slides. Decapitate and pith several males and females. Dissect the testes and the (usually pigmented) vasa efferentia and macerate them thoroughly in 10 ml. of pond or spring water or 10% Holtfreter solution. Dissect out the oviducts, place them on glass plates, and very carefully slit them or cut them open and set the eggs free. They are soft and delicate and must be handled with utmost caution. Mount them singly on the slides; do not moisten them. With a fine pipette, drop a few drops of the sperm suspension over each egg so that it is well coated. Place the slides in the moist chambers for 5–10 minutes, then submerge them in water. After the membranes are swollen, rinse off the sperm suspension and remove the eggs from the slides with a scalpel."

Some commonly used species

For reasons already given *Xenopus* and the axolotl are probably the most generally useful amphibians for embryological purposes. But the following notes, based partly on Fankhauser (1963), will give some idea of the advantages and disadvantages of other species. In general, urodeles will lay eggs in aquaria, whereas anurans, with a few exceptions, will not (although the eggs can often be obtained by stripping after induced ovulation). For some types of experiment urodele eggs have been found easier to manipulate; but anurans lay eggs in far larger numbers and spawn them rapidly, providing large batches of embryos of similar age.

Detailed information on the natural history of many different species of amphibia can be found in such works as Bishop (1943, salamanders of North America), Cochran (1961), Frommhold (1954, amphibia of Central Europe), Klingelhöeffer (1956), Noble (1931), Smith (1964, British amphibia), Stebbins (1951, 1954, amphibia of Western North America), Wright and Wright (1949, anura of North America). The diseases of amphibia are described (in German) in Reichenbach-Klinke (1961) and (in English) in Reichenbach-Klinke and Elkan (1965).

Urodeles

European newts of the genus *Triturus*

T. vulgaris. The common or smooth newt.
T. cristatus. The crested newt.
T. helveticus. The palmate newt.
T. alpestris. The alpine newt.

T. helveticus is the most aquatic of the four species, and may be found in and out of ponds and pools at all times of the year. The others are more terrestrial and return to water only to breed. During the breeding season, April–July, 200–400 eggs are laid singly on the leaves of water plants. Under carefully controlled conditions the adults can be kept in the laboratory but they are difficult to keep through the winter. It is usually better to collect fresh breeding stock each spring and place them in aquaria, where the females will deposit their eggs. Small frog tadpoles, which are often found in the same ponds as the newts, provide an excellent food for the adults. The larvae can easily be raised to metamorphosis.

Triturus (=*Diemictylus*) *viridescens.* The common newt of the U.S.A.
Found throughout the United States and southern Canada, particularly in the East. After metamorphosis it has a terrestrial phase (the "red eft" stage) lasting 2–3 years, and then returns to a fully aquatic existence for the rest of its life. Courtship and mating begin in the autumn and the eggs are laid March–June. 200–400 eggs are laid attached singly to leaves. Fertilised eggs may also be obtained

during the winter months from late October onwards by implantation of frog pituitaries; from about 10 to over 100 eggs are then laid over a period of 6 to 10 days. The outermost layer of the jelly capsule is adhesive and opaque and firmly attached to the inner clear layer. It cannot be removed in large pieces, as is possible with eggs of European and Japanese newts, but when the eggs are freed from the leaves to which they are attached, portions of the opaque layer remain behind and leave one or more transparent windows. Larvae can be reared to metamorphosis on *Artemia* and *Tubifex*, and for some time afterwards on *Drosophila*. It is necessary to collect fresh breeding animals each year.

Triturus pyrrhogaster. The Japanese newt.

The Japanese newt is more resistant to laboratory conditions than *T. viridescens*. Its life history has no prolonged terrestrial phase, and newly metamorphosed animals can often be induced to return to the water after a few days. The adults may be kept in a large aquarium on a diet of *Tubifex*, earthworms or beef liver, and will breed for at least two successive years. Spawning can be induced during the winter by implantation of frog pituitaries (2 per animal); a single female may then deposit from 30–90 eggs over a period of 2 weeks. This species has been reared to sexual maturity.

Pleurodeles waltlii. The Spanish salamander.

This urodele can conveniently be kept in the laboratory (see Hamerton 1957 for a full account). It is one of the most highly aquatic of the salamanders and will thrive in simple aquaria. The species is native to the Iberian peninsula and North Africa, where it occurs in small ponds, especially those with much vegetation. In captivity eggs can be obtained at most times of the year, each female laying batches of 200–500 every 2–3 months. The eggs are rather smaller than those of *Triturus cristatus*, but about the same size as or slightly larger than those of *T. vulgaris* or *T. palmatus*. The larvae hatch at about 10 days, and metamorphose at 2–6 months; they can be reared in the laboratory and the first spawning may be obtained at an age of 16 months.

Taricha torosa (= *Triturus torosus*). The California newt.

It is doubtful whether these animals will mate and deposit eggs normally in the laboratory. But the relatively large size of the eggs and embryos, and the fact that they are laid in clusters of up to 30 all at the same stage of development, makes them favourable material for embryological work. They may be collected during the breeding season from December to May. From the oviducts a large number of eggs can be obtained for artificial fertilisation. The larvae can be raised on *Artemia*, and the metamorphosed animals reared to sexual maturity, but this is rarely worth doing because growth is slow and sexual maturity is not attained for three years (Stebbins 1951).

Ambystoma maculatum ($=A.$ *punctatum*). The spotted salamander.

This is the commonest of the large American salamanders, and is found over a wide range in the eastern United States. The eggs and embryos are excellent for operative procedures and are laid in batches of 125–250, but they can only be obtained by collecting the spawn from ponds, or bringing into the laboratory adults on the point of spawning. For the latter it is necessary to wait for a night of warm rain during the breeding season (March–April), which induces the animals to migrate to their spawning ponds, and then to collect them during the same night. Eggs in the one-cell stage can be found in the pond on the morning after a rain. The animals do not spawn spontaneously in the laboratory at any other time, and do not respond to the usual methods of inducing spawning. The larvae can be raised easily to metamorphosis but are difficult to rear to maturity.

Ambystoma tigrinum. The tiger salamander.

Found through the U.S.A., and in Canada and Mexico this is one of the largest of the salamanders (adult length about 25 cm.). Hutchinson (1950) was able to maintain a breeding colony for three years, but only under special, and rather elaborate conditions. The animals, after they had spawned in the spring, were placed in a large enclosure which simulated their natural swamp-wood habitat. To prevent the animals' escape, and to protect them from predators, the enclosure was covered with wire netting and surrounded by deeply sunken cement walls. In the autumn they were transferred to a cold room ($3°$–$5°$C) to hibernate. When eggs were required a few animals were removed from the cold room to a warmer tank, and usually spawned on the third night after being transferred. In this way it was possible to extend the normal breeding season (January to March) as late as June.

Anurans

Discoglossus pictus. The painted toad.

This small toad is widely distributed in south-west Europe, north Africa and most of the islands of the western Mediterranean. Its eggs have proved valuable for embryological work (e.g. Dalcq 1938, Waddington 1941) and, like Xenopus, it readily spawns in response to gonadotrophin injections. Descriptions of the care and breeding of Discoglossus in the laboratory are given by Bruce, Parkes and Lantz (1947), from whose paper the following details are taken, and by Gallien (1950).

The animals must have access to land and water. A covered aquarium containing water to a depth of 20 cms., with a platform supported above the water on bricks and covering about half the area of the tank, seems to be adequate. All food is given on the platform, which should carry pieces of hollow stone or bricks under which the animals can retire. The water must be changed about once a week.

Discoglossus does not feed readily on dead meat; but worms, snails, insects and mealworms are accepted. If newborn mice are available these are an excellent food; 3–4 mice per week have proved sufficient to keep a pair of toads in good condition for over a year, in spite of frequent oviposition and without any other food.

Fertile eggs can be obtained throughout the year. From March to October the animals spawn spontaneously every few weeks, laying several hundred eggs at a time with a high level of fertility. During the winter months ovulation and oviposition can be induced by hormone injection; if 200 i.u. chorionic gonadoptrophin is injected into the dorsal lymph sac of the female, and 100 i.u. into the male, during the afternoon, eggs are laid and fertilised the following night.

The eggs are laid singly, and are 1–1·5 mm. diam. with a thick jelly coat. They are darker than those of *Xenopus* and the cleavage divisions are harder to see. At 20°C the larvae hatch on the 3rd day and become free-swimming on the 5th day. They can easily be raised to metamorphosis, which occurs around 5 weeks, but it is more difficult to rear the juvenile toads.

Bufo bufo. The common European toad.

Found throughout most of Europe, northern and temperate Asia and North Africa. Absent from Ireland. According to Smith

(1964) this toad "has been called an 'explosive' breeder, by which is meant that all the sexually mature individuals in a district migrate from their hibernation quarters to their breeding ground within a few days of one another. . . . With remarkable directness they make straight for one particular spot, passing all other ponds or ditches of which they might avail themselves, on the way. . . . The same pond is returned to year after year." Spawning occurs in April, each female laying about 4,000 or 5,000 eggs in strips of jelly 2–3 metres in length. The eggs are $1\frac{1}{2}$–2 mm. in diameter and almost entirely black. Hatching usually occurs after about 3 weeks and metamorphosis after 10–12 weeks, but these times can vary greatly with temperature.

Bufo americanus. The American toad.

Common in north-eastern U.S.A. Breeding occurs in April and May, the eggs being laid in long spiral tubes of jelly. The average number of eggs spawned by each female is about 6000. Hatching occurs after 2 to 17 days, depending on the temperature, and metamorphosis after about 60 days. The temperature tolerance is from about 10°C to 30°C (Rugh 1962).

Rana temporaria. The common European frog.

Widely distributed throughout Europe and parts of Asia. This frog is tolerant of cold and breeds early in the year. Spawning occurs from February to April according to latitude and mildness of the season. According to Smith (1964) "these frogs spawn in a great variety of ponds, but specially favour those that have water flowing in and out of them. They return to the same ponds and to the same part of the pond year after year. They choose shallow water when it is available, sometimes only a few inches in depth and exposed to the sun." The eggs are laid in jelly masses, each female spawning 1,000–4,000. Each egg is 2–3 mm. in diameter, black, with a light area at the vegetal pole. Subject to temperature, hatching occurs after 2 weeks and metamorphosis after 10 weeks.

Rana pipiens. The leopard frog.

The frog most commonly used in the U.S.A., where it is found in most areas except the Pacific Coast. It breeds in March and April and the eggs are laid in masses near the surface, each female spawning about 3000 eggs. In the laboratory, females kept at 4°C can be induced to ovulate at most times from September to May by injection of pituitary glands. A few days after the injection the eggs are obtained by stripping, and can then be artificially fertilised. The larvae can be reared on a diet of *Drosophila*, and later on mealworms, small earthworms or liver.

Tables of normal development of some amphibian species
(as compiled by Fankhauser 1963)

URODELA

Triturua viridescens: Fankhauser, G. (Unpublished—available in mimeographed form from the author).
Taricha torosa: Twitty, V. C. and Bodenstein, D. (1962).
Triturus pyrrhogaster: Oyama, J. (1930).
        Anderson, P. L. (1943).
        Okada, Y. K. and Ichikawa, M. (1947).
Triturus vulgaris: Glaesner, L. (1925).
        Glücksohn, S. (1931).
Triturus helveticus: Gallien, L. and Bidaud, O. (1959).
Triturus alpestris: Knight, F. C. E. (1938).
Pleurodeles waltlii: Gallien, L. and Durocher, M. (1957).
Salamandra atra: Wunder, H. (1910).
Ambystoma maculatum (=A. punctatum): Harrison, R. G. (1960 and 1962).
Eurycea bislineata: Fankhauser, G. (Unpublished—available in mimeographed form from the author).
Necturus maculosus: Eycleshymer, A. C. and Wilson, J. M. (1910).
Megalobatrachus japonicus: Kudo, T. (1938).

ANURA

Rana chalconata: Hing, L. M. (1959).
Rana fusca (temporaria): Moser, H. (1950).
        Kopsch, Fr. (1952).
Rana dalmatina: Cambar, R. and Marrot, Br. (1954).
Rana pipiens: Shumway, W. (1940).
        Shumway, W. (1942).
        Taylor, A. C. and Kollros, J. K. (1946).
Rana sylvatica: Pollister, A. W. and Moore, J. A. (1937).
Bufo arenatum: Del Conte, E. and Sirlin, J. L. (1952).
Bufo bufo: Cambar, R. and Gipoulaux, J. D. (1956).

Bufo regularis: Sedar, S. N. and Michael, M. I. (1961).
Bufo valliceps: Limbaugh, B. A. and Volpe, E. P. (1957).
Hyla regilla: Eakin, R. M. (1947).
Xenopus laevis: Gasche, P. (1944).
                  Weisz, P. B. (1945).
                  Nieuwkoop, P. D. and Faber, J. (1956).
Discoglossus pictus: Gallien, L. and Houillon, Ch. (1951).

BASIC TECHNIQUES FOR EXPERIMENTING WITH AMPHIBIAN EMBRYOS

It is outside the scope of this book to describe the immense number of studies that have been made with amphibian embryos. But the following general techniques are basic for many experiments. Among recent papers describing special techniques are those of Elsdale, Gurdon and Fischberg (1960) on nuclear transplantation, Blackler and Fischberg (1961) on transfer of germ cells, Curtis (1962a) on cortical grafting between uncleaved eggs and (1962b) between blastulae, and Tuft (1962) on the uptake and distribution of water in embryos, calculated from determinations of their density and weight in water. Deuchar (1956, 1958a) has studied amino acids and (1958b) catheptic activity in the embryo. Brown and Littna (1964) have used density gradient centrifugation methods for characterising the different types of RNA formed at various stages of development. All these workers used *Xenopus laevis*. Hegenaur and Nace (1962) describe a method for parabiosis of two or more embryos (*Rana pipiens* or *Ambystoma maculatum*), and Wallace (1962) describes the prolongation of life of anucleolate *Xenopus* tadpoles by joining them parabiotically to normal tadpoles. Fox has studied the effects of unilateral pronephrectomy in embryos of *Triturus cristatus* (1956), the axolotl (1960), and *Rana temporaria* (1962). Selman (1958) has used implanted magnets to measure the forces of neural fold closure in *Triturus alpestris* and the axolotl. Shaffer (1963) has maintained the isolated *Xenopus* tail in culture and used it for studying metamorphosis.

Saline

The jelly coats round amphibian eggs help to maintain the correct pH and ionic composition for embryonic development, and enable the embryos to be fairly tolerant of variations in the surrounding water. If these coats are removed, as is necessary in many experiments, the embryos grow only in a carefully balanced saline. Holtfreter's saline (p. 4) is the most widely known and gives excellent results. As originally devised (Holtfreter 1931) the pH of this saline was rather high (over 8) but Holtfreter has since reduced the concentration of bicarbonate to 0·02 gms./litre (Hamburger 1960) which, in equilibrium with normal CO_2 concentrations in the air, gives a pH of about 7·5. The saline is isotonic with embryonic amphibian cells, and the relative concentrations of the different metallic ions have been found empirically to be the best for embryonic development.

Although neurulae and older embryos will tolerate full strength Holtfreter saline, early embryos develop abnormalities if left in it for any length of time, and for these 10% Holtfreter saline should be used. But wounds heal very much better in the stronger solution, and the best procedure is to place the embryos in the full strength saline while performing any operation involving wounding (e.g. transplanting grafts), to leave them in it until the wound is completely healed, and then to transfer them to the 10% saline.

Removal of the jelly coats also robs the embryos of an important protection against bacterial and fungal infection. The culture saline must therefore be sterilised, and antibiotics should be added. A concentration of 0·025 gm. streptomycin sulphate and 1000 units of penicillin per litre of saline gives good results (Hamburger 1960). Without antibiotics losses from infection are liable to be heavy.

Removal of egg membranes (*decapsulation*)

Amphibian eggs are surrounded by a vitelline membrane and several layers of jelly. The number and consistency of these jelly layers varies greatly from one species to another. The jelly of anuran eggs is usually fairly soft and can often be removed without much difficulty by means of forceps, scissors, or rolling the eggs on filter paper. But urodele eggs commonly have at least one tough jelly layer, or capsule, with or without other soft layers, and the removal of this capsule is more difficult. Fortunately between the vitelline membrane and the capsule there is a layer of fluid in which the egg moves freely, so that it is possible to tear the capsule open without the egg being damaged. In general the best instruments to use are a pair of watchmakers forceps in each hand. To get sufficient grip on the jelly to tear it apart, it is often necessary before closing the forceps to pass one prong inside the capsule. This can be done without injuring the egg, particularly if the operation is performed under a low power dissecting microscope.

The following is a convenient method for the rapid decapsulation of *Ambystoma mexicanum* eggs. A batch of eggs in their jelly is placed on the back of the experimenter's left hand, and the soft jelly is cut away and pushed aside, using fine scissors held in the right hand. Each capsule is then given a single cut with the scissors, and if this is done carefully a hole is left through which the undamaged egg pops out. The decapsulated eggs are transferred to a dish of saline by inverting the left hand over the dish, so that the back of the hand is just below the surface and the eggs fall off.

Removing the vitelline membrane from amphibian eggs is usually fairly easy from neurula stages on, but is considerably more difficult in younger embryos. The eggs must be placed under a dissecting microscope, and the vitelline membrane torn open with watchmakers forceps, the points of which have been ground as fine as possible. A certain amount of practice is necessary before this can be done with the minimum of injury to the eggs, and the details vary slightly according to the particular species and instruments used. With some eggs (e.g. axolotls') the membrane is best removed by puncturing it with a very fine tungsten needle (pp. 2–3) when it will often split spontaneously and can then easily be torn off with forceps. Small injuries usually heal well, particularly if the egg is placed for a time in full strength Holtfreter saline.

Methods of removing the vitelline membrane by chemical digestion have been devised (Spiegel 1954 with papain and sodium thioglycolate; Steinberg 1957 with cysteine hydrochloride). They are worth trying with embryos at cleavage and morula stage, where removal of the membrane with forceps is exceedingly difficult. But chemical treatment has considerable hazards for the embryo, and a good deal of trial and error is necessary before the exact conditions can be found for rupturing the membrane without doing any further damage. In general, chemical digestion is a less reliable method than tearing the membrane open with forceps.

Eggs and embryos from which the vitelline membrane has been removed are usually extremely delicate and must be handled with great care. At all times they must be completely immersed in fluid; any contact with surface tension forces causes serious distortion or disruption. They can be transferred from one container to another by means of wide pipettes, provided that care is taken to hold the tip of the pipette below the saline surface before ejecting them. All instruments brought in contact with the eggs must be sterile and the culture vessels should not be left uncovered any longer than is absolutely necessary. The naked eggs and embryos tend to stick to glass surfaces and it is advisable to line glass culture vessels with a layer of 2% agar in Holtfreter saline.

Narcosis

Late embryos or larvae may be too active for close examination or precise operations. Hamburger (1960) recommends as narcotics for urodeles either chloretone (acetone chloroform) at a concentration of 1 : 3,000, or MS 222 (methane sulphonate) at 1 : 5000 or 1 : 6000. These concentrations are usually satisfactory, but the heart beat should be watched; its stoppage is a sign of too high concentration, and the embryos will recover only if transferred immediately to normal medium. Old larvae may require a stronger concentration. Embryos and larvae become immobile within a few minutes and recover within 5–10 minutes. They can be kept under light narcosis for hours or even days.

Anuran larvae are much more sensitive, and Hamburger considers that narcosis for them is too risky. Instead he recommends placing them on a bed of moist cotton. However, MS 222 has been used successfully at a concentration of 1 : 7,000–10,000 for anaesthetising *Xenopus* larvae (Lehman 1953). Fox (1964) finds that tolerance of *Rana temporaria* larvae to anaesthetics decreases with age; MS 222 at 1 : 1000 gives good results with very young larvae (Fox 1962) but is fatal to advanced tadpoles, and for these he uses a strength of 1 : 10,000, allowing 15 minutes for anaesthetisation and 1 or 2 minutes for the operation, followed by immediate transference to full strength Holtfreter solution.

Vital staining

Amphibian embryos are excellent for tracing morphogenetic movements by means of vital dyes. The cells stain intensely and the colour persists for a considerable time. Moreover there is little or no diffusion of the dyes to neighbouring cells, and any movement of the colour can be regarded as a convincing indication of cell movement.

Movements may be traced at various stages of development but they can be particularly well demonstrated during gastrulation. Following the classic experiments of Vogt (1925, 1929) blocks of agar impregnated with nile blue or neutral red (see p. 7) are applied to the dorsal surface of an early gastrula fairly close to the blastopore lip. The positions of the stained areas are carefully noted at the time of staining and at intervals during gastrulation.

To do this experiment, all the jelly layers must be removed from the embryo. The vitelline membrane can remain, but the results are sometimes better if it also is removed. A small shallow dish (e.g. embedding dish) is prepared with a layer of wax in the bottom about as deep as the diameter of the embryo. A depression is made for the embryo in the wax with a warmed ball-tip glass rod. The depression must be made deep enough to cover at least the lower hemisphere of the embryo and should fit it fairly tightly (Fig. 30).

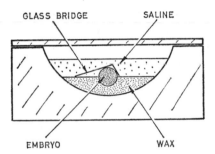

Figure 30.   Operating dish for amphibian embryos. The embryo lies in a depression made in the wax with a heated glass rod. To minimise the possibilities of infection the cover is removed from the dish only during the actual operation.

The edges of the depression must be smoothed carefully. The embryo is arranged with the blastopore upwards, and the agar block is placed on it and, if necessary, held firm by a glass bridge (p. 2). If the wax does not grip the embryo sufficiently tightly it will rotate and carry the blastopore below the surface of the depression. Embryos in this position can be stained by pushing the agar block between the embryo and the depression wall at a point just above the blastopore. (The tendency of the embryo to rotate can be reduced by puncturing the vitelline membrane and releasing the perivitelline fluid, or by removing the membrane.)

The agar should be left in place until the cells under it are very strongly stained. Usually this requires about half an hour. The embryo is then gently lifted out of the depression and transferred to a culture dish. If the stain has been applied close to the blastopore lip the stained cells will pass in through the blastopore, but can then often be seen through the covering ectoderm. At the end of the experiment their location can be accurately determined by dissection of the embryo.

Shah (1960) describes a method for applying several accurately spaced marks simultaneously, by staining through holes in a piece of tin foil.

Isolation, excision and grafting operations

A dissecting microscope is essential. Details of the other instruments required are given on pp. 1–3. The operations are best carried out in small dishes (e.g. embedding dishes) containing full strength Holtfreter solution and lined with wax. A depression is made in the wax of a size and shape to fit the decapsulated embryos (as in Fig. 30). All the coverings, including the vitelline membrane, are removed and the required part of the embryo is cut out with glass or metal needles. The loss of the vitelline membrane and perivitelline fluid makes it impossible for the embryo, once lodged in the wax depression, to rotate, and it can be placed there in any required orientation. Isolated parts grow best in full strength Holtfreter saline; whole operated embryos should be returned to 10% saline as soon as wound healing is complete.

In making grafts, the host and donor embryo should be arranged side by side in the same dish and close enough to be viewed together in the field of the dissecting microscope. The hole cut in the host embryo to receive the graft should usually be slightly smaller than the graft itself, so that it fits tightly and facilitates healing. The graft must be held in place for an hour or so until it is healed in; a glass bridge can be used for this, or sometimes the embryo can be rotated so that it lies over the graft. To make it easier to distinguish subsequently the graft from the host tissues, the whole of the donor embryo can be stained in 0·1% nile blue sulphate in saline before taking the graft.

Details of many operations on amphibian embryos are given by Hamburger (1960) and Rugh (1962), with particular reference to their use as classroom experiments.

REFERENCES

ANDERSON, P. L. (1943). The normal development of *Triturus pyrrhogaster*. *Anat. Rec.*, **86**, 59–74. See also Rugh, 1962, p. 88.

BILLETT, F. S. (1964). Personal communication.

BISHOP, S. C. (1943). *Handbook of salamanders. The salamanders of the United States, of Canada, and of Lower California*. Comstock Publishing Co., New York.

BLACKLER, A. W. & FISCHBERG, M. (1961). Transfer of primordial germ-cells in *Xenopus laevis*. *J. Embryol. exp. Morph.*, **9**, 634–41.

BRIGGS, R. & HUMPHREY, R. R. (1962). Studies on the maternal effect of the semilethal gene v, in the *Mexican axolotl*. *Devl. Biol.*, **5**, 127–46.

BROWN, D. D. & LITTNA, E. (1964). RNA synthesis during the development of *Xenopus laevis*, the South African clawed toad. *J. Mol. Biol.*, **8**, 669–87.

BRUCE, H. M. & PARKES, A. S. With a note by L. A. LANTZ (1947). Observations on *Discoglossus pictus*. Otth. *Proc. Roy. Soc. B.*, **134**, 37–56.

BRUNST, U. V. (1955). The axolotl (*Siredon mexicanum*). 1. As material for scientific research. *Lab. Investigation*, **4**, 45–64.

CAMBAR, R. & GIPOULAUZ, J. D. (1956). Table chronologique du développement embryonnaire et larvaire du crapaud commun: *Bufo bufo* L. *Bull. biol.*, **90**, 198–217.

CAMBAR, R. & MARROT, Br. (1954). Table chronologique du développement de la grenouille agile (*Rana dalmatina* Bon.). *Bull. biol.*, **88**, 168–77.

COCHRAN, D. M. (1961). *Living amphibians of the world*. Doubleday, New York.

CURTIS, A. S. G. (1962a). Morphogenetic interactions before gastrulation in the amphibian, *Xenopus laevis*—the cortical field. *J. Embryol. exp. Morph.*, **10**, 410–22.

CURTIS, A. S. G. (1962b). Morphogenetic interactions before gastrulation in the amphibian, *Xenopus laevis*—Regulation in blastulae. *J. Embryol. exp. Morph.*, **10**, 451–63.

CURTIS, A. S. G. (1964). Personal communication.

DALCQ, A. M. (1938). *Form and causality in early development*. Cambridge University Press.

DEL CONTE, E. & SIRLIN, J. L. (1952). Pattern series of the first embryonary stages in *Bufo arenarum*. *Anat. Rec.*, **112**, 125–35.

DEUCHAR, E. M. (1956). Amino acids in developing tissues of *Xenopus laevis*. *J. Embryol. exp. Morph.*, **4**, 327–46.

DEUCHAR, E. M. (1957). Famous animals—8. The axolotl. *New Biology*, **23**, 102–22.

DEUCHAR, E. M. (1958a). Free amino acid changes during cleavage in *Xenopus laevis* embryos. *Exp. Cell Res.*, **14**, 84–7.

DEUCHAR, E. M. (1958b). Regional differences in catheptic activity in *Xenopus laevis* embryos. *J. Embryol. exp. Morph.*, **6**, 223–7.

EAKIN, R. M. (1947). Determination and regulation of polarity in the retina of *Hyla regilla*. *Univ. California Publ. Zool.*, **51**, 245–88. See also Rugh, 1962, pp. 68–9.

G

ELKAN, E. (1957). Amphibia IV—*Xenopus laevis* Daudin. In *The UFAW handbook on the care and management of laboratory animals* (A. N. Worden and W. Lane-Petter, eds.). The Universities Federation for Animal Welfare, London.

ELSDALE, T. R., GURDON, J. B. & FISCHBERG, M. (1960). A description of the technique for nuclear transplantation in *Xenopus laevis*. *J. Embryol. exp. Morph.*, **8**, 437–44.

EYCLESHYMER, A. C. & WILSON, J. M. (1910). Normal plates of the development of *Necturus maculosus*. F. Keibel's *Normentafeln zur Entwicklungsgeschichte der Wirbeltiere*, Heft 11. Fischer Verlag, Jena.

FANKHAUSER, G. (1963). Amphibia. In *Animals for research* (W. Lane-Petter, ed.). Academic Press, London and New York.

FOX, H. (1956). Compensation in the remaining pronephros of *Triturus* after unilateral pronephrectomy. *J. Embryol. exp. Morph.*, **4**, 139–51.

FOX, H. (1960). Internal factors influencing normal and compensatory growth of the axolotl pronephros. *J. Embryol. exp. Morph.*, **8**, 495–504.

FOX, H. (1962). Degeneration of the remaining pronephros of *Rana temporaria* after unilateral pronephrectomy. *J. Embryol. exp. Morph.*, **10**, 224–30.

FOX, H. (1964). Personal communication.

FROMMHOLD, E. (1954). *Heimische Lurche und Kriechtiere*. Die Neue Brehm-Bücherei, Heft 49. A. Ziemsen, Wittenberg/Lutherstadt.

GALLIEN, L. (1950). *Élévage du Discoglosse au laboratoire*. General Embryological Information Service (Hubrecht Laboratory), 2nd issue, 152-3.

GALLIEN, L. & BIDAUD, O. (1959). Table chronologique du développement chez *Triturus helveticus*. *Bull. Soc., Zool. France*, **84**, 22–32.

GALLIEN, L. & DUROCHER, M. (1957). Table chronologique du développement chez *Pleurodeles waltlii* Michah. *Bull. biol.*, **91**, 97–114.

GALLIEN, L. & HOUILLON, Ch. (1951). Table chronologique du développement chez *Discoglossus pictus*. *Bull. biol.*, **85**, 373–6.

GASCHE, P. (1944). Beginn und Verlauf der Metamorphose bei *Xenopus laevis* Daud. Festlegung von Umwandlungsstadien. *Helv. Physiol. et Pharmacol. Acta*, **2**, 607–26.

GITLIN, D. (1944). The development of *Eleutherodactylus portoricensis*. *Copeia* **2**, 91–8.

GLAESNER, L. (1925). Normentafel zur Entwicklungsgeschichte des gemeinen Wassermolches (*Molge vulgaris*). F. Keibel's *Normentafeln zur Entw. gesch. der Wirbelthiere*, **14**, Fischer Verlag, Jena.

GLÜCKSOHN, S. (1931). Aeussere Entwicklung der Extremitäten und Stadieneinteilung der Larvenperiode von *Triton taeniatus* Leyd. und *Triton cristatus* Laur. *Arch. entw. mech.*, **125**, 341–405.

GOIN, C. J. (1947). Studies on the life history of *Eleutherodactylus ricordii planirostris* (Cope) in Florida. *Univ. Florida Studies, Biol. Sci. Ser.*, **4**, 1–66.

GURDON, J. B. (1964). Personal communication.

HAMBURGER, V. (1960). *A manual of experimental embryology*. Revised ed. University of Chicago Press.

HAMERTON, J. L. (1957). Amphibia II—The spanish salamander. In *The UFAW handbook on the care and management of laboratory animals* (A. N. Worden and W. Lane-Petter, eds.). 2nd ed. The Universities Federation for Animal Welfare, London.

HARRISON, R. G. Stage series of *Ambystoma maculatum* (published in Hamburger, 1960, pp. 211–13, and Rugh, 1962, pp. 82–7).

HEGENAUER, J. C. & NACE, G. W. (1962). A simplified method for the fusion of two or more amphibian embryos. *J. Embroyl. exp. Morph.*, **10**, 99–102.

HING, L. K. (1959). The breeding habits and development of *Rana chalconata* (Schleg.) (Amphibia). *Treubia*, **25**, 89–111.

HOLTFRETER, J. (1931). Über die Aufzucht isolierter Teile des Amphibienkeimes *Arch. EntwMech. Org.*, **124**, 404–66.

HUGHES, A. F. W. (1959). Studies in embryonic and larval development in Amphibia. I. The embryology of *Eleutherodactylus ricordii*, with special reference to the spinal cord. *J. Embryol. exp. Morph.*, **7**, 22–38.

HUGHES, A. F. W. (1962). An experimental study on the relationships between limb and spinal cord in the embryo of *Eleutherodactylus martinicensis*. *J. Embryol. exp. Morph.*, **10**, 575–601.

HUGHES, A. F. W. (1964a). The innervation of supernumerary and replacing grafts of limbs in *Eleutherodactylus martinicensis*. *J. Embryol. exp. Morph.*, **12**, 27–41.

HUGHES, A. F. W. (1964b). Further experiments on the innervation and function of grafted supernumerary limbs in the embryo of *Eleutherodactylus martinicensis*. *J. Embryol. exp. Morph.*, **12**, 229–45.

HUGHES, A. F. W. (1964c). The innervation of xenografted limbs in the embryo of *Eleutherodactylus martinicensis*. *J. Anat. Lond.*, **98**, 385–96.

HUMPHREY, R. R. (1959). A linked gene determining the lethality usually accompanying a hereditary fluid imbalance in the Mexican axolotl. *J. Hered.*, **50**, 279–86.

HUMPHREY, R. R. (1962). A semilethal factor (v) in the Mexican axolotl (*Siredon mexicanum*) and its maternal effect. *Devl. Biol.*, **4**, 423–51.

HUMPHREY, R. R. & BURNS, R. K. Jr. (1939). An incompatibility manifested in heteroplastic parabiosis or grafting in Amblystoma due to a toxin of cutaneous origin. *J. exp. Zool.*, **81**, 1–42.

HUTCHINSIN, R. C. (1950). Amphibia. *The care and breeding of laboratory animals* (J. Farris, ed.). John Wiley & Sons, New York. Chapman & Hall, London.

KLINGELHÖEFFER, W. (1956). *Terrarienkunde*. 2. Teil, Lurche Alfred Kernen, Stuttgart.

KNIGHT, F. C. E. (1938). Die Entwicklung von *Triton alpestris* bei verschiedenen Temperaturen, mit Normentafel. *Arch. EntwMech. Org.*, **137**, 461–73.

KOPSCH, FR. (1952). Die Entwicklung des braunen Grasfrosches *Rana fusca* Roesel (dargestellt in der Art der Normentafeln zur Entwicklungsgeschichte der Wirbelthiere). Stuttgart.

KUDO, T. (1938). Normentafel zur Entwicklungsgeschichte des Japanischen Riesensalamanders (*Megalobatrachus japonicus* Temminck), F. Keibel's

Normentafeln zur Entwicklungsgeschichte der Wirbeltiere, Heft 16. Fischer Verlag, Jena.

LEHMAN, H. E. (1953). Observations on macrophage behaviour in the fin of *Xenopus* larvae. *Biol. Bull.*, **105**, 490–5.

LESTER, J. W. (1957). Amphibia I.—General. In *The UFAW handbook on the care and management of laboratory animals*. (A. N. Worden and W. Lane-Petter, eds.). 2nd ed. The Universities Federation for Animal Welfare, London.

LIMBAUGH, B. A. & VOLPE, E. P. (1957). Early development of the Gulf Coast toad, *Bufo valliceps* Weigmann. *Amer. Mus. Novitates*, No. 1842, 32 pp.

LYNN, W. G. (1942). The embryology of *Eleutherodactylus nubicola*, an anuran which has no tadpole stage. *Contr. Embryol. Carneg. Instn.*, **190**, 27–62.

LYNN, W. G. (1948). The effects of thiourea and phenylthiourea upon the development of *Eleutherodactylus ricordii*. *Biol. Bull.*, **94**, 1–15.

LYNN, W. G. & LUTZ, B. (1946a). The development of *Eleutherodactylus guentheri* Stdnr. *Boletim do Museu Nacional Zool. Brazil*, **71**, 1–46.

LYNN, W. G. & LUTZ, B. (1946b). The development of *Eleutherodactylus nasutus* Lutz. *Boletim do Museu Nacional Zool. Brazil*, **79**, 1–30.

LYNN, W. G. & PEADON, A. M. (1955). The role of the thyroid gland in direct development in the anuran, *Eleutherodactylus martinicensis*. *Growth*, **19**, 263–86.

MOSER, H. (1950). Ein Beitrag zur Analyse der Thyroxinwirkung im Kaulquappenversuch und zur Frage nach dem Zustandekommen der Frühbereitschaft des Metamorphose-Reaktionssystems. *Rev. Suisse Zool.*, **57**, 1–144.

NEWTH, D. R. (1959). Black axolotl, and white. *Proc. roy. Instn.*, **37**, 353–50.

NIEUWKOOP, P. D. & FABER, J. (eds.) (1956). *Normal table of Xenopus laevis* (Daudin). *A systematical and chronological survey of the development from the fertilised egg till the end of metamorphosis.* North-Holland Publishing Co., Amsterdam.

NOBLE, G. KINGSLEY (1931). *The biology of Amphibia*. McGraw-Hill, New York.

OKADA, Y. K. & ICHIKAWA, M. (1947). A new normal table for the development of *Triturus pyrrhogaster* Boie. *Exp. Morphol. (Tokyo)*, **3**, 1–6 (in Japanese).

OYAMA, J. (1930). Normentafel der früheren Entwicklung des *Diemictylus pyrrhogaster* (Boie). *Zool. Mag.*, **23**, 465–73.

POLLISTER, A. W. & MOORE, J. A. (1937). Tables for the normal development of *Rana sylvatica*. *Anat. Rec.*, **68**, 489–96. See also Hamburger, 1960, pp. 209–10; Rugh, 1962, pp. 64–5.

REICHENBACH-KLINKE, H. H. (1961). *Krankheiten der Amphibien*. Gustav Fischer, Stuttgart.

REICHENBACH-KLINKE, H. H. & ELKAN, E. (1965). *The principal diseases of lower vertebrates*. Academic Press, London and New York.

ROSE, S. M. (1960). A feedback mechanism of growth control in tadpoles. *Ecology*, **41**, 188–99.

RUGH, R. (1962). *Experimental embryology. Techniques and procedures*, 3rd ed. Burgess Publishing Co., Minneapolis.

SEDAR, S. N. & MICHAEL, M. I. (1961). Normal table of the Egyptian toad, *Bufo regularis* Reuss, with an addendum on the standardisation of the stages considered in previous publications. *Českoslov. Morfol.*, **9**, 333–51.

SELMAN, G. G. (1958). The forces producing neural closure in amphibia. *J. Embryol. exp. Morph.*, **6**, 448–65.

SHAFFER, B. M. (1963). The isolated *Xenopus laevis* tail: A preparation for studying the central nervous system and metamorphosis in culture. *J. Embryol. exp. Morph.*, **11**, 77–90.

SHAH, R. V. (1960). A modified vital staining technique for amphibian eggs. *Experientia*, **16**, 165.

SHUMWAY, W. (1940). Stages in the normal development of *Rana pipiens*. I. External form. *Anat. Rec.*, **78**, 139–48. (See also Hamburger, 1960, pp. 205–7; Rugh, 1962, pp. 56–63.)

SHUMWAY, W. (1942). Stages in the normal development of *Rana pipiens*. II. Identification of the stages from sectioned material. *Anat. Rec.*, **83**, 309–16.

SMITH, M. (1964). *The British amphibians and reptiles*. 3rd. Collins, London.

SPIEGEL, M. (1954). The role of specific surface antigens in cell adhesion. Part II. Studies on embryonic amphibian cells. *Biol. Bull.*, **107**, 149–55.

STEBBINS, R. C. (1951). *Amphibians of Western North America*. University of California Press.

STEBBINS, R. C. (1954). *Amphibians and reptiles of Western North America*. McGraw-Hill, New York.

STEINBERG, M. (1957). In *Carnegie Institution of Washington Year Book*, **56**, 348.

TAYLOR, A. C. & KOLLROS, J. K. (1946). Stages in the normal development of *Rana pipiens* larvae. *Anat. Rec.*, **94**, 7–24. See also Rugh, 1962, 70–4.

TUFT, P. H. (1962). The uptake and distribution of water in the embryo *Xenopus laevis* (Daudin). *J. exp. Biol.*, **39**, 1–19.

TWITTY, V. C. & BODENSTEIN, D. (1962). Normal stages of *Triturus torosus* (published in Rugh, 1962, p. 90).

VOGT, W. (1925). Gesaltungsanalyse am Amphibienkeim mit örtlicher Vitalfärbung. I. Methodik. *Arch. EntwMech. Org.*, **106**, 542–610.

VOGT, W. (1929). Gesaltungsanalyse am Amphibienkeim mit örtlicher Vitalfärbung. II. Gastrulation und Mesodermbildung bei Urodelen und Anuren. *Arch. EntwMech. Org.*, **120**, 384–706.

WADDINGTON, C. H. (1941). Translocation of the organizer in the gastrula *Discoglossus*. *Proc. zool. Soc. Lond.*, **111**, 189–98.

WALLACE, H. (1962). Prolonged life of anucleolate Xenopus tadpoles in parabiobis. *J. Embryol. exp. Morph.*, **10**, 212–23.

WEISZ, P. B. (1945). The normal stages in the development of the South African clawed toad, *Xenopus laevis*. *Anat. Rec.*, **93**, 161–9. See also Rugh, 1962, pp. 66–7.

186   THE CULTURE OF VERTEBRATE EMBRYOS

WRIGHT, A. H. & WRIGHT, A. A. (1949). *Handbook of frogs and toads.*
Comstock Publishing Co., New York.
WUNDER, H. (1910). Die Entwicklung der äusseren Körperform des Alpen-
salamanders (*Salamadra atra* Laur.). *Zool. Jb., Abt. Anat.*, **29**, 367–414.
ZWARENSTEIN, H., SAPEIKA, H. & SHAPIRO, H. A. (1946). *Xenopus laevis,
a bibliography.* African Bookman, Cape Town. (A supplement to this
bibliography has been published by ZWARENSTEIN, H. & BURGERS, A. C.
(1955). Medical Library, University of Cape Town).

CHAPTER 6

Fish

A variety of fish have been used for embryological experiments, but in this account detailed consideration will be restricted to three that have proved particularly valuable—the killifish, *Fundulus;* the trout, *Salmo;* and the medaka, *Oryzias.* The first two have large eggs suitable for vital marking or grafting experiments, but the eggs are only obtainable during two or three months of the year. *Oryzias* lays smaller eggs, but the adults are easily maintained in laboratory aquaria and will supply eggs throughout the year.

Both embryonic and adult fish are easily poisoned by certain impurities in the water. Metallic ions, particularly of copper, are often a source of trouble, and as far as possible containers should be of glass or plastic, and any water that has been in contact with metal should be treated as suspect. Tap water is very variable, and it is always wise to test the water from a particular source on a few embryos before taking risks with large numbers. Excess chlorine, which is the commonest poison in tap water, can easily be removed (p. 165).

So far it has not proved possible to induce breeding in fish by pituitary injections, as in amphibia. However, eggs and sperm for artificial fertilisation can be obtained without difficulty by stripping the adults of *Fundulus* or *Salmo;* and *Oryzias* lays so regularly that a well managed aquarium should yield eggs almost daily.

In common with other teleosts the eggs of these three species are protected by a tough transparent membrane, the chorion. This membrane is termed by some authors the "shell" or "vitelline membrane"; it is non-cellular and is not related in any way to the embryonic membrane of the same name found in amniotes. After experimental removal of the chorion the embryo becomes highly vulnerable to bacterial infection, and aseptic precautions must be taken.

Details of several other fish useful for experimental embryology are given in Rugh (1962). Pentelow (1957) describes the maintenance for experimental purposes of *Salmo, Carassius* (goldfish), *Phoxinus* (minnow) and *Gasterosteus* (stickleback) in laboratory tanks and ponds, and Stuart (1957) gives general instructions for keeping tropical and sub-tropical fish. The book by Dettlaff and Ginsburg (1954) describes (in Russian) the development of sturgeon embryos with instructions for culturing them. The work of Vandebroek (1936) on morphogenetic movements in *Scyllium canicula* is one of the few notable studies on the experimental embryology of elasmobranch fish. Newth (1951, 1956) has successfully cultured lamprey embryos, and has used them for experiments involving transplantation of parts of the neural crest.

Experimental work on the epigenetics of fish has been discussed by Oppenheimer (1947) and Rudnick (1955), the latter author comparing the embryos of fish and of the chick. Smith (1957) gives a comprehensive review of the physiology of fish embryos, Yamamoto (1961) reviews studies on the physiology of fertilisation, and Devillers (1965) discusses the respiration of the teleost embryo.

Among the recently published tables of fish development are the well illustrated table by Swarup (1958) of *Gasterosteus aculeatus*, and the tables by Armstrong and Child of the bullhead, *Ictalurus nebulosus* (1962—with exceptionally beautiful illustrations), and of *Fundulus heteroclitus* (1965—reproduced here in abbreviated form on pages 193–221).

Much information on the diseases of fish is given in the book by Reichenbach-Klinke and Elkan (1965).

THE KILLIFISH (*Fundulus heteroclitus*)

This species is one of the commonest of the North American cyprinodonts. Both adults and young are remarkably tolerant of a wide range of salinities and are found abundantly in brackish waters of the east coast from Maine to Mexico. The adults are about 8–12 cm. in length. The males are a dark dull green with orange-yellow belly and numerous narrow bands of silvery spots on the sides (the colours are brighter in the breeding season); the females are olive, lighter below and without spots. The eggs are about 2 mm. in diameter, spherical, amber in colour and surrounded by a chorion covered with very fine adhesive threads. They are spawned in very shallow water, usually among weeds and where the salinity is low. The time of spawning varies with temperature and latitude; from Maine to Rhode Island it begins about June 1st and continues until mid July; at the marine Station of Duke University at Beaufort, North Carolina, it lasts from early June to August.

The adults can be kept in salt water aquaria, but eggs taken from freshly caught fish are likely to be in better condition for experiments. The eggs can be obtained only in the natural breeding season.

Culturing whole eggs

Both eggs and sperm can be obtained by stripping the adults, i.e. stroking the abdomen with gentle pressure from anterior to posterior. The eggs must not be left in water for long before the sperm are added because they lose their fertilisability within 15–20 minutes of immersion (Kagan 1935). Oppenheimer (1964b) strips some eggs, and then some sperm, into fingerbowls containing seawater to a depth of about 1 cm., and then after an hour transfers them to tap water. When the fertilised eggs are about 4–8 hours old they are rolled gently on filter paper to take off the sticky threads and prevent them from clumping.

The eggs must not be overcrowded. A bowl 10 cm. in diameter will accommodate up to 50 eggs, and if the water is kept at a depth of 1 cm. no aeration pumps or other special oxygenating devices are necessary. The water should be changed twice a day.

Fundulus eggs, and explants, develop well at temperatures between 18°C and 28°C. Varying the temperature alters the rate of development, but it should not be allowed to fall below 18°C. When eggs are kept at 15°C, even for as short a time as overnight, a proportion develop abnormally.

A full description of the embryonic development of Fundulus, illustrated with photographs, is given in the table of normal stages by Oppenheimer (1937). The more recent table by Armstrong and Child (1965) is reproduced here, in abbreviated form, on pp. 193–221 with the corresponding Oppenheimer stage numbers inserted for comparison.

Experiments with Fundulus eggs and embryos

The eggs are protected by a tough membrane, the chorion. This membrane is transparent and allows a clear view of the developing embryo, but for many experiments it is necessary to cut a window in it or to remove it entirely. This is a delicate operation which is best done under a dissecting microscope. Great care must be taken to avoid any pressure on the thin layer of elastic cytoplasm—the

G*

"surface gel layer" of Trinkaus (1949)—covering the yolk and blastoderm, which ruptures very easily. Fortunately, between the chorion and the surface gel layer there is a thin fluid-filled space, the perivitelline cavity, so that if the chorion is opened carefully it comes away without any damage to underlying structures.

In the method first devised by Nicholas (1927) the chorion is cut with iridectomy scissors, the movable blade of the scissors having been sharpened to a fine point. The egg is held either with blunt watchmakers forceps, or in a small cavity made in plasticine, wax or other soft material, and the sharp blade of the scissors is inserted through the chorion into the perivitelline cavity, care being taken to hold the blade tangential to the egg so that the point does not damage the yolk or embryo. A good place to make the insertion is just above or to the side of the blastoderm, where the chorion is often slightly raised. The scissors are then lifted slightly so that the egg is raised off the bottom of the dish, and the blades are closed together sufficiently to make a short cut in the chorion but not enough for the points to meet. This ensures that the tip of the sharp blade remains within the chorion, and if the membrane is now pushed farther up the blade the cut can be continued. In this way a window can be made over the embryo, or the membrane can be cut into two halves and removed.

Trinkaus (1951) describes an alternative method for removing the chorion, using two pairs of watchmakers forceps with the points polished to a high lustre. One of the points on one pair must be made very fine so that it will puncture the chorion with the minimum of pressure. It is inserted as far as possible into the perivitelline cavity, and the two points are brought together so that the chorion is grasped firmly. The egg is then raised and the remainder of the operation is made with the egg held well clear of the bottom of the dish. One of the points of the unsharpened forceps is rubbed against the chorion at the place where it is held by the grasping forceps, so as to cut it. The grasping forceps are then released, the egg eased further onto the sharp point into a position suitable for a further cut, and this procedure repeated until a complete window has been made or the chorion cut into two halves.

If the eggs are handled carefully, the embryos can be reared to feeding stages, after removal of the chorion at any time from fertilisation onwards. Dechorionated eggs, like intact eggs, develop normally in sea water, tap water, distilled water, and Ringer or Holtfreter saline (p. 4). It is advisable, however, to immerse them in double strength Ringer or Holtfreter saline while removing the chorion, or during any operation on the embryo, because wounds heal more rapidly in the more concentrated solutions.

The chorion is the embryo's main defence against bacterial infection. Fundulus yolk is a good bacterial medium, and if infection occurs the bacteria multiply extremely rapidly. Dechorionated eggs can be protected by adding antibiotics to the water or saline; Trinkaus and Drake (1956) found 0·001–0·002% sulphadiazine satisfactory. But Oppenheimer (1964b) successfully avoids infection without using antibiotics, by washing the eggs very thoroughly; after the eggs have been rolled to remove their covering of threads, and before the chorion is opened, they are washed in seven successive baths of sterile tap water; aseptic precautions (pp. 3–4) are then taken during all subsequent operations.

Morphogenetic movements in the Fundulus blastoderm can be studied by vital staining, as in the classic experiments of Oppenheimer (1936c). Nile blue or neutral red may be used, separately or together. The nile blue diffuses less than the neutral red, and remains definitely localised for longer when used in combination with neutral red than when used alone. The method is a modification of Vogt's technique for amphibia, small pieces of cellophane being used instead of agar as a carrier for the stain. The cellophane is rigid and easily handled and, after a small window has been cut in the chorion, can be easily slipped in between the chorion and egg and manipulated into the required position over the blastoderm. When the cellophane is held in place in this way the pressure is so slight that no damage is done to the developing embryo.

The cellophane is prepared by soaking it in an aqueous solution of equal parts of 1% nile blue and 1% neutral red and then allowing it to dry. It is left in contact with the embryo for 15 to 45 minutes, and can be used for staining individual blastomeres of cleavage stages, or parts of the embryonic shield during gastrulation. The stain remains sufficiently localised in the embryo to be traced for up to 48 hours. Good results, however, are only obtained if the staining operation is made in a medium of the right tonicity, e.g. double strength Ringer saline. Oppenheimer found that if the stain was applied in distilled water or tap water the cells took up too much in too short a time and were sloughed off immediately; if it was applied in normal Ringer saline or sea water the cells took up too little, and the small amount that entered the egg concentrated at all the cleavage planes irrespective of the place of application.

For some purposes carbon particles can also be used for tracing movements in the Fundulus egg, as in the studies by Trinkaus (1949, 1951) on the surface gel layer and the mechanism of epiboly, and by Brummett (1954) on the formation of the tail bud.

The early embryo has considerable powers of regulation, and Nicholas and Oppenheimer (1942) showed that up to the 16-cell stage the embryo could survive removal of up to half the blastomeres. They found that a convenient method for removing individual blasto-meres, or small parts of later embryos, was to suck the material away with a micropipette. The pipette is prepared with a terminal bore slightly smaller than the blastomere or other material to be removed, and inserted through a small window in the chorion. If necessary the blastomere can be loosened by a circular movement of the pipette.

Grafts can readily be made to the blastoderm (Oppenheimer— 1959 and earlier papers). The tissues to be transplanted are removed from the donor with finely sharpened steel knives (Oppenheimer used knives made from dissecting or sewing needles sharpened on an oil stone) and placed in sites previously prepared in the host blastoderm by cutting away or pushing aside the superficial cells. The operation on the host can be made through a window in the chorion, or after removal of the entire chorion. The host cells sur-rounding the graft immediately close in around it and hold it fast; healing is very rapid and no special provision is necessary to retain the graft in place. Secondary embryos can be induced in the host egg by grafted tissues, as in amphibia (Oppenheimer 1936b).

Fundulus blastoderms at certain stages can develop without the yolk. Oppenheimer (1936a) explanted blastoderms between the 1- and 128-cell stages and found that, whereas those explanted before the 32-cell stage merely developed into large balls of cells, many explanted after this stage gastrulated and developed embryonic organs, though the arrangement of the organs was often abnormal, particularly in the trunk. In making the explants, the eggs were dechorionated and the blastoderm dissected away with steel knives and cultured in double strength Holtfreter solution without bicarbonate or additional nutrients. Trinkaus and Drake (1956) obtained very little differentiation of blastoderms isolated in 2 × Holtfreter saline, but much more in a complex synthetic medium (White 1946) containing glucose, amino acids and vitamins. They found, however, that in all media there was little growth in size of the embryos, which remained abnormally small. Blastoderms fused or crowded together in culture (Trinkaus and Drake 1959) developed further than single controls.

Oppenheimer (1964a) cultured embryonic shields, removed from blastoderms of (Oppenheimer) stage 13 and 14, in amphibian Ringer solution (p. 4). In most of the cultures a little periblast and yolk were included, but no other nutrients were added. Usually the explants did not enlarge appreciably, but 89% of them formed embryos or differentiated embryonic structures including axial organs, eyes and ears.

STAGES IN THE NORMAL DEVELOPMENT OF
FUNDULUS HETEROCLITUS

The following table of normal development of *Fundulus heteroclitus* is an abbreviated version of the table by Armstrong and Child (1965) (Figs. 31–44). The numbering of the illustrations corresponds with the numbering of the stages. (The original table contains more detail of several of the stages and some general information on the fish.)

A few notes are added (in brackets) to the description of some of the stages, from the table by Oppenheimer (1937). The numbering of the corresponding Oppenheimer stages is also given (in brackets), although in the later stages the correspondence can only be approximate, because the description of Fundulus development by Oppenheimer differs in one or two particulars (e.g. the moment of onset of the blood circulation, and of fin movements), from that by Armstrong and Child.

The time (hours after fertilisation) indicated for each stage, applies to development at 20°C ±0·2°. Solberg (1938) gives times for the more rapid development obtainable at 25°C; at this temperature the 16 cell stage is attained in 3 hours, the blastopore closes at 26 hours, melanophores appear at 30 hours, and rudiments of the pectoral fins (stage 27) develop at 78 hours.

The magnification of all the illustrations is ×22.

FERTILISATION AND CLEAVAGE

Stage 1. 0 hours. (Oppenheimer, Stage 1.)

The fully matured unfertilised ovum is about 2 mm. in diameter. The cortical granules (yolk platelets) are uniformly distributed over the surface of the yolk, just below the chorion, together with an aggregation of oil droplets of various sizes. There are a few small oil droplets scattered through the yolk which otherwise is a clear yellow viscous fluid, not granular as in some teleost eggs. The micropyle is most readily seen immediately after stripping the eggs from the fish. It shows up best when viewed on the horizon of the egg and appears as a small funnel-shaped indentation on the external surface of the chorion.

Immediately after fertilisation the cortical granules disappear in a progressive wave spreading out from the micropyle, the process being completed in 2–3 minutes. In Fundulus the chorionic membrane, which functions as a fertilisation membrane, does not lift from the egg but rather the egg shrinks away from the membrane, beginning first in the area encircling the micropyle, as the perivitelline space appears. This progressive formation of the perivitelline space closely parallels the disappearance of the cortical granules.

Stage 2. 1·75 hours. (O.S. 2.)

1 cell. Following fertilisation, cytoplasmic condensation in the submicropylar area gradually forms a protoplasmic cap which bulges above the curve of the egg and develops into a single cell.

Stage 3. 2·5 hours. (O.S. 3.)

2 cells.

Stage 4. 3·25 hours. (O.S. 4.)

4 cells.

Stage 5. 4·25 hours. (O.S. 5.)

The 8-cell stage results from a vertical division of the cells of the four-cell stage, the lines of cleavage paralleling that of the first cleavage.

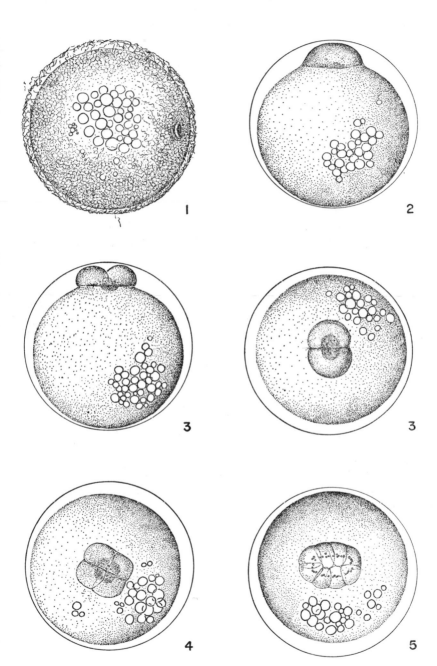

Figure 31.

Stage 6. 5 hours. (O.S. 6.)

Another vertical cleavage produces 16 cells in a single layer of four parallel rows of four cells each, though minor variations in cell alignment may occur.

Stage 7. 6 hours. (O.S. 7.)

The cells of stage 6 appear columnar as they approach cleavage, particularly the central cells. The cleavage spindles are perpendicular to the egg surface, this cleavage being latitudinal. The central cells continue as a two-celled layer. There is some rearrangement of peripheral cells as cleavage proceeds, with irregularities in the layering of the cells.

Stages 8–9–10. 7·5–10 hours. (O.S. 8–9.)

With successive cleavages there is a progressive increase in the number of cells with a reduction in cell size. However, there is little apparent increase in the size of the blastoderm. (Nuclei from the marginal cells, which are open peripherally, wander out of the cells to enter the *periblast*, the part of the plasma membrane which adjoins the blastoderm.)

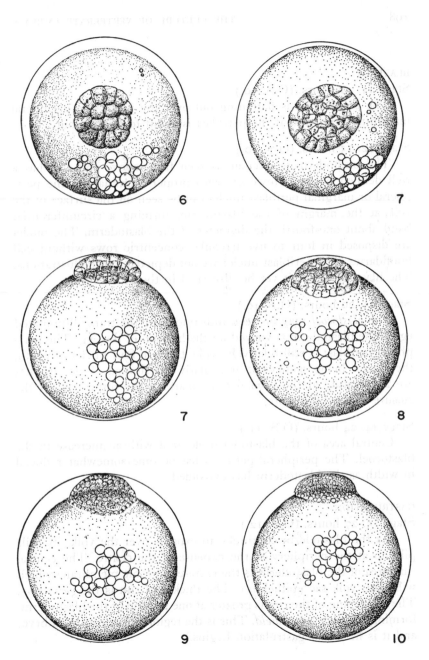

Figure 32.

BLASTULA
Stage 11. 11 hours. (O.S. 10.)

The blastoderm is flattening out over the yolk. The peripheral margin is serrated as if the periblast is about to migrate out.

Stage 12. 15 hours. (O.S. 10.)

The blastoderm is circular as seen from above and still has a well defined border. However, with proper illumination, the peripheral or marginal periblast nuclei can be seen on the surface of the yolk at the margin of the blastoderm, forming a circumferential band about one-fourth the diameter of the blastoderm. The nuclei are disposed in four to five irregular concentric rows without cell boundaries. The periblast nuclei are not depicted in the illustrations. The blastocoel cannot yet be discerned in the intact egg.

Stage 13. 20 hours. (O.S. 10.)

The *blastocoel* may be seen indistinctly in the trans-illuminated egg if the blastoderm is viewed on the horizon of the egg. The peripheral periblast is still relatively wide, three to four nuclei in width, the nuclei being somewhat irregularly distributed. Fine droplets are aggregating at the vegetal pole, marking the future site of the closure of the blastopore.

Stage 14. 24 hours. (O.S. 11.)

Central area of the blastoderm elevated with an increase in the blastocoel. The peripheral periblast has become somewhat reduced in width as the blastoderm has expanded.

GASTRULATION
Stage 15. 27 hours. (O.S. 12.)

(As the blastoderm continues to expand over the yolk, its cells pile up at the periphery at the expense of the centre. The central thin area of the blastoderm is the extra-embryonic membrane which will form yolk sac epithelium. The thickened rim is the *germ ring*. The thickening of the rim is greater at one portion of the blastoderm, forming the *embryonic shield*. This is the region of the future embryo, and it is here that gastrulation begins.)

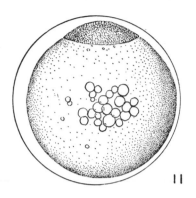 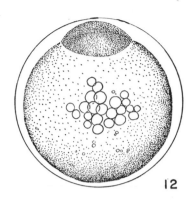

11 12

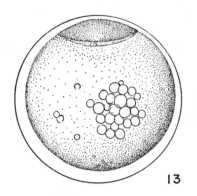 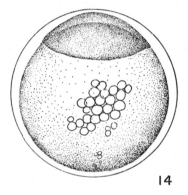

13 14

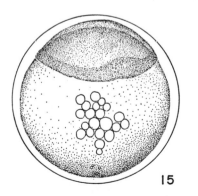 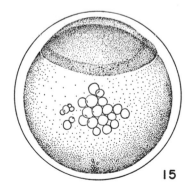

15 15

Figure 33.

Stage 16. 30 hours. (O.S. 13.)

(As gastrulation continues, the embryonic shield enlarges by the addition of cells anteriorly, laterally and posteriorly.) There is a further accumulation of fine droplets at the vegetal pole at the future site of the closure of the blastopore.

Stage 17. 33 hours. (O.S. 13.)

The gastrula has expanded to cover one-half of the yolk. The germ ring is little if any wider but the embryonic shield and axis have extended with epiboly. The latter is about one-sixth the circumference of the egg in length. (A refractive streak of cells is visible in the midline of the shield; this is the solid *keel* which forms the beginning of the central nervous system.)

Stage 18. 37 hours. (O.S. 14.)

The extra-embryonic ectoderm covers three-fourths of the surface of the yolk. (As the blastoderm continues to expand over the yolk, gastrulation continues, and the shield narrows; the keel of the central nervous system is more clearly marked.)

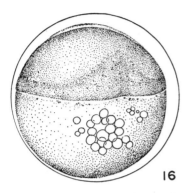
16

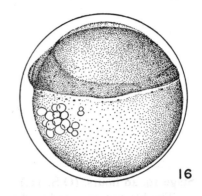
16

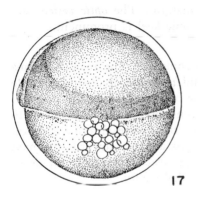
17

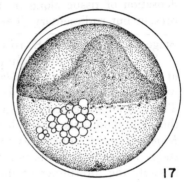
17

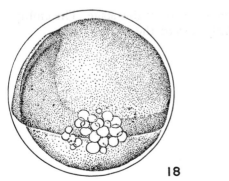
18

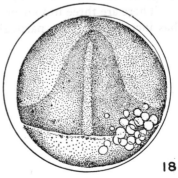
18

Figure 34.

Stage 19. 40 hours. (O.S. 15.)

The blastopore is reduced to a small opening through which the yolk may bulge. The embryonic axis is well defined with some condensation of tissue along its lateral margins. The *optic vesicles* are present but rudimentary. The embryonic keel is prominent.

Stage 20. 46 hours. (O.S. 16.)

The closure of the blastopore is complete. The main divisions of the brain, the *forebrain*, *midbrain*, and *hindbrain*, are distinguishable with a well defined keel, ventral to the brain, indenting the yolk sac. There is an increased but variable condensation of cells lateral to the embryonic axis in the location of the future anterior somites. *Kupffer's vesicle* appears as the embryos advance towards the next stage. The ectoderm lifts to form a large vesicle anterior to the head, possibly the forerunner of the pericardial cavity.

GROWTH AND ORGANOGENESIS

Stage 21. 52 hours. (O.S. 17.)

There are three to four pairs of *somites* at this stage. The embryo has increased in size, particularly toward the caudal end.

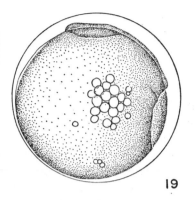

19

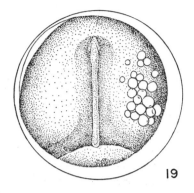

19

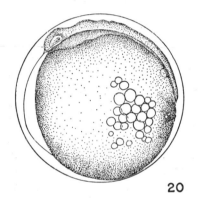

20

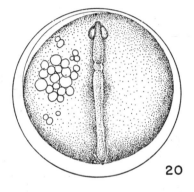

20

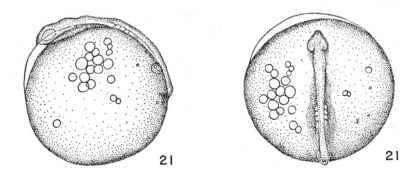

21

21

Figure 35.

Stage 22. 56 hours. (O.S. 18.)

The *optic cup* can be seen but the lens is not discernible. The pericardial cavity is present anterior to the head, but has not yet extended posteriorly under or lateral to the head, which is flush with the yolk. There is some condensation of tissue at the future site of the pectoral fin. There are no pigment cells either on the embryo or yolk sac, but the *blood islands* are forming as fine strands on the surface of the yolk. The Kupffer vesicle is deep and anterior to the tip of the tail, which is flush with the surface of the yolk.

Stage 23. 66 hours. (O.S. 19.)

The main divisions of the brain are better defined as are also the *otic vesicles*. The *lens* appears as a thickening but does not bulge out of the optic cup. The earliest indication of the olfactory placode can be noted. The outlines of the *pericardial cavity*, bilateral to the midbrain and hindbrain, are well defined; this cavity extends under the head, which has lifted off the yolk sac beneath the optic lobes and anterior hindbrain. The anterior extremity of the forebrain is still flush with the yolk sac. In most specimens the *heart* rudiment can be seen. Small *pigment cells* are present, scattered sparsely over the yolk sac with occasional cells on the dorsolateral aspect of the hindbrain. The tip of the tail is rounded but not free of the yolk sac.

Stage 24. 74 hours. (O.S. 20.)

The *brain ventricles* are forming, initially in the optic lobes with rapid extension into other divisions of the brain. The lens of the eye fills the optic cup. There is an increased number of melanophores and, as the embryos develop toward the next stage, erythrophores appear on the under side of the hindbrain region and trunk. Most of the melanophores are still unexpanded. Cardiac contractions are beginning and the blood islands of the yolk are linking up with each other, forming a syncitium, but as yet there is no circulation.

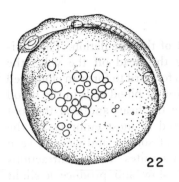

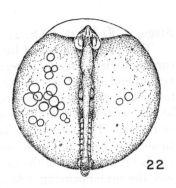

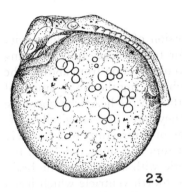

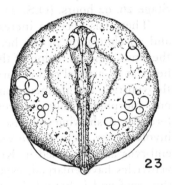

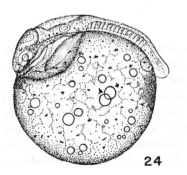

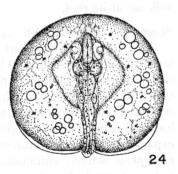

Figure 36.

Stage 25. 84 hours. (O.S. 21–22.)

This period is marked by the onset of the circulation. The peri-cardial cavity extends forward, lifting the head off the yolk; the venous end of the heart likewise extends forward to form an elongated tube. Also, there develops a concentration of blood cells in the blood islands on the yolk at the venous end of the heart and near the root of the tail. The circulation is established in most embryos by the 19-somite stage. The first contractions of somitic muscles are seen involving only a few of the most anterior somites. These contractions and the accompanying relaxations are slow and produce a slight bending of the body axis. The tip of the tail is now free of any yolk sac attachment.

Stage 26. 92 hours. (O.S. 23.)

There has been an increased extension of the pericardial cavity and an elongation of the heart anterior to the head, fully exposing the sinus venosus region of the heart to observation from above. The heart at its arterial end is curved, foreshadowing the development of the ventricle as a defined chamber. Although the heart chambers are not morphologically differentiated they are physiologically dif-ferentiated, showing stepwise depression of contractility progressively involving the presumptive ventricle, atrium and sinus venosus if the embryos are immersed in KCl isosmotic with sea water. The brain ventricles have enlarged, especially the fourth ventricle which has a thin roof and is bounded anteriorly by a well defined rhombic lip. The paired *otoliths* are first observed at this stage as aggregations of very fine dark granules. The tail has elongated and has lifted off the yolk sac at its root.

Stage 27. 112 hours. (O.S. 24.)

The ventricle of the heart forms a definite chamber. The otoliths are dense concrete bodies. There is a bilateral condensation of cells just posterior to the emerging anterior vitelline arteries, the rudi-ments of the *pectoral fins*. The *body cavity* is forming bilaterally but the *gut* rests ventrally on the yolk sac bisecting the body cavity longitudinally. The menalophores on the surface of the yolk sac are expanding. Body movements have increased in frequency. The *pronephros* actively eliminates dyes, though the urinary bladder is not yet formed (Armstrong, 1932).

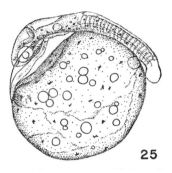 25 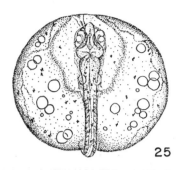 25

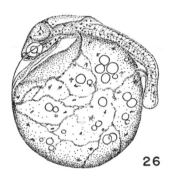 26 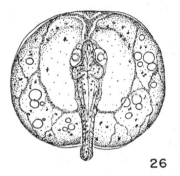 26

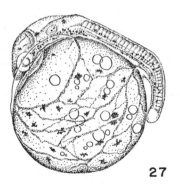 27 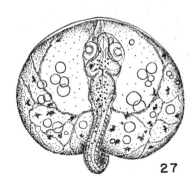 27

Figure 37.

Stage 28. 128 hours. (O.S. 25.)

This stage is marked by the earliest development of *retinal pigment* imparting a dusky tone to the eye. The body cavity has extended under the trunk, usually lifting the gut off the yolk sac. There is a blood vessel coursing caudally along the gut. The *urinary bladder* is small, bilobed but contains no precipitate. The tail has grown in length and lifted further off the yolk sac but contractility of the somites is limited to those anterior to the ventral flexure of the tail. The pectoral fin juts up above the surface of the yolk sac parallel to the body axis.

Stage 29. 144 hours. (O.S. 26.)

The eye has enlarged so that the lens does not completely fill the optic cup. The pectoral fin is a small pointed projection on the horizon of the egg as viewed along the body axis. The urinary bladder is a small bilobed organ grooved above and anteriorly by a ventrally coursing blood vessel. There is no precipitate in the urinary bladder, but selected dyes injected into the embryos at this stage are eliminated by the pronephros and colour the bladder contents.

Stage 30. 156 hours. (O.S. 27–28.)

Although the retinal pigment has markedly increased, the outline of the lens can still be discerned on transillumination of the eye. The pectoral fin extends slightly above the lateral line. The tail is completely straightened out. On lateral flexion, the tip of the tail passes over the hindbrain. The aorta terminates in a small glomus in the base of the rudimentary caudal fin which is just beginning to flatten out.

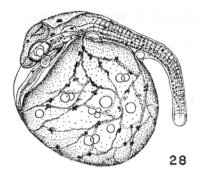

28

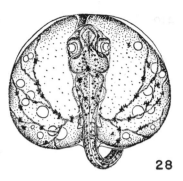

28

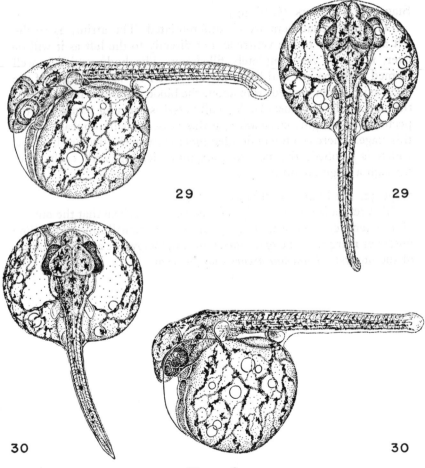

29

29

30

30

Figure 38.

Stage 31. 168 hours. (O.S. 29.)

The heart chambers are all differentiated. The atrium is to the left and anterior to the ventricle, not directly to the left as it will be later, nor is it yet completely filled out. The body cavity is well formed with the gut and liver in view. The liver is to the left of the body axis; when viewed from above the blood can be seen circulating through the liver sinusoids. A small vessel is forming parallel to the pectoral fin margin; circulation in this vessel usually appears late in this stage. There is a finely divided precipitate in the urinary bladder, which is bilobed, the two lobes communicating with each other through a large opening.

Stage 32. 192 hours. (O.S. 29.)

The retina is more heavily pigmented, so much so that the outline of the lens can be seen only with strong transillumination. The posterior margin of the *operculm* is forming below the anterior margin of the otocyst. *Branchial arches* may be seen.

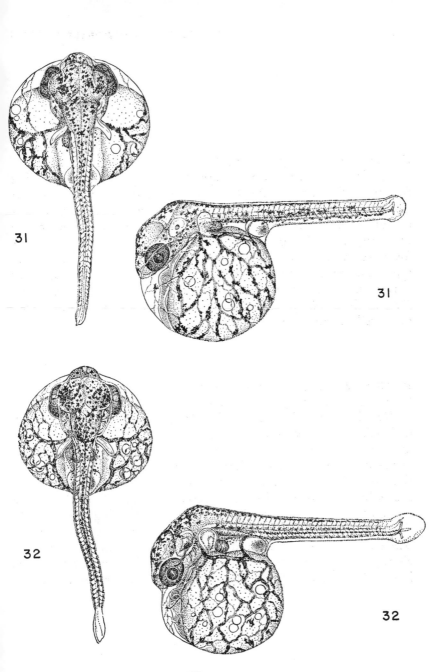

Figure 39.

Stage 33. 216 hours. (O.S. 30.)

During the past several stages there has been a developing flexure of the head at the level of the hindbrain, which is most marked at this stage. In the succeeding stages the head gradually straightens out. The ectoderm of the yolk sac comes off the embryo anteriorly at the lower level of the forebrain. The rudiment of the *lower jaw* is posterior to this, under the head. The retina is heavily pigmented, masking the deep part of the lens. There may be sporadic movements of the fins but no co-ordinated rhythmic movements. *Rays* in the *caudal fin* are faintly seen, with some unexpanded pigment cells along them.

HATCHING AND ABSORPTION OF THE YOLK

Stage 34. 228 hours. (O.S. 31–32.)

The lower jaw is well developed; the mouth is open and occasionally lower jaw movements are observed, but these movements are not co-ordinated with movements of the gills, which are still immobile. The yolk sac ectoderm comes off the lower jaw just below the mouth. The pectoral fins may occasionally show fluttering movements between long periods of quiescence. The rays in the caudal fin are well developed, with blood vessels radiating out between the rays. There is a *ventral fin* along the entire length of the tail. The *swim bladder* is small and inconspicuous. Hatching takes place shortly after the mouth has come open, due in part to an enzyme liberated by cells in the mouth and gill cavities (Armstrong, 1936).

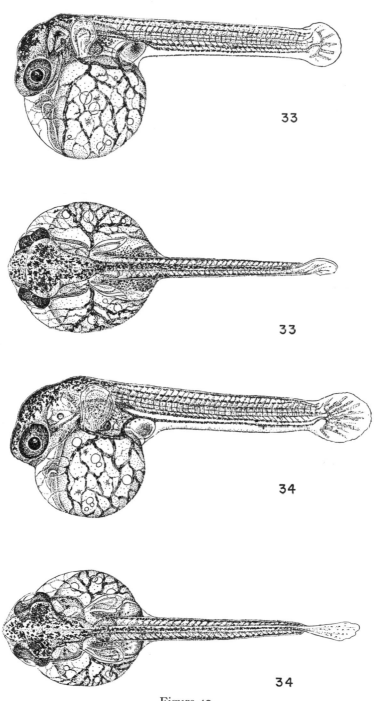

33

33

34

34

Figure 40.

Stage 35. 252 hours. (O.S. 32.)

Some extension of the head has taken place. The ectoderm of the yolk sac now comes off the ventral aspect of the head just in front of the continuity of the conus arteriosus with the ventral aorta. The margins of the operculum are well defined. Undulatory swimming movements occur but are transitory and are not sustained enough to propel the embryo; however, there are well sustained alternating movements of the pectoral fins with intervals of quiescence. A *dorsal fin* is forming but is not as extensive as the ventral fin.

Stage 36. 288 hours. (O.S. 33.)

There has been some further extension of the head and an apparent decrease in the size of the yolk sac. There is little if any significant change in the functional features of these embryos as compared with the preceding stage.

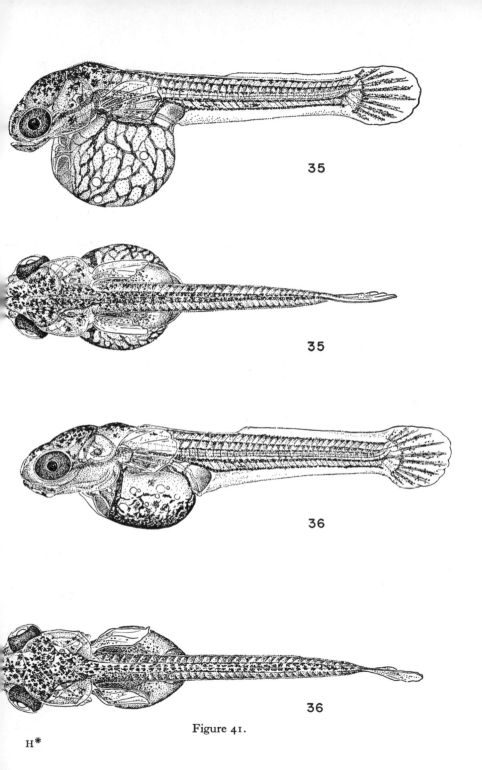

35

35

36

36

Figure 41.

Stage 37. 336 hours. (O.S. 33.)

The reduced size of the yolk sac, the extent of the development of the dorsal and ventral fins, and the serrations of the caudal fin, are aids in differentiating this stage which is also marked by the maturation of motor activity. There is co-ordination of the lower jaw and opercular movements, and of the undulating swimming and pectoral fin movements.

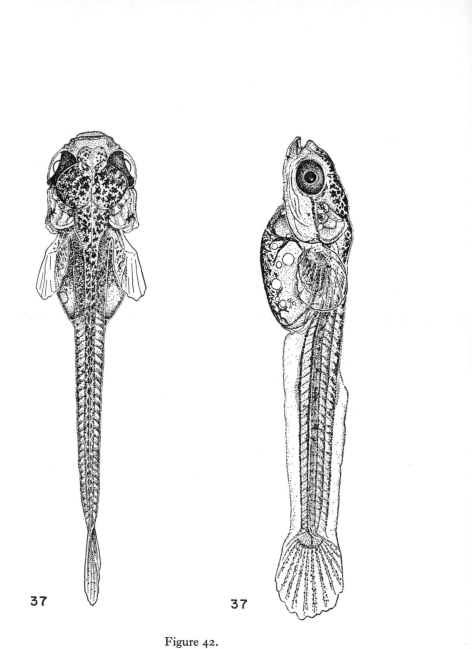

37   37

Figure 42.

Stage 38. 360 hours. (O.S. 33.)
    There is further reduction in the yolk and a strengthening of swimming activity.

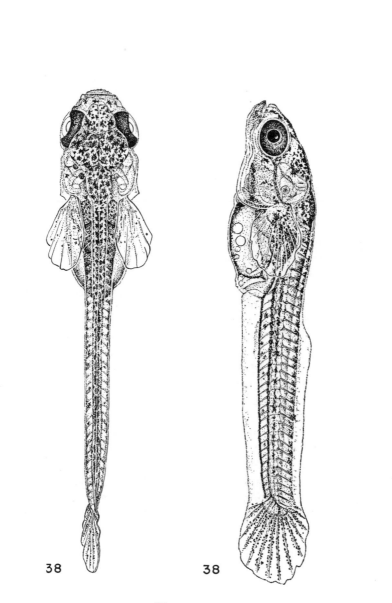

38   38

Figure 43.

Stage 39. 384 hours. (O.S. 34.)

This is a transition stage from the embryonic to the larval state with the complete absorption of the yolk. The operculum and pectoral fins are almost continuously rhythmically active. The swim bladder has increased in size and the embryos commonly swim at the surface of the water, but will swim to the bottom of the aquarium if disturbed, the pectoral fins being in constant motion. (The designation of the stage where the yolk is absorbed as the final step of the series is purely arbitrary; it must not be thought that at this stage the fry are miniature adults. Many more changes must ensue before adult proportions are attained: skin and scales must be differentiated, much of the skull and axial skeleton remains to be elaborated, the definitive pigment pattern is yet to be laid down, and the anal fins are still to be formed, to mention only a few of these changes. In addition the body as a whole is to undergo considerable change of proportion, and its parts varying degrees of heterogonic growth. Since all these processes are gradual and a continuation of the earlier processes described, there can be chosen no exact moment when the embryo metamorphoses into an adult. The stage of yolk absorption is a convenient stopping place because the primitive organ systems are all represented at this stage.)

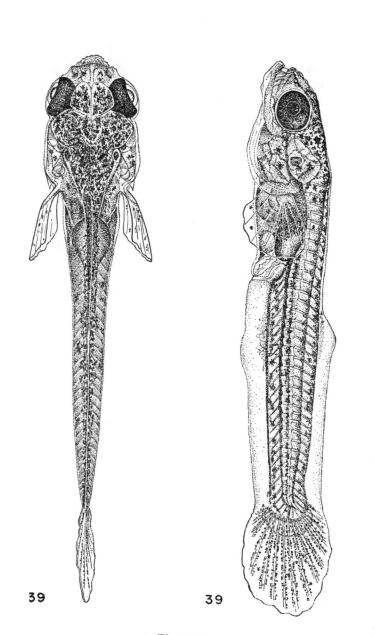

39   39

Figure 44.

THE TROUT (*Salmo*)

The two species most commonly used are the brown trout, *Salmo trutta* (=*S. fario*) and the rainbow trout *Salmo gairdneri* (=*S. irideus*). These fish can live in laboratory ponds or tanks but do not breed naturally under such conditions. Eggs are best obtained, already fertilised, from trout farms; or adults on the point of breeding may be bought, and eggs and sperm obtained from them by stripping. The breeding season is fairly short; in southern England it is usually possible to obtain living eggs only between November and January.

Ripe males and females are stripped by gentle anteroposterior pressure towards the anus. Both eggs and sperm rapidly lose their capacity for fertilisation in fresh water, and it is best to fertilise "dry" in glass (not metal) bowls, stirring the eggs and sperm together for a few seconds and then adding water. After 5 minutes the eggs are rinsed well with clean water.

Eggs can be transported in bottles immediately after fertilisation when respiration is low. At this time they withstand journeys of up to 24 hours provided they are kept cool. Later they become very sensitive to mechanical agitation and cannot again be safely moved until the eyes are easily visible (i.e. after about 18 days at 10°C).

Single fertilised eggs develop satisfactorily in small covered dishes (e.g. petri dishes or embedding dishes) containing tap water. But to obtain development of numbers of eggs, aerated water must be kept circulating round them, and it is usual to place the eggs on grills of glass rods, or on perforated earthenware trays, in gently flowing water. Fig. 45 shows the arrangement used by Smith at the University of Cambridge. Trout eggs require cool conditions to develop properly and temperatures of around 10°C give good results. According to Gray (1928) the eggs of the brown trout will tolerate temperatures between 3° and 13°C, but above 15°C mortality is high. However, older embryos (i.e. after the eyes are pigmented) appear unharmed by temperatures of 18°–20°C (Smith 1965).

The chorion is only semi-transparent, but the developing embryo can be seen fairly clearly through it with strong side illumination. Embryo formation is similar to that of *Fundulus* (pp. 193–221) though considerably slower. The relative rates of development of the embryo and the yolk sac, however, are very different in the two species; in *Salmo* the embryo is much more advanced by the time the blastoderm has completely surrounded the yolk to form the yolk sac, and the young fish is more developed when the yolk is finally absorbed.

Smith (1965) gives the following times for the development of *S. gairdneri* at 10°C:

24 hours	16–32 cells
5 days	Gastrulation begins
10 days	,, ends
16–17 days	Eyes become pigmented
34–37 days	Hatching
65 days	External yolk sac almost entirely absorbed.

The young fish feed from about the 60th day onwards and can be started on live *Daphnia* or *Artemia* (p. 14).

Illustrated accounts of the normal development of the trout are

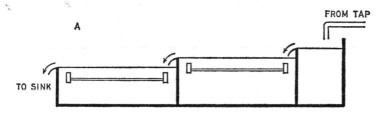

Figure 45. Method of culturing trout (*Salmo*) eggs. A. Arrangement of tanks of different heights with overflows providing a continuous current of water; the eggs are placed on a grill of parallel glass rods in each tank. B. Detail of glass rod grill; the rods are 25-30 cms. long, 6 mm. diameter, spaced 2·5 mm. apart, and inserted at each end into a wood (teak) bar; a wide slot cut through the bar above the level of the rods permits better flow of water over the eggs and provides a convenient handle for lifting the grill (Smith 1965).

H**

given by Henneguy (1888) and Keibel (1906); Witschi (1962) provides a table of development of salmonid fishes, without illustrations.

Experiments with trout eggs and embryos

Techniques for experiments with trout embryos are very similar to those described for *Fundulus*. Pasteels (1936) has made fate maps of the early blastoderm, based on vital staining experiments in which parts of the blastoderm were marked with pieces of nile blue agar after removal of the chorion. The mechanism of gastrulation has been studied by Devillers (1951, 1952), and the grafting experiments of Luther (1935, 1937) have shown that the invaginated chordamesoderm acts as an organiser closely resembling that of *Fundulus* and amphibians. Devillers (1947, 1949) and Devillers, Colas and Richard (1957) have studied the very limited development shown by blastoderms explanted from the yolk. The physiological studies of Smith and others are discussed in Smith's (1957) general review of the physiology of fish embryos.

THE MEDAKA (*Oryzias latipes = Aplocheilus latipes*)

The medaka is a small (adult length 2–4 cm.), egg-laying, freshwater fish native to Japan, Korea and China, where it is found in both static pools and running streams. The natural breeding season is from April to September.

The fish is hardy and thrives under laboratory conditions. Colonies of breeding adults can be kept in aquaria and have proved particularly suitable for studies in genetics and reproductive physiology. Briggs and Egami (1959) in their bibliography of the medaka list 376 publications.

For embryological purposes the medaka is particularly valuable because of its long breeding season and the regularity with which it spawns. Japanese workers who have kept the fish in large outdoor tanks have been able to obtain eggs for six months of the year; in laboratory aquaria eggs may also be available even in the winter months if the aquaria are kept at 25–28°C. The eggs are smaller (diameter about 1 mm.) than those of *Salmo* and *Fundulus* but they are excellent for observations on normal embryonic development and for physiological studies.

In Europe and the U.S.A. the medaka is readily obtainable from suppliers of aquarium fish. It requires little space, and up to 40 fish can be kept satisfactorily in a 40-litre tank. It thrives best at about 25°C, but can withstand a wide range of temperatures. Artificial aeration of the water is unnecessary, but some plants should be present in the aquarium. The fish can be fed adequately on *Tubifex*, *Enchytraeus*, *Daphnia*, *Artemia* (pp. 14–17) or small-grained dried fish food as supplied by dealers.

To obtain a regular supply of eggs it is best to keep the fish 30–50 per tank, with an excess of females; in such colonies eggs will be found almost daily throughout most of the year. The males and females can be distinguished by the shape and length of the dorsal and anal fins (Fig. 46); breeding females are also distinguishable by the obviously swollen abdomen.

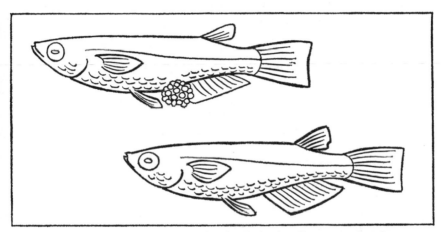

Figure 46. The medaka (*Oryzias latipes*). *Above:* egg-bearing female; *below:* male. The male can be distinguished by the larger dorsal and anal fins, and by the indented membrane between the last two dorsal fin rays (Briggs and Egami 1959).

A healthy female usually produces 20–40 eggs at each spawning, and may continue to lay a new cluster of eggs every day for 3 or 4 months—sometimes longer. Reproductive activities in the medaka are photoperiodic and the time of egg laying can be controlled by suitable lighting arrangements. Spawning normally occurs shortly after dawn, and if the fish are kept in artificially regulated periods of 12 hours light and 12 hours darkness, they will lay at the time of change from dark to light, which can be adjusted to suit the experimenter's convenience.

The eggs remain attached to the female for a few hours after laying but can be safely removed by hand. Fertilisation takes place during or immediately after oviposition, the male holding the female with his dorsal and anal fins while spreading the milt over the eggs with the pectoral fin.

The eggs vary slightly in size from one batch to another, the smaller females usually laying smaller eggs. The size of the mouth of the adults is such that the smaller fish cannot eat the larger eggs, but the larger fish can and do eat the smaller eggs. Also the adults prey on the newly hatched young. The eggs should therefore be removed as soon as possible from the aquarium containing the adults. They can be kept in any small glass container convenient for observation, provided overcrowding is avoided.

Ova of the medaka become unfertilisable within a few minutes after they have been immersed in fresh water. Yamamoto, in the course of detailed studies on the fertilisation mechanism of this fish, found that in a salt solution isotonic with the osmotic pressure of the egg (Yamamoto 1941) the eggs retained their fertilisability for several hours and could be artificially fertilised as required (Yamamoto 1939, 1944). The composition of this saline is given on p. 4.

Yamamoto (1961) describes his method of obtaining and artificially fertilising eggs as follows: "The female medaka exhibits a maturation cycle of 24 hours and spawns a batch of eggs at dawn of every day during a certain period of the breeding season. In order to obtain ripe ova, females known to have spawned should be removed from males on the day before the experiment is to be performed. While ripe eggs could be stripped out from the fish, it is wise to sacrifice the females and remove the ova gently. This is because ordinary stripping methods frequently injure ova and cause them to manifest mechanical activation. On the day of the experiment, the fish is found to contain ripe eggs which would have been spawned had they been left with males. The belly of the fish is incised after pithing the brain, and the ovary removed and put into Ringer's solution (formula as given on p. 4). The ripe unfertilised eggs which can be distinguished by size and translucency, are isolated with glass needles and kept in the Ringer's solution. Only a few eggs (5–6%) show autoactivation (i.e. separation of the chorion and other cortical changes normally occurring at fertilisation) in Ringer's solution. These are discarded. An adult male is cut open and the testis also isolated and kept in the Ringer's solution.

Insemination of ova in Ringer's solution is performed by teasing the testis in Ringer's solution."

The fertilised eggs will develop in aquarium water, tap water free of excess chlorine (p. 165), or Yamamoto isotonic saline.

Attached to the outer surface of the chorion are threads and sticky filaments which entangle with those of other eggs forming clusters. Between the chorion and the yolk is a perivitelline space, and on the surface of the yolk are a number of oil droplets which during early development merge into a single large globule at the vegetal pole. This oil globule is presumably a food reserve and gradually disappears.

Cleavage and later developmental stages can be easily observed through the chorion, which is clear and transparent. If necessary, the chorion can be removed (Trinkaus 1951) by the same methods as for *Fundulus* (p. 190).

Development follows the usual teleost pattern (pp. 193-221) and is rapid. At 25°C the first cleavage takes place 1 hour after fertilisation, the sixth cleavage after four hours; by the end of the first day a few somites have formed and by the end of the second day the heart is beating. Embryonic movements begin on the fourth day and hatching occurs at about the eighth day. The newly hatched fish is about 4·5-5 mm. in length and grows during the first month to about 12 mm. Maturity is reached in 1-1½ months in summer and the life span is 4 years.

REFERENCES

ARMSTRONG, P. B. (1932). The embryonic origin of function in the pronephros through differentiation and parenchyma-vascular association. *Amer. J. Anat.*, **51**, 157-88.

ARMSTRONG, P. B. (1936). Mechanism of hatching in *Fundulus heteroclitus*. *Biol. Bull.*, **71**, 407.

ARMSTRONG, P. B. & CHILD, J. S. (1962). *Stages in the development of Ictalurus nebulosus*. Syracuse University Press. New York.

ARMSTRONG, P. B. & CHILD, J. S. (1965). Stages in the normal development of *Fundulus heteroclitus*. *Biol. Bull.*, **128**, 143-68.

BRIGGS, J. C. & EGAMI, N. (1959). The medaka (*Oryzias latipes*). A commentary and a bibliography. *J. Fish. Res. Bd. Canada*, **16**, 363-80.

BRUMMETT, A. R. (1954). The relationship of the germ ring to the formation of the tail bud in *Fundulus* as demonstrated by carbon marking technique. *J. exp. Zool.*, **125**, 447-86.

DETTLAFF, T. A. & GINSBURG, A. S. (1954). The embryonic development of the sturgeons (*Acipenser stellatus, A. güldenstadti colchicus* and *Huso*

huso) in connection with the problem of breeding. USSR Acad. Sci., Moscow. (In Russian.)

DEVILLERS, C. (1947). Explantations *in vitro* de blastodermes de poissons. (*Salmo, Esox.*) *Experientia*, **3**, 71–2.

DEVILLERS, C. (1949). Explantations en milieu synthétique de blastodermes de truite (*Salmo irideus*). *Cyto-embryol. belgo-neerland*, 67–73.

DEVILLERS, C. (1951). La couche envelloppante du blastoderme de *Salmo*. Son role dans la mécanique embryonnaire. *C.R. Acad. Sci., Paris*, **232**, 1599–600.

DEVILLERS, C. (1952). Coordination des forces épiboliques dans la gastrulation de *Salmo*. *Bull. Soc. zool. Fr.*, **77**, 304–9.

DEVILLERS, C. (1965). Respiration et morphogenèse dans l'oeuf des téléostéens. *Année biologique*, **4**, 157–86.

DEVILLERS, C., COLAS, J., et RICHARD, L. (1957). Différenciation *in vitro* de blastodermes de truite (*Salmo irideus*) dépourves de couche enveloppante. *J. Embryol. exp. Morph.*, **5**, 264–73.

GRAY, J. (1928). The growth of fish. III. The effect of temperature on the development of the eggs of *Salmo fario*. *J. exp. Biol.*, **6**, 125–30.

HENNEGUY, F. (1888). Recherches sur le développement des poissons osseux. Embryogénie de la truite. *J. Anat. Paris*, **24**, 413–502.

KAGAN, B. M. (1935). The fertilisable period of the eggs of *Fundulus heteroclitus* and some associated phenomena. *Biol. Bull.*, **69**, 185–201.

KEIBEL, F. (1906). Die Entwickelung der äusseren Körperform der Wirbeltierembryonen, insbesondere der menschlichen Embryonen aus den ersten 2 Monaten. In *Handbuch der vergleichenden und experimentellen Entwicklungslehre der Wirbeltiere*. Erster Band. Zweiter Teil. Gustav Fischer, Jena.

LUTHER, W. (1935). Entwicklungsphysiologische Untersuchungen am Forellenkeim; Die Rolle des Organisationszentrum bei der Entstehung der Embryonalanlage. *Biol. Zbl.*, **55**, 114–37.

LUTHER, W. (1937). Transplantations- und Defektversuche am Organisationszentrum der Forellenkeimscheibe. *Arch. EntwMech. Org.*, **137**, 404–34.

MYERS, G. S. (1952). Easiest of all to spawn and raise—the medaka. *Aquarium J.*, **23**, 189–94.

NEWTH, D. R. (1951). Experiments on the neural crest of the lamprey embryo. *J. exp. Biol.*, **28**, 248–60.

NEWTH, D. R. (1956). On the neural crest of the lamprey embryo. *J. Embryol. exp. Morph.*, **4**, 358–75.

NICHOLAS, J. S. (1927). The application of experimental methods to the study of the developing *Fundulus* embryos. *Proc. Nat. Acad. Sci.*, **13**, 695–9.

NICHOLAS, J. S. & OPPENHEIMER, J. M. (1942). Regulation and reconstitution in *Fundulus*. *J. exp. Zool.*, **90**, 127–53.

OPPENHEIMER, J. M. (1936a). The development of isolated blastoderms of *Fundulus heteroclitus*. *J. exp. Zool.*, **72**, 247–69.

OPPENHEIMER, J. M. (1936b). Transplantation experiments on developing teleosts (*Fundulus* and *Perca*). *J. exp. Zool.*, **72**, 409–37.

OPPENHEIMER, J. M. (1936c). Processes of localisation in developing *Fundulus*. *J. exp. Zool.*, **73**, 405–44.

OPPENHEIMER, J. M. (1937). The normal stages of *Fundulus heteroclitus*. *Anat. Rec.*, **68**, 1–15.

OPPENHEIMER, J. M. (1947). Organisation of the teleost blastoderm. *Quart. Rev. Biol.*, **22**, 105–18.

OPPENHEIMER, J. M. (1959). Extraembryonic transplantation of sections of the *Fundulus* embryonic shield. *J. exp. Zool.*, **140**, 247–68.

OPPENHEIMER, J. M. (1964a). The development of isolated *Fundulus* embryonic shields in salt solution. *Acta Embryol. Morph. exp.*, **7**, 143–54.

OPPENHEIMER, J. M. (1964b). Personal communication.

PASTEELS, J. (1936). Études sur la gastrulation de vertébrés méroblastiques. I. Téléostéens. *Arch. Biol.*, *Paris*, **47**, 205–308.

PENTELOW, F. T. K. (1957). Freshwater fish. In *The UFAW Handbook on the Care and Management of Laboratory Animals*. 2nd ed. (A. N. Worden and W. Lane-Petter, eds.) Universities Federation for Animal Welfare. London.

REICHENBACH-KLINKE, H. & ELKAN, E. (1965). *The principal diseases of lower vertebrates.* Academic Press. London and New York.

RUDNICK, D. (1955). Embryogenesis in teleosts and birds. Pages 297–314 in *Analysis of Development*. (B. H. Willier, P. A. Weiss, V. Hamburger, eds.). W. B. Saunders Co., Philadelphia and London.

RUGH, R. (1962). *Experimental embryology. Techniques and procedures.* 3rd ed. Burgess Publishing Co., Minneapolis.

SMITH, S. (1957). Early development and hatching. In *The Physiology of Fishes*, Vol. I. (M. E. Brown, ed.) Academic Press, New York.

SMITH, S. (1965). Personal communication.

SOLBERG, A. N. (1938). The susceptibility of *Fundulus heteroclitus* embryos to X-radiation. *J. exp. Zool.*, **78**, 441–69.

STUART, T. A. (1957). Exotic freshwater fishes. In *The UFAW Handbook on the Care and Management of Laboratory Animals*. 2nd ed. (A. N. Worden and W. Lane-Petter, eds.) Universities Federation for Animal Welfare, London.

SWARUP, H. (1958). Stages in the development of the stickleback. *Gasterosteus aculeatus* (L.). *J. Embryol. exp. Morph.*, **6**, 373–83.

TRINKAUS, J. P. (1949). The surface gel layer of *Fundulus* eggs in relation to epiboly. *Proc. Nat. Acad. Sci.*, **35**, 218–25.

TRINKAUS, J. P. (1951). A study of the mechanism of epiboly in the egg of *Fundulus heteroclitus*. *J. exp. Zool.*, **118**, 269–319.

TRINKAUS, J. P. & DRAKE, J. W. (1956). Exogenous control of morphogenesis in isolated *Fundulus* blastoderms by nutrient chemical factors. *J. exp. Zool.*, **132**, 311–48.

TRINKAUS, J. P. & DRAKE, J. W. (1959). Enhancement of morphogenesis in *Fundulus* blastoderms by fusion and crowding *in vitro*. *Devl. Biol.*, **1**, 377–95.

ULMER, R. E. (1942). Breeding the medaka, *Aplocheilus latipes*. *Aquarium*, **10**, 152–5.

VANDEBROEK, G. (1936). Les mouvements morphogénétique de la gastrulation chez *Scyllium canicula*. *Arch. Biol.*, *Paris*, **47**, 499–584.

WHITE, P. R. (1946). Cultivation of animal tissues in nutrients of precisely known constitution. *Growth*, **10**, 231–89.

WITSCHI, E. (1962). Characterisation of developmental stages: Salmonid fishes. In *Growth. VII. Prenatal Vertebrate Development*. (P. L. Altman and D. S. Dittmer, eds.) Biological Handbooks of the Federation of American Societies for Experimental Biology.

YAMAMOTO, T. (1939). Changes of the cortical layer of the egg of *Oryzias latipes* at the time of fertilisation. *Proc. Imp. Acad.* (*Tokyo*), **15**, 269–71.

YAMAMOTO, T. (1941). The osmotic properties of the egg of the freshwater fish, *Oryzias latipes*. *J. Fac. Sci. Tokyo Imper. Univ.*, *Sec. IV*, **5**, 461–72.

YAMAMOTO, T. (1944). Physiological studies on fertilisation and activation of fish eggs. I. Response of the cortical layer of the egg of *Oryzias latipes* to insemination and to artificial stimulations. *Annot. Zool. Japan.*, **22**, 109–25.

YAMAMOTO, T. (1961). Physiology of fertilisation in fish eggs. *Int. Rev. Cytol.*, **12**, 361–405.

Author and Subject Index

Italics indicate page numbers of text-figures
Bold figures indicate plate numbers